Guilty by Definition

Susie Dent is a writer and broadcaster on language. She recently celebrated thirty years as a co-presenter and the resident word expert on Channel 4's *Countdown*, and also appears on the show's comedy sister *8 Out of 10 Cats Does Countdown.* Susie comments regularly on TV and radio on words in the news, and is the author of several non-fiction books on words and language. *Guilty by Definition* is her first novel.

@susie_dent

Guilty by Definition

SUSIE DENT

ZAFFRE

First published in the UK in 2024 by
ZAFFRE
An imprint of Zaffre Publishing Group
A Bonnier Books UK company
4th Floor, Victoria House, Bloomsbury Square, London, WC1B 4DA
Owned by Bonnier Books
Sveavägen 56, Stockholm, Sweden

A CIP catalogue record for this book is
available from the British Library.

Hardback ISBN: 978-1-80418-394-6
Trade paperback ISBN: 978-1-80418-395-3

Also available as an ebook and an audiobook

1 3 5 7 9 10 8 6 4 2

Typeset by IDSUK (Data Connection) Ltd
Printed and bound in Great Britain by Clays Ltd, Elcograf S.p.A.

Zaffre is an imprint of Zaffre Publishing Group
A Bonnier Books UK company
www.bonnierbooks.co.uk

For Malcolm Michael Dent

1931–2023

1

quaesitum, *noun (seventeenth century)*:
that which is searched for

THE DAY THE FIRST LETTER arrived was warm for the time of year. A Thursday in late April when Oxford was at its most charming, the sunlight washing over the buttery sandstone of the college buildings, their spires looking obligingly dreamy against a pale blue sky. Easy to love the city in the sunshine, unless, of course, you were one of the students contemplating their upcoming finals. In a few weeks they would be hurrying towards the Examination Schools in the regulation attire of black gowns known as sub fusc – long and billowing for scholars, shorter and skimpier for commoners – chattering like jittery magpies.

When Martha Thornhill had been appointed senior editor at the *Clarendon English Dictionary* six months earlier, she had quickly discovered that a desk overlooking the street was one of the perks of the job. She wasn't convinced it was an advantage to her employer, however. Too often, when she looked away from her screen to try and think her way through a word or tweak a definition, she found her attention snagged by a passing figure on the pavement. A girl with long blonde hair, head down and walking fast; a young man, hands in his pockets, at ease with himself and his future; an older couple, arm in arm, enjoying a stroll past the grand frontage of the dictionary's offices, pausing to look up and catching her eye. She'd look away guiltily, knowing she'd been caught wool-gathering yet again.

Berlin, where she'd spent the last ten years learning her trade as an editor, had felt starkly different. History pressed up against you more urgently there; its upheavals and reinventions so recent they seemed to linger in the air and give the city a restless energy. In Oxford, the history had settled into the fabric of the stone; a subtle perfume breathed out by the street names and college spires. It comforted. Welcomed contemplation.

Martha touched her necklace, slowly running the pair of silver hearts back and forth along their chain, her private rosary. Another group of tourists, eager and neon-coated, was gathering beneath Martha's window, trying to catch a glimpse of the ornate fountain in the grassy courtyard beyond the gates. Martha could have done the tour guide's speech for him.

'The *Clarendon English Dictionary*, known throughout the world as the *CED*, is one of the greatest ongoing intellectual endeavours of our age. The project was begun in the nineteenth century under the auspices of the university, and continues apace as new words come into use and existing ones change.'

This opening gambit was traditionally followed by a pause as one of the tourists asked a question. Martha seldom heard the exact words, but the guide's answer frequently told her that it was some variation on spellcheckers, Google, and why anyone these days writes dictionaries at all. *Well, certainly not for the money*, she thought, as she half listened to the guide's reply. Their answer usually involved a fluffy version of how language and civilisation are inseparable; that to understand the history and development of one is to appreciate the evolution of the other.

Martha wanted to seize his audience by their neoprene lapels and tell them there was so much more to it than that. That language defines us and is the framework of our thought, an endless, shifting, complex dance through time and human nature. It is about patterns of life and the need to communicate them; it is about dying, renewal, and everything in between, about chaos and the order we make from chaos, the blood and bones of every history. Above all, it is about the slow, insistent pull into the secret lives of the ordinary.

'Is it *Looney Tunes* time?'

Martha flinched and turned from the window to see her colleague hovering by her desk, holding two coffees and proffering her one as though he might withdraw it at any moment. His wardrobe, on the other hand, was anything but tepid. He was embracing the warm weather by wearing a Hawaiian print shirt in a violent purple, patterned erratically with white hibiscus flowers that drew the eye to an incipient beer belly. She glanced down at her watch – one minute past two – before accepting the coffee with a grin.

'Thanks, Simon. Yes, let's get cracking. Safi, do you have the bundle?'

Safiya Idowu – Safi to anyone who mattered – was the youngest editor on Martha's team. Fiercely intelligent, she crackled with enthusiasm for the work. It lifted them all.

'Yup!'

Safi pulled a folder from her in-tray containing the enquiries to the dictionary that had come in by post, and began passing them out. Alex Monroe, the fourth editor on the team, swivelled her chair towards the others. 'The emailed ones are on the shared drive. Tuesday's crossword in *The Times* seems to have caused a flurry from the usual suspects. The answer to two across was "lasagne". I've put in a draft response.'

'Ah, that old ch—amber pot,' Simon said, and looked pleased with himself. It was a joke that only an etymologist could possibly find funny, knowing that the word 'lasagne' had begun with a Latin word for a potty.

Martha accepted her share of the written queries and flicked through the half dozen she'd been allotted. She already recognised some of the handwriting. In today's bundle, a regular correspondent named Barbara Wilson was insisting that her grandmother was offering a 'ploughman's lunch' to friends and family long before the 1950s, as the dictionary currently had it. Martha would, as always, use the template on the shared drive to thank her and ask for any printed or dateable proof. Ms Wilson's traditional response was silence.

'Right, Safi, what truffles have you found for me today?' Alex said, tapping her stack together neatly. 'Any good phobias?'

Martha's team all had their preferences. Alex had a predilection for fears, folklore and the supernatural. She might have been a Goth in her youth, Martha thought, as she considered her across the room. Alex was in her fifties and effortlessly elegant, with a marked fondness for dark colours that seemed to suit her intellectual love of the shadows.

Safi had a passion for regional words, which she would throw into conversation whenever possible – a one-woman popularisation society. That day had begun with her gleefully announcing that the politician on the front page of *The Times* was positively 'crambazzled', explaining (glancing rather too directly at Simon, Martha had thought), that it was an old Yorkshire word for looking prematurely aged from excess drinking. Then again, Safi had added, she was a little too familiar with 'crapulence' – the hungover companion to crambazzlement – herself.

Simon was keen on the senses: tastes, smells, colours. He'd published a book on the language of taste some years ago, and Martha reminded herself to read it. She knew he'd applied for her job and that it must have been galling to be passed over for a woman in her early thirties. He'd been friendly and welcoming enough when she arrived, but his eyes rarely warmed when they spoke. It would be politic to be able to praise his work, particularly as reviewers and book buyers had largely ignored it. It was now sitting on the shelves of their shared office among the leather-bound historical lexicons and glossaries.

'Ah, here's one!' Alex said, unfolding one of her allocated queries. 'Is there a word for the fear of peanut butter sticking to the roof of your mouth?'

'Well, is there?' Martha asked, assuming Alex wanted to tell them.

'There is. Arachibutyrophobia. Someone made it up in the eighties, if I remember rightly – it may even have been one of our lot. It's a clumsy Greek joke of a word, really.' Alex turned to her computer and pursed her lips. 'Scattered across the internet on various medical sites – not in the dictionary, though. Obviously.'

They worked on in silence for a while. Safi had handed Martha a query about the first use of 'fuckwit', written in a spidery hand on incongruously elegant stationery. The correspondent had found a record from the 1940s, some twenty years before the *CED*'s earliest finding to date. Antedatings like these were always betwittering, and Martha put it to one side for verification and sharing. For all that she chose her own swearing moments carefully, she found tracing taboos and profanities fascinating. They were part of a shifting scale of squeamishness over the centuries, a rebellious lexicon that was largely spoken and rarely printed until the twentieth century. She consequently had to go digging for its vocabulary herself, in transcriptions of trials, scribbled marginalia, and letters or diaries never intended to be shared with the world at large. Searching for them made her feel like an archaeologist smothered in linguistic mud – not a curator admiring the preserved artefacts of language that had been cleaned and smoothed by propriety.

'Oh, is it my turn for the Shakespeare crank letter *again*?' Simon sighed theatrically.

'I did it last week,' Alex replied. 'Have you got an Oxfordian?'

'Yours was a one-line email!' Simon protested. 'This person has sent five thousand words. No, they're not disputing authorship,' he turned the page to check the signature, 'Ms Burnside has worked out, apparently, which lines of *Timon of Athens* were written by Shakespeare and which by Thomas Middleton. Huge, if true.' His fingers strummed the table as he considered.

'We have a list of Shakespearean resources for this sort of thing, don't we?' Martha asked.

Simon nodded. 'To be fair to her, Ms Burnside does seem familiar with the scholarship.' He scanned the page. 'And has *roundly* dismissed it all, preferring instead her own system detailed below.' He started typing out a reply. 'I shall congratulate her on her diligence, apologise that we haven't got the resources to fully explore her system ourselves, and suggest she writes directly to our expert on the subject, consultant editor Jonathan Overton!'

Martha smiled. Jonathan would not like that much, although she imagined his reply to Ms Burnside would be resolutely diplomatic. On his last visit he had lectured them all on how even the most aggressive critic could be converted into an enthusiastic ally with proper handling.

'Behave yourself,' Alex said dryly, then added, 'Are we all going to Jonathan's launch tonight? It's at the Ashmolean, isn't it?'

'Free champagne and canapés? I'm willing to endure a couple of speeches on his greatness for that,' Simon said, finishing off his email with a flourish like a pianist polishing off a cadenza.

'Do we have to go?' Safi asked. 'I'm rubbish at these things. And what's with all the fiddly canapés? What are you supposed to do with the little sticks? I find them in my pockets for weeks.'

'We'll look after you, Safi.' Alex flicked open her next letter. 'And it would be good for you. All the great and good come up from London to Jonathan's launches. Maybe we'll find a radio producer for a series on dialect. Will you be coming, Martha? Do you have any suitable shoes?'

Martha glanced at her footwear. She opted to wear Doc Martens all year round, beneath long flowing dresses in a variety of prints. She preferred to wait for fashion to come to her rather than endlessly chase its coat-tails. 'I don't do heels.'

'I would expect a senior lexicographer to know the meaning of compromise.' Alex stuck her leg out from behind the desk and waggled her ankle, all without looking away from her screen. 'A kitten heel in black or beige. On sale in the Covered Market – you can pop in before the reception.'

Martha smiled and looked at her next written enquiry. It had been typed on an old-fashioned mechanical typewriter that obviously wasn't quite working perfectly. The lines were so close in places that they almost overlapped, yet the double returns were incongruously large. The letter 'e' had been worn into shadows.

She bent down to study it more closely.

'Safi, what's this one?'

Her colleague glanced up from her own letter. The pencil she was using to make notes had a pink pompom dangling from its end.

'Sorry, boss. It just came this morning. I glanced at it and thought it looked weird, so gave it to you. Not a regular correspondent.'

Another perk of leadership. Martha had told Safi to pass on the odd, angry, disturbed or threatening letters to her. They weren't many in number – people looking to troll the dictionary or its writers tended to confine themselves to bashing out unpleasantness on social media – and it seemed the least she could do in return for the chair by the window and a few extra thousand a year.

'Of course.' She read it again carefully, and felt her unease growing. It was neither threatening nor abusive, yet there was something deeply discomfiting about it.

The worry must have shown on her face. When she looked up again she found the others were watching her with expressions of confusion or expectation.

'What is it, Martha?' Alex asked.

Martha cleared her throat and read it out loud:

Dear Editors,

This is not a confession, but it contains one. I have been afraid of the truth; I have kept secrets. I believe I am not the only one to have done so, and so I come to you.

Time – its glory is to calm contending kings, to unmask falsehood, and bring truth to light. Who could want to prevent such a thing? That would be roguery indeed.

You are the secretaries of English, and I've decided to make you mine. Some of you at least should make common cause with me, till the poisoned fountain clears itself again. You are detectives too, are you not?

Have you the appetite? You are not newsmongers, but you are upholders of the truth.

Made men can be unmade. Your first loyalty is to the evidence, and no legacy is so rich as honesty. After all, 'evidence' is a term used as much by dictionary writers as by detectives.

Two professions that are very similar: in each we hunt for clues, the thread that leads back to the beginning, the impetus that set everything in train. We look at the story before it has even started. And as the evidence builds so the picture completes itself, and a life is exposed.

Maidens betrayed themselves with blushing in the past, so I read. I doubt that is the case any longer. If circumstances lead me, I will find where truth is hid, though it were hid indeed within the centre.

Cross your fingers, and work with me, the voice of freemen. I ask you to learn of me, who stand i' the gaps to teach you, the stages of our story. Truth will come to light. Murder cannot be hid long.

Yours in waiting,
Chorus

Simon was the first to break the silence that followed.

'Murder? Bloody hell! Guess Ms B's got serious competition for Shakespeare Crank of the Week.' Martha stared at the paper; it felt hot and dangerous in her hand. Simon continued: 'I'm not going mad, there are loads of Shakespeare quotes in there, aren't there?'

'Don't think Shakespeare had much to say about evidence or detectives,' Alex replied, wrinkling her nose, 'but I recognise the "I will find where truth is hid" – that's Polonius playing detective in *Hamlet*.'

'"No legacy is so rich as honesty" is from *All's Well That Ends Well*, I think,' Simon added, tugging unconsciously on his beard.

'I don't get it.' Safi's voice sounded high and tight. 'Is it meant to be a joke?'

'Doesn't sound like someone who's joking.' Alex got up from behind her desk and approached Martha's, her hand out. 'May I look?'

Martha felt a spasm of protectiveness, as if the letter was hers and hers alone, but that would be ridiculous. After the briefest of pauses she handed it over. As Alex studied it an open-topped tourist bus passed outside; its guide was getting the passengers to cheer about something. The racket made an awkward backdrop to the mutedness of the room.

'Well, it suggests that somebody is lying about something. But it's not very specific. I'm pretty sure that in *Much Ado* Claudio says Hero's blushes are born of guilt, not innocence. Is she the "maiden" here?'

Safi and Simon came out from behind their desks to join her, forming a small huddle in the middle of the blue carpet tiles. Martha had a sense the room was holding its breath somehow: that the old volumes, trailing houseplants, and coffee cups were all waiting. The only discernible sound was the insistent buzzing of computers.

Eventually, Simon tapped the page. 'This might be another one for Jonathan. I'm not teasing this time – look, "roguery", "newsmonger". Those were both thought to be Shakespearean coinages until, what, five years ago? Then the reading group found previous usages.'

'"Truth will come to light" – that one is definitely Shakespeare, too,' Alex said.

'But what truth are they talking about?' Safi said. 'It sounds like they're hinting at a crime. But murder? There was a murderer who worked for the dictionary once, wasn't there?'

'More than one. But that's hardly a secret. There was that film about one of them a few years ago,' Alex said, still staring at the page.

'Any more recent scandal?' Martha asked.

'Not that I know of,' Alex said, glancing at Simon, who shrugged without looking at her. 'Not here.'

'"The fountain clears" . . . Are they talking about the fountain in our quadrangle?' Safi frowned. '"Some of you at least should make common cause with me" . . . I mean that suggests some of us *wouldn't* want to. Because we're liars?'

Simon curled his lips. 'Hold the front page. Has someone been shredding Ms Wilson's proof about her mother's neologistic brilliance all these years?'

'Don't.' Martha got up from behind her desk. 'I had a letter from her today. Safi, will you scan this?' She took it from Alex and passed it over, then leant against her desk and folded her arms. 'No return address, of course. What are we supposed to do exactly? God, I don't know; I'll take it to the reception this evening and perhaps Jonathan will make something of it.'

'"You will be my secretaries,"' she said quietly, returning to her chair. It was a nice metaphor: of lexicographers attending upon a language – serving it, assisting it, and organising it into something ruly. What's more, she also knew that some words wear their hearts on their sleeves. The very first *secret*aries were keepers of secrets.

Safi carried the letter over to the scanner which worked only for her, and even then only intermittently. 'Yes, but it seems like this "Chorus" wants us to be detectives and bring secrets to light, not keep them buried.'

'Chorus: they're a key part of ancient Greek theatre, aren't they?' Simon asked rhetorically. 'They express what the main characters can't say.'

'And they wear a mask,' Alex replied. 'Shakespeare uses one in *Henry V*.'

Safi pressed a button on the scanner and it whirred reassuringly into action. 'Perhaps it is for Jonathan. A joke, I mean, as his new book is coming out.'

'Last place it would reach him would be in the office! And it's addressed to "The Editors", so to all of us, isn't it?' Simon sighed. 'Well, I suppose we'll see what he makes of it this evening. I'm going to the pub before this launch. Anyone joining me?'

'I have to buy shoes apparently,' Martha said, with a teasing eyeroll in Alex's direction. 'I'll see you at the Ashmolean.'

They worked on quietly until the bells of the clock tower signalled the end of the working day.

2

perceivance, *noun (seventeenth century)*:
the capacity or action of perceiving

'GOOD CHOICE!' ALEX SAID, GLANCING at Martha's low-heeled black shoes as she came into the lobby of the museum. 'Elegant but manageable.'

'I should have gone home and changed,' Martha replied abstractedly. She had paused in front of a vast gilt-edged mirror that allowed guests to give their appearance one final check before entering the mêlée of the atrium, where Oxford's finest were gathered to offer Jonathan Overton his due.

Alex stood beside her. She looked, Martha noted ruefully, gorgeous. Her grey-streaked black hair, bobbed fashionably short, had a salon glossiness to it, and she had swapped the earth tones she preferred for the office for a black and white tunic top, an understatedly expensive motif of chains running across it. Alex had what the Italians called *sprezzatura* – the kind of studied nonchalance that implies no time has been taken at all to look a certain way, even if it has been achieved through considerable effort.

Martha had tied up her own coppery hair in a high ponytail and refreshed her eyeliner, but now, eyeing the satin and silk edges of the crowd gathering for Jonathan, she wondered whether it was enough.

'Rubbish, Martha, you look like you've just fallen out of one of the Pre-Raphaelite paintings upstairs. But maybe, in that spirit, let down your hair?'

It wasn't the first time someone had compared her to those pictures of pale pensive Victorians. Martha pulled the scrunchie out of her hair and ran her fingers through it to liberate the soft curls. Her face looked a little less thin now. But didn't the Pre-Raphaelites all look rather sickly? She was trying to regain the weight she'd lost during those last months in Berlin, but with only partial success.

Alex gurned at the mirror to check her reflection for lipsticked teeth, whereupon she put her arm through Martha's and they swooped together down the dramatic modern staircase into the atrium.

It was the largest of the event spaces available at the Ashmolean, but the crowd filled it easily, gathered among white walls and glass and milling around the feet of a huge plaster cast of the Apollo from Olympia. Lightwells on either side allowed natural light to filter vertically through the building to the lower ground, where the sound of a hundred voices was echoed and multiplied. The museum was reinventing itself, Martha thought as she descended the stairs. Like the dictionary, it was a palimpsest, overwritten by the discoveries and tastes of each new generation of scholars. When the museum moved to its new home on Beaumont Street, the original site had been taken up as office space for the *Clarendon*

English Dictionary, leaving an invisible thread between the two institutions.

They found Simon and Safi at the bottom of the staircase, hovering next to a Greek mask of tragedy that stared in apparent horror at the circulating guests. As they exchanged greetings and Simon and Safi admired Martha's new shoes, a loud and gravelly voice interrupted the steady stream of chatter.

'Martha! You're so naughty, how can you have been in Oxford six months and not come to see me yet?'

A woman in a shimmering peach dress and a necklace of oversized pearls had grabbed Martha by the shoulders and was enthusiastically kissing each cheek.

'Look at you, you must weigh less than most of the manuscripts I get these days!'

'Hello, Gemma,' Martha said. 'So good to see you – it's a wonderful party.'

'I know,' the woman replied with no trace of humility, scanning the crowd with obvious satisfaction. 'Jonathan's parties always attract the loveliest people. The usual Oxford lot naturally, but a good supply of Londoners too. Most of them have houses near here, mind you. Nevertheless, it is a *quality* turnout, which I will remind his publishers of repeatedly. Getting them to give him the marketing spend he deserves is an absolute nightmare.' She turned her gaze on Martha's companions. 'And are these your colleagues, Martha? So happy you could come and support Jonathan tonight.'

'Yes, this is Safiya, Alex and Simon. Everyone, this is Gemma Waldegrave. My godmother, and Jonathan's agent.'

They shook hands. 'Actually, we've met a couple of times before,' Simon said, his smile a little tight.

'Oh, have we? Well, how lovely to see you again.'

'Don't the manuscripts come as email these days?' Safi asked.

'What? Oh, yes. But they still weigh a metaphorical ton. So, how is Martha as a boss? I was thrilled to hear she was coming home and taking the job.' She turned to her goddaughter: 'Though I struggle to think of you as a working woman. It seems only five minutes ago I was in your garden spraying you and Charlie with a hose during those long summer evenings.'

'Is Charlie your brother?' Safi asked Martha, smiling.

'Older sister,' Martha replied quickly. 'Short for Charlotte.'

She felt her throat tighten as she said her sister's name. But before anyone could respond, a murmur in the assembled crowd heralded the arrival of the man of the moment.

Martha had been to many book launches during her time in Berlin. She had worked for a small academic press, where most celebrations had taken the form of a gathering in a pub over a few bottles of cheap beer. The author had always been the first one there, rearranging the copies for sale and terrified no one would turn up, but the evenings invariably ended with them all spilling out of the pub onto Kreuzberg's cobblestoned streets, still talking and gossiping as they headed for the tram home. This was the first book launch she'd been to where they served champagne, and the first where the author made a late, film-star entrance like this.

Jonathan Overton, scholar, author, broadcaster and consultant editor of the *Clarendon English Dictionary*, was greeted with applause. He paused at the top of the stairs to acknowledge the crowd, his wife Olivia on his arm. They were matched in understated elegance, their body movements fluid and aligned in some unspoken agreement. They made a stunning couple; fitting, Martha thought, that they should appear alongside these plaster casts of ancient gods and muses. Jonathan had always been a striking man, blessed with sharp cheekbones, a square jaw and a naturally lithe physique.

Undoubtedly brilliant too. No wonder so many young women in Oxford had fallen for him over the years. From time to time he would mention the delicate complications of letting down some girl or other in his previous life. Now he had added the patina of wealth thanks to years of good food and supervised exercise, and, courtesy of his TV career, more than a little fame.

'I must go and greet him,' Gemma whispered in Martha's ear. 'Now, you've promised. Tea. Very soon. My treat.'

She swept halfway up the stairs, arms outstretched to welcome the conquering hero as he descended. Even above the general noise they could hear her exclaiming loudly just how beautiful Olivia looked in that dress.

'She's your *godmother*?' Simon said, staring at Martha. 'Jonathan's agent?'

'Yes. My mother was at school with Gemma. She introduced them.'

'Martha Thornhill. Charlie . . .' he said, then his eyes widened. 'God, all these months, I hadn't made the connection. I suppose it's been more than ten years . . .'

Martha shook her head, focusing her attention on Jonathan. One of the events team was setting up a microphone on the half-landing of the staircase where Jonathan and Gemma were exchanging air kisses.

'No reason you should have done.'

If Simon noticed Martha was uncomfortable, he didn't let it stop him. He leant in. 'I always thought of you as "Martha dropping in from your shining career in Berlin". I didn't realise this was a homecoming. You must know half the people here.'

As Jonathan was clearly preparing to make his speech, Martha felt no need to respond with anything more than a nod. Her eyes scanned the crowd. She did indeed recognise quite a few people, including friends of her parents, most of whom she hadn't seen in a very long time.

Over the last ten years she'd spent living in Berlin, her visits to Oxford had been for family. She'd returned for Christmases and odd weeks in the summer, when a few of the present guests had dropped in for cocktails or picnics in the garden. Then her mother had become ill, and Martha's visits had grown longer but more private. Some of these same people had appeared with food, books, and comfort; some had not. Perhaps they feared contagion: not from the cancer, but from the liminal sadness that had seeped into the walls of Martha's family home. Gemma had fought it off with colour, filling her old friend's bedroom with vibrant quilts for her bed and scarfs for her hair in deep reds and blues. She had worn this evening's same jewel-like colours at Rebecca's funeral two years before.

Tonight's gathering involved both town and gown: the masters of a couple of the colleges and their wives, a fistful of retired academics, local writers and journalists, and a few editors from the Oxford University Press. The famous and semi-famous present this evening Martha didn't know at all; presumably they were all friends Jonathan had made when his first book on Shakespeare, *Think Like a Genius*, became such a mammoth success. A superior sort of self-help book, it had topped the bestseller lists on both sides of the Atlantic. Martha hadn't paid much attention at the time, but she was aware he'd parlayed that triumph into a series of presenting jobs on TV and radio, and turned out to be very good at it, looking thoughtful as he wandered through an empty Globe Theatre and the garden of Anne Hathaway's Cottage, or interviewing creative geniuses – mostly rich men, the occasional artist – in time-soaked rooms, all timber beams and burnished floors.

'Good evening!' he said, spreading his arms wide. 'I promise not to make this a long speech, but I can't let this occasion pass without a few mentions. "I can no other answer make, but thanks, and thanks."'

Light laughter and nods proceeded from sections of the crowd, eager to show they had caught the quotation.

'I want to begin with my most important and personal thank you. To my wife, without whom I would be nothing, and our wonderful children, Miranda and Edgar . . .' Martha's attention drifted, reducing Jonathan's words to a staticky hum as she cast her eye over his wife. Olivia was watching her husband, head tilted to one side, smiling at his thanks and witticisms. She and Martha had met a few times, though Martha had always suspected that Olivia had been looking around for someone more important to talk to when they had. All Martha really knew about her was that she was a golden child with brains, daughter of a self-made millionaire with a life peerage. Arrestingly beautiful, too, with long blonde hair that was plaited tonight and tied up around her delicately featured face. Amid the sea of sartorially questionable, slightly shambling academics she had an almost preternatural aura.

Suddenly everyone was applauding, and Martha realised the speech was over. Browsing the faces of the audience she noted a few people who, like her, were 'nod-crafty': adept at nodding along to a speaker even when they had entirely tuned out. The entertainment continued with a group of musicians – students probably – playing from an upper gallery. It was a Renaissance and contemporary mash-up – Beyoncé and P!nk songs that Martha vaguely recognised from the bars in Berlin, played with crumhorns and fiddles. The musicians wore loose white shirts and Converse, and performed with the ease that comes from hard-won expertise.

The crowd shifted and Martha and Alex were separated from their colleagues.

'Well, the speech was mercifully brief. Good for Jonathan,' Alex said. 'Now do you need to go and circulate?'

Martha wrinkled her nose. 'I'd rather not. I hate small talk.' The room was growing warm and she could feel a prickle of sweat at the back of her neck.

'You must practise then.' Alex took a sip of her drink and shook her head. 'I'll never understand cheap champagne. A decent Cava is so much better.' Then, without waiting a beat, 'Do you miss Berlin?'

'Shall I practise my polite conversational response, or tell you the truth?'

'The truth, please.'

'Yes, I do. Very much.'

Alex waited, then laughed. 'Gosh, yes, you are bad at this. And why do you miss it?'

The room was becoming increasingly crowded. They found themselves squeezed together by waiters who looked equally clammy in their tuxedos, carrying plates of mini burgers, thumb-nail towers of chilli-jammed halloumi, and prawn tempura. Martha noted that they were all held together with bamboo sticks, and thought of Safi.

'It's a special city. Big enough to lose yourself, but small enough to find friends. Full of forgotten corners, dive bars, endless parks, offbeat museums . . . It's as though it has invention – reinvention – at its core. I think that's it: you can leave yourself behind, and nothing of your old life really counts anymore.'

Alex blinked. 'Honestly, Martha, that might be the most I've heard you say about anything since you arrived. But then why on earth come back here? I mean, Oxford is glorious, but it's also very pleased with itself. Was it family? Your father's on his own now, isn't he?'

Martha gave a faint nod. She didn't agree with Alex's appraisal of her birthplace: she was with Keats, who thought it the finest city in the world. But she also sorely missed the anonymous comforts of Berlin.

'Watch your six: the great man approaches.'

Martha twisted round and saw Jonathan making a beeline for them. She hadn't really expected to speak to him this evening, but he clearly had other ideas.

'Martha!' he called, brushing off the approach of a lesser guest with a business card in his hand. 'Hi, Alex. Thank you both for coming!'

They exchanged kisses. The fabric of his suit was strangely smooth under her fingertips, and his aftershave was heavy with cedar wood and leather. 'Congratulations on the new book.'

He grimaced. 'Thank you, it's a tie-in with the new TV series really. Not rigorous scholarship, I'll be the first to admit.'

Martha searched her mind for something ordinarily appropriate to say, and failed. Alex stepped in.

'We had a very curious letter today, Jonathan. It's so loaded with Shakespeare references that we wondered if it was meant for you.'

He smiled. 'That sounds exciting. Do you have it with you?'

Martha took the original from her shoulder bag and gave it to him. He pulled a pair of reading glasses from his pocket and flicked them open, then read in silence for a minute.

'A rather strange tone, isn't it? All secrets and suggestions of skullduggery.'

'Not wishing to step on your alliteration, but there's a mention of murder, too,' Alex added. 'Though I suppose that might have been because the writer couldn't resist the quotation.'

Jonathan lifted his glass with his free hand, silently toasting someone behind them. 'Probably an undergraduate art project or something. I can see why you thought it might be for me with its hints of roguery, etc. I mention those antedatings in my TV series. Still, it's addressed to the team, and it looks like its focus is the dictionary. Though why our mothership should be accused of hiding secrets is beyond me.'

'Any idea who it might be from? Or what it's about?' Martha asked.

He tucked his reading glasses away and handed the letter back to her.

'None! I've had some pretty strange letters over the years. They normally go to my publisher. Can you send me a copy?' Martha nodded. 'Otherwise ignore it. It's almost certainly a crank of some sort, so they'll either write again and make themselves plainer, or go and bother someone else.' He turned away but then looked back with a frown. 'That truth quote is wrong though. It's a song from *The Rape of Lucrece* and it should be "Time's glory is to calm contending kings, to unmask falsehood, and bring truth to light" not "Time – its glory", etc. Ruins the scansion.'

With that he was sucked back into the throng and Safi took the chance to dart into the gap created by his wake.

'You said you'd look after me!' she said.

'Sorry, Safi,' Alex replied. 'I thought you were with Simon.'

She rolled her eyes. 'He's found a TV producer.'

'And how have you managed your canapés?' Martha asked.

The younger woman brightened considerably and opened her fist to show a handful of wooden skewers. 'New approach. I'm going to wash and paint them and hang them on a chain as a reminder to avoid sticky social gatherings. I don't want to measure out my life with cocktail sticks. Beer labels and gig flyers for me. Did Jonathan have anything to say about the letter?'

The pressure of the crowd shifted again, travelling with Jonathan towards a signing table. The three women moved in the direction of the stairs where they wouldn't need to shout to be heard, and Martha told Safi about the misquote Jonathan had spotted. She took out the letter once more and they all studied it together.

'Why misquote that line? Could just be a mistake, but a mistake that mucks up the rhythm is odd.' Safi chewed her lip. 'Perhaps they wanted that sentence to start with "Time", not "Time's".'

'Possibly,' Alex continued. 'The whole thing is very odd, yet it seems carefully constructed. Perhaps if the first words of each sentence are important, it might be an acrostic? Must be whole words rather than just the first letter, though, otherwise the distinction between "Time" and "Time's" wouldn't matter.'

'That makes no sense,' Martha said, recoiling slightly as a waiter with another bottle of champagne tried to fill her glass. 'This, I, I, I, time, who, that, you . . .'

'I'll have some!' Safi waved at the waiter and grinned as he filled her glass. She noticed Alex's raised eyebrow. 'I've student loans to pay off! I'm not going to waste the chance to drink free champagne.'

'That's fair,' Alex replied, extending her glass. 'I shall keep you company.'

Martha studied the page. The noise of the room became muffled as her attention narrowed to the paper in front of her. She knew *The Rape of Lucrece* herself, and remembered the one line that had always sung to her: 'To blot old books and alter their contents'. Isn't that what lexicographers did, overwrite old dictionaries as time rescripted their contents?

Then she noticed something else.

'That paragraph break is strange,' she said, half to herself, 'the one between "detectives" and "Two". It's not a change of subject, so why the double return?'

'Perhaps it's the first words of the *paragraphs* that matter then,' Safi said, swigging her drink while still staring at the page.

'That works!' Martha felt a quiver of delight as the first word of each paragraph swam up into a coherent sentence. Or nearly coherent. "This Time You Have Made Two Maidens Cross."'

'Yes! That does sound like it should mean *something*,' Safi said.

'Perhaps a crossword clue?' Alex leant close to Martha, her shadow passing over the letter.

'You three look a picture!' Simon emerged from the back of the crowd, his cheeks flushed. 'Like Klimt's painting of "The Three Ages of Woman" or something . . .'

'And I'm the crone?' Alex asked. 'Thank you very much.'

His cheeks went from pink to scarlet. 'I didn't . . . sorry, I thought you all look great, just . . .' He waved his glass. 'Too much of this . . . didn't think.'

Alex shook her head but was smiling. 'Don't fret, Simon. You know full well you'd have to try harder than that to offend me. Come over here and look at this. You like crosswords, don't you?' He approached them sheepishly. 'Look, the first words of each paragraph seem to form a sort of acrostic. "This time you have made two maidens cross." Doesn't that sound like a crossword clue?'

He furrowed his brow. 'Yes . . . Fuck, that's cool. Right in front of us . . . This time . . . so that means the answer is a date or day, perhaps. Two maidens and cross. M and X? Or two maidens so M, M, and X. Perhaps it could refer to the year, in Latin numerals.'

'MMX,' Safi said, punching Simon on the shoulder. 'Dude, that's brilliant. So two thousand and ten. What happened that year?'

Martha felt a rushing in her ears, but Safi was still speaking. 'This Chorus thing – it sounds like he's going to tell us a story. And he says he's the voice of freemen – can that mean anything? Stands out from the other stuff a bit. Who is Chorus speaking for?'

Then she knew. Secrets. Falsehoods. The poisoned fountain. The rushing became a roar, like the thrumming of an enormous bell. She couldn't hear her own voice as she replied.

'Charlotte. The name. It's derived from the Old English for "free man". The letter is about Charlie. I'm sorry, I have to go.'

Alex put her hand on Martha's arm. 'Of course, are you all right?'

She could only nod. She folded the letter, tried to put it back in the envelope, her fingers shaking.

'Jesus fucking Christ,' Simon said, staring at her.

'What's going on?' Safi asked, looking between them.

Martha couldn't speak, so Alex did it for her.

'Charlie, Martha's sister, went missing in 2010. She was working in our office at the *CED* at the time. And she hasn't been seen since.'

'Goodnight,' Martha said. The words felt like stones in her mouth; she couldn't breathe for trying to spit them out. 'I'll . . . in the morning.'

She turned and fled through the crowd, down the wide flight of stone steps, and out into Beaumont Street, looking at nothing but the ground. Three corners later she found a side road and turned into it. She put her back against the wall and tried to breathe.

3

eidolon, *noun (seventeenth century)*:
a spirit, phantom, or apparition

SHE'D KNOWN THERE WOULD BE ghosts in Oxford. Martha wasn't afraid of any headless horsemen, or nuns haunting the local ruins; it was Charlie, always Charlie she was afraid would find her. There had been times in the first year after her sister's disappearance when Martha's heart would stop as she spotted her through the crowd: the long blonde hair, the shapeless cardigan draped over a thin cotton dress. She'd hear a laugh, throaty and sudden, or catch a movement, a walk, a twist in the shoulders, and she'd be certain. Just for a moment. Then the illusion would shatter and the person she *knew* to be her sister would resolve into a stranger.

As the years passed, so the ghost of Charlie aged. Now it was women in their mid thirties who made Martha stop dead in the streets. In Berlin, once a month perhaps, she'd felt that same flickering certainty before realising the woman with a child on her lap as she drank a coffee at a pavement café was not her sister, just an echo of Martha's own image of who Charlie might be now, thirteen years after fleeing Oxford and her family.

Martha pressed her palm against the wall behind her. She reminded herself of her therapist's mantra for the moments when she was in danger of being overwhelmed. What can you see now? *The shiny cobbles of the side street, the white brick of the wall opposite.* What can you feel? *The bricks under my fingers, a breeze ruffling my hair.* What can you smell? *Cooking oil, the Black Opium perfume I put on this morning.*

Her breathing slowed.

She pulled the letter out of her bag again and stared at it. Could it be *from* Charlie? Impossible. What could this Chorus know? Should she burn it? Throw it in the river? Take it to the police?

Ah, the police. She heard the scrape of her mother's chair on the kitchen floor as she leapt up at the sound of the doorbell. They had found Charlie's bike not far from the ring road. Did she hitchhike? How was her PhD going? Martha couldn't remember their faces, just their hands around tea mugs as they sat at the table, the low rumble of their voices as they talked about stress and pressure. Most runaways come back in time, they'd said. They left literature, helpline numbers, and world-weary sympathy behind them.

Martha realised she was at her own front door. Her body had picked her up and carried her here through the gathering dark. She looked up. All the lights were off; her father must be in bed.

Charlie had been living here when she went missing, taking advantage of the space, their mum's cooking, and the glow of parental approval while she slogged through her PhD. Martha had just left for university, and was starting to experiment with life out of Charlie's orbit.

As she put her key in the lock, she remembered Alex's shadow moving across the folded letter at the museum. Now it was Charlie's. Always here: the shadows of the past thrown against the walls and floors. She pushed open the door.

Every house has a signature scent. It gives you the first hint of its story, setting off a stream of associations the moment you enter. For Martha, the smell of her parents' house was as integral a part of home as its worn rugs and floorboards. She stepped over the loose panel in the hall that squeaked, a habit of her teenage years, and breathed in once more as she headed for the kitchen. Old books, beeswax, coffee. Her mind searched automatically for the one note which was missing: the floral echoes of her mother's perfume.

Even after two years, you could catch a breath of it in the wardrobe in her parents' room where most of her mother's clothes were still hanging. Martha and Charlie had always loved sitting on the enormous bed as Rebecca got ready for a party, looking on spellbound as she picked up her bottle of Coco Chanel and dabbed it behind her ears. Later, they would sneak back in and explore the jewellery box and make-up drawer, Charlie using Martha as a model on whom to experiment with eyeshadow and mascara. Then they would pick up the glass-stoppered bottle and imitate their mother's final touch. No matter how much they tried to tidy away all traces of their presence and scrub their faces clean, some lingering stain of stolen lipstick on their pillows the next morning would always betray their games. Their mother never once mentioned it, respecting it as part of a private ritual played out for years.

Martha knew that it wasn't just the scent of those days that had evaporated. Her family home was fading. The gold mirror whose gaze her mother had once shared with her children was now speckled with age. Martha looked into its apologetic frame and was surprised by the depth of her frown. 'Aspectabund', she thought: wearing your emotions on your face. Quite.

Rebecca had kept the house beautiful, always ready to welcome Charlie home until sickness had narrowed her vision. She had never stopped believing that Charlie was coming back. Every birthday or Christmas became an agony of repressed, unspoken hope, followed by its painful retreat. Then she would call some of the helplines or post on the forums for families of the missing, and set to, cleaning, mending, saying only that she was certain Charlie was well and just needed time. So much time. Disconnected memories fizzed through Martha's head as she switched on the kitchen light and dropped her bag; a lurch of associations, free-flying, free-falling.

Her father had either not noticed the slow decline of the house or didn't care. He would habitually remove himself to the study when they were children, the clatter of his typewriter ceasing only when his wife teased him out of his sanctuary. In her absence his reclusiveness simply deepened. Martha did not think any friend of his had come to the house since she'd been back. Gabriel's reserve had always been in stark contrast to his wife, whose Mediterranean descent was writ large in everything she did. Martha often thought of the dark tale of Thomas Mann's *Death in Venice*, whose antihero is caught between the warring impulses of his parents, between his mother's sensual embrace of life and his father's cool detachment. There was an image in the story that had implanted itself in Martha's mind as a summary of her family: of the father living with his fists tightly clenched, and of the mother holding out her hands to receive everything life could offer her. And so it was for Rebecca, who embraced even the pain of loving her absent daughter with passionate intensity.

Martha had vowed to live with her own palm outstretched. Had she managed it? Her years in Berlin had been full and spontaneous, but even there she had absented herself at times, finding corners of the city where she could sit in silence, her guilt sharing a park bench with her like an old friend.

She took the letter out again and laid it on the kitchen counter while the kettle boiled.

Truth will come to light. Murder cannot be hid long.

4

throng, *noun (eighteenth century)*:
a gathering; close association

ALEX WEAVED HER WAY THROUGH the crowd to where Safi and Simon had managed to find a table, and set down the drinks. Pints of something called Neck Oil for them, which came in glasses decorated with candy-coloured skulls, and a double whiskey for her.

They'd done well to get a table here after leaving the launch, and it was a pleasant enough evening to sit outside in comfort. Turf Tavern, known to everyone as simply the Turf, was tucked into an ancient courtyard among the twisting cobbled alleyways that lay behind the elegant eighteenth-century façades of Holywell Street. Alex loved the incongruities of the fourteenth-century pub, the centuries of building and rebuilding apparent in its layered architecture, the different window styles and shapes, doors sunk at odd angles, and uneven surfaces. The courtyard was full of young people, squeezed together in groups, all talking a bit too loudly, overplaying popular, confident versions of themselves like mediocre actors grappling with their lines.

She dug a selection of crisps, nuts, and pork scratchings out of her pockets and dropped them on the table.

'Help yourselves. Woman cannot live by canapés alone.'

Safi fell on the pork scratchings with glee.

'So this is weird,' Simon said, picking up a crisp packet, oblivious to the fact that he regularly took Safi to task for starting so many of her sentences with 'So'.

'Uh-huh,' Alex replied noncommittally, crossing her legs and sipping her whiskey.

Safi tried to crunch her pork scratching in a respectful manner. 'Did you both know her? Martha's sister?'

Alex and Simon exchanged glances.

'We did.'

Safi swallowed. 'Are we allowed to talk about it? I mean, that's why we came to the pub, isn't it? To conjobble? Eat, drink, and talk?'

Simon had opened up the crisp packet to form a sort of platter. Alex took one and enjoyed the tangy shock of salt and vinegar on her tongue.

'You're right, Safi,' she said. 'It is why we came, but it feels a lot like tattling behind someone's back now, and I'm having one of those uptight British moments.'

Simon seemed to have inhaled half his pint already. 'Apparently gossip is a positive thing. It's community bonding. I mean, look at all the vocabulary for it we have to deal with: gabbering, yaddering, gasbagging, jaffocking, chamragging . . .'

A crowd of stickily gelled young men bumped up against Safi's chair.

'Watch it, sunshine,' she said over her shoulder. 'You spill this, you're buying me another.'

The young man who had jogged her turned scarlet and mumbled an apology. Safi flashed him a brilliant smile before turning back to her colleagues. She was unaware, Alex was sure, that given the opportunity the man would follow her to the ends of the earth after that smile. 'Be newsmongers then,' Safi went on. 'Give me the facts at least.'

Alex nodded. 'Charlie was a PhD student at Somerville and worked at the *CED* as an editorial assistant. Not full time, just two days a week.' She slipped her feet out of her shoes under the table and pressed them upon the cool stone flags. *Am I grounding myself?* she wondered, even as she spoke. 'I had already been here a couple of years, and Simon, you had been on the dictionary a while by then, too, hadn't you?'

'Not quite a year,' Simon said, and looked down. 'My beer's evaporated. I'll get another round in while you do the facts, Alex. And return for the wild conjecture.'

'Just a half,' Safi said.

'Same again,' Alex raised her glass. 'Jameson, please. No ice.'

He elbowed his way back towards the entrance through the echoing bubble of conversation.

'And what?' Safi scraped her chair closer to the table. 'She just disappeared?'

'Pretty much. I've been trying to remember. She was in the office at the beginning of the week – she normally worked Monday and Tuesday. I got a call from the police on the Saturday afternoon, asking if she had said anything about going away as the family had reported her missing.' A nudge of memory and Alex was her younger self on a sunny autumn afternoon, checking her reflection in the window of an estate agent's office. She recalled the stab of excitement as she wondered if she could afford one of those neat little houses in

Jericho by the canal. She heard her own voice answering the calm, polite police officer on her phone. The shock and strangeness of it.

Safi arched her eyebrows questioningly and Alex blinked her way back to the present, to the pub, its drifting smell of tobacco and the fruity vapours softened by the evening air.

'Charlie hadn't said anything to me about it. It was the week that Jonathan's first book came out and there was a party at Blackwell's on the Thursday. Not as grand as this evening, of course, just crisps and warm white wine, but the book was already generating a lot of buzz. Charlie had been invited, but she didn't show up. I think it was the next day that her parents began to get worried.'

'I forget there must have been a time when Jonathan wasn't famous,' Safi interjected. 'My mum almost forgave me my career when she discovered I'd be working with him.'

'Yes, you could have mistaken him for a mere mortal back then,' Alex said wryly. 'What did your mum want you to do?'

'Medicine. Bit of a long shot with an English degree from Oxford, but she kept hoping. Was it a big party?'

'Yes, packed. I was surprised Charlie missed it. Her parents were there.' She caught Safi's questioning look. 'Martha's father was an archivist, working at the Bodleian, and he was part of the *CED* seminar group with Jonathan, but then Charlie was working hard and it's not extreme for PhD students to disappear in the final stages of writing their thesis.'

Safi looked shocked.

Alex smiled. 'Not "disappear", disappear, I just mean they often ditch social obligations in a panic over footnotes and word counts.'

'Why did the police ring you? Were you and Charlie close?'

Alex shook her head vigorously. 'God, no. They were ringing everyone. Her supervisors, work colleagues, friends, family. After that we heard everything through Jonathan and Mike.'

Mike. Alex should ring him. She had never liked her old boss that much, thinking him snobbish and a little smug, but he had been in the job that Martha now held for fifteen years, retiring reluctantly at sixty with vague plans to pursue independent study. He had never married, choosing an almost-Edwardian life of scholarship despite being born in the heart of the twentieth century. She wondered what Safi had thought of him during the few months her career at the dictionary was beginning and his was ending.

'And what did you hear?'

'First that she hadn't been seen since the Thursday morning of Jonathan's launch. Then her bike was found, I think probably a week or so later? Her cards hadn't been used and her phone was switched off. She'd taken her laptop, so we thought perhaps she'd gone somewhere to work.' Alex settled back into the memories. For weeks after, months even, the air around her had felt charged. Life had become a series of small, static shocks as they were confronted each day with the fact of Charlie's disappearance. She had sat down with her mildly embarrassed teenaged sons and had long talks with them about their mental health, making them promise to share their feelings, giving them assurances of her love and support. 'It was awful. I didn't know Charlie that well, had only met Dr Thornhill and his wife in passing a few times, but someone just disappearing like that was upending. I felt . . . I felt like I couldn't trust things to stay in place. Buildings, people . . . everything might just wink out of existence at any moment.'

Safi moved her glass in small circles on the table, making patterns with the condensation, watching the water sink into the wood and vanish.

'What did they think had happened?'

'The police? I've no idea . . .'

'No,' Safi replied without looking up. 'Her family. And Jonathan and Mike.'

Alex finished the rest of her whiskey. Darkness had settled around them, but the moon and the light from the pub windows lifted the shadows. A girl peered out at the crowd from an upstairs window, watching the mild revelry from a distance. She reminded Alex of Martha: wistful, removed, locked in thought.

'They hoped she'd gone away for a few days, taken a break from Oxford. Perhaps ditched the bike and hitched a lift somewhere. Mike, I think, assumed after a while that she'd killed herself.'

'How horrible,' Safi said with a passion that surprised Alex. She was blinking rapidly. It always impressed Alex: the capacity of the younger generation to openly display their feelings rather than euphemise them.

'Yes. I think her mother always refused to believe it. Must have been so grim for Martha. I'm sure it still is.'

Simon reappeared with the drinks and more crisps. 'Sorry, bar was packed. Are we ready for the fantastical speculation yet?'

Safi took her drink with a nod of thanks. 'Almost. Did you like her?'

She was asking them both. Alex glanced at Simon; she had done her share.

'She was very clever,' Simon said, picking up the conversational baton. 'And beautiful. Double First; played the violin; rowed. Could be charming. Funny. Dry sense of humour.'

'You didn't answer the question,' Safi said, pursing her lips.

Alex pressed her feet into the cool flags again and took a swallow from her fresh glass of whiskey. 'Of course he didn't,' she said. 'Charlie disappeared, devastating her family. It would be in poor taste to say she could be arrogant, dismissive, but she seemed to reduce the rest of us to ciphers. I was just a mother; Mike was a dinosaur.'

'I got my first degree at Leeds, which she seemed to think was quaintly amusing,' Simon added. 'It was subtle – she wasn't outwardly rude, but you came away feeling . . .'

'Elf-shot,' Alex finished. 'A conversation with Charlie left you with tiny wounds dealt by invisible archers, and they festered.'

'Yeah, that's about right.'

Safi frowned, absorbing this new information. 'But that doesn't sound like someone who'd have a breakdown in the middle of their PhD and run away.'

Alex wrapped her coat around herself, feeling the expensive whisper of silk against her skin while the whiskey warmed her blood and the chill of the old stone under her feet kept her connected to the ancient streets, their flow of language and story.

'Exactly. But we can never know what's really going on in another person's head. We're all so obsessed with our own problems and with how people see us that we create simple silhouettes for everyone else. I don't know about you, Simon, but I felt so guilty after she disappeared. There was something going on with Charlie, and I thought I'd been too blinded by her looks and her brains to notice. I know it's a platitude, but I kept wondering if there was something I could have done.'

He drank his pint, considering the question. 'I don't think I felt guilty. My daughter Chloe was only six months old. I felt afraid for her, tried harder in my marriage, then had Stephine eighteen months later. I probably would have been divorced five years earlier if Charlie hadn't disappeared.'

'It must be an awful pressure to be that beautiful and brilliant,' Safi said.

Alex laughed softly. 'So how do you cope, Safi?'

Safi laughed, spluttering into her beer. 'I have four housemates and a phalanx of Nigerian aunties to keep my feet on the ground. So what's with the letter? Is someone playing a prank on Martha now she's back in town?'

'Possibly,' Simon said. 'Sick thing to do, though, isn't it?'

'We should go back through the files,' Alex said, swilling the last of the whiskey. The courtyard was emptying out now and a couple of staff were threading through the remaining drinkers, collecting glasses. 'What if Chorus has written before, and we simply haven't noticed?'

'I'll look tomorrow,' Safi said.

'Horrible,' Simon said. His face was flushed. Alex wished he hadn't mentioned his divorce or his daughters. Both subjects made him morose; add in some alcohol and it was not a happy combination. 'Why would anyone dredge all this up again?'

'There is another possibility – beyond it being some sort of joke,' Safi said, finishing her drink and passing the glass to a waiter sporting a sleeve of swirling Celtic tattoos. 'Chorus might actually know something.'

5

wone, *noun (thirteenth century)*:
a dwelling-place

THE WORDS ACCOMPANIED ALEX AS she walked back to her house in the narrow streets of Jericho, turned her key in the lock, and switched on the hall lights. Her cat, black from her paws to the tip of her tail, weaved his way around her ankles. She bent down, offering her hand to be rubbed.

'Yes, home at last, Rags.'

She'd resisted the idea of a cat at first, anticipating the cliché of a single woman of a certain age looking for a child or lover substitute. But her sons had cajoled her out of her qualms, and she was glad they had. Raglan was an absurdly affectionate creature and padded around the ornaments and oddments that crowded Alex's bookshelves with exaggerated care.

Wearily, she set her bag on the hall table before walking into the living room and opening the French windows that led to her small back yard.

Chorus might actually know something.

What could anyone know about Charlie's disappearance? Her eye was drawn to a picture of the boys that had been taken at about that time. They were grinning, arms locked around each other's shoulders, half-silouetted against an anonymous stretch of lush greenery and screwing up their eyes to the sun. But Alex knew perfectly well where it had been taken: at the nature reserve near C. S. Lewis's house, a secret patch of Narnia among the oblivious residential streets.

I would have been divorced five years earlier if it hadn't been for Charlie.

It was late, and Alex was tired and a little drunk, but she wasn't ready for bed yet. Her laptop sat under the window on the old dining table she used as a desk. The whiskey decanter and glasses were set ready on its elegantly weathered surface. Nothing was out of place, but then Sue, who cleaned for her twice a week, was as careful with her home as the cat was. 'Instagram-ready', her daughter-in-law, Ethan's wife, had called it. Alex's aesthetic, according to Ayesha, was cottage-core. A good thing apparently. On the other hand, her younger son, Jacob, accused his mother of being a borderline hoarder.

The only man she'd had a serious relationship with since her divorce had complained that there was no room for him in her house. She'd looked at him, and at the house, concluded he was right, and promptly ended the romance.

She poured the whiskey but ignored the computer, picking up instead her journal from the table next to her armchair and letting her hand wander over its pages, tuning into the soundscape of Oxford at night. A car in the distance; someone calling an over-loud farewell; a door slamming; students heading home from the Jericho Tavern; the cicada rattle of a freewheeling bicycle. Sometimes she would hear the fingernail screech of a barn owl, hunting at dusk in Port Meadow. Too late for that now.

Alex looked down at her latest doodle. She remembered the creed of all graphologists: that the accidental graffiti on our pages reveal our subconscious thoughts. She saw that she had sketched a word, its block capitals carefully shaded. CHARLIE. She stared at the retro, rotary dial phone sitting next to the computer.

The things we do to protect our families. The ones we are born into, the ones we make. The quiet compromises.

Was it time to make the call?

Not yet. She closed the book, finished her drink and closed the doors.

'Time for bed, Rags.'

She picked up the cat, who settled on her shoulder, and went to climb the stairs. Her chest rumbled with Raglan's throaty purrs as she paused to glance at the post Sue had picked up from the mat and set on the hall table. Two or three bills, and a postcard with a picture of a familiar portico on the front. The *CED*. Alex shifted Raglan in her arms and turned it over. Her name and address were digitally printed on a neat label, glued over the right side of the card. On the other side someone had written in neat block capitals:

I DO DESPISE A LIAR

Alex's eyes flicked to the front door. Yes, the security chain was attached.

'Shit,' she whispered. The cat rubbed against her chin, kneading her shoulders with his night-black paws.

6

shrine, *noun (fifteenth century)*:
an object of veneration

MARTHA TOOK HER TEA UPSTAIRS to her room. She had been trying to make it less childlike since she returned to Oxford, but whenever she decided to reorganise it she found herself paralysed, unable to grapple with this space that hovered between her past and future. The former felt clouded, troubling; the latter ineluctable yet impossible at the same time.

Her bedroom clung unsteadily to the expectations for her life she'd had growing up here. She had anticipated being married by now, a mother. Not that she'd ever asked herself if she wanted to be married or have children – she'd just assumed it would happen. What would her sixteen-year-old self think of her now? Would she be disappointed? Angry? Baffled probably.

That makes two of us.

The letter from Chorus was back in the bag she'd flung onto the desk where she had studied for her A-levels. Her set texts were still on the shelf above it, full of her painstaking annotations. *Hamlet*, *Ariel* by Sylvia Plath, and *Middlemarch*. Her advanced German grammar was there, too, its spine cracked, alongside dozens of second-hand Virago classics and a bunch of CDs she'd abandoned here when she first moved to Berlin.

She left the room to escape the insistent stare of her bag and went next door into Charlie's room. She switched on the light.

Her father's cleaner obviously came in regularly. Martha had been expecting it to smell musty, unused, but however much Gabriel had let the rest of the house run to seed, this room had been looked after according to her mother's wishes. It was far more grown-up than Martha's space, but then Charlie had had it redecorated when she moved back in to start her PhD.

Martha sat down carefully on the bed and looked around. When they were young this room had always been an assault on the senses: clothes everywhere, posters of Destiny's Child and Eminem on the walls, cork boards with drifts of postcards and flyers accreted haphazardly. Then Charlie had wiped out her younger self and replaced it with something smoother, unwrinkled by the past. Martha remembered going to Kettles Yard in Cambridge with her sister, how they'd lingered over its elegantly understated collections. There were echoes of that look here, but something was missing. Emotion, Martha realised. She recalled a conversation with Charlie about a word she'd discovered one day: 'shibui', from Japanese. She'd tried to convey its essence to her sister, explaining that it was about simple and unobtrusive beauty, a quiet state of being that shuns ostentation and, crucially, improves with age. Shibui, she'd concluded, was a smile-wrinkled face or a time-honed piece of wood. She'd expected Charlie to share her delight in the idea. Instead, she recognised that her sister feared invisibility and imperfection. A life was either ablaze, public, or not fulfilled at all.

Nothing really to fire the soul here, Martha noted flatly. A woven bamboo carpet almost completely covered the pale wooden floorboards. The curtains pulled back from the sash windows were a pale yellow, and the bookshelves were painted in dark green. Charlie's desk waited for her, its A4 notepads of PhD research neatly stacked. A fountain pen lay poised on the green leather cover of the desk itself, a newly upholstered armchair of the same colour tucked behind it. On either side of the bed, floor-to-ceiling wardrobes housed expertly folded clothes. Only a pair of old abstract prints by Sonia Delaunay hung over the bed, their muted greens and blues occasionally interrupted by splashes of scarlet. Even the books looked as if they'd been picked for their bindings: reds, golds, and browns in crinkled cloth or leather to harmonise with the prints.

There was just one photograph, of Charlie herself, grinning, one hand holding back her hair against the wind. Martha had spent a lot of time staring at the picture in the weeks after Charlie had disappeared, sitting on the bed and wondering at the terrible absence of her sister. It had been taken in the sunny courtyard of some country house, a wall and the edge of its roof and windows just visible behind her.

Martha opened the closet and switched on the light. To her surprise it still worked. So this was where the other Charlie was hiding – along the narrow shelves where her sister had consigned herself to overflowing shoeboxes. Martha picked up the last one and returned to the bed. Her stomach clenched in a familiar anticipation of sadness and fear. The box was labelled '2010'. Had Charlie kept all this for some future biographer? 'Portrait of the genius as a young woman'? Martha leafed through the concert flyers, the postcards from friends, invitations, and scrawled notes bearing the handwriting of strangers.

'Are you looking for something?'

Martha looked up sharply. Her father stood in the doorway, filling its narrow frame. He was wearing a long burgundy dressing gown over his pyjamas. Blue cotton with white piping – he had never worn any other design, but these were looking decidedly worse for wear. Martha felt a spasm of concern. Her mum had always bought Gabriel's pyjamas for him. Where did she get them? Were they even replaceable?

'No,' Martha said, setting down the box. 'I haven't been in here since I came home. I was at Jonathan's launch this evening and . . .' Should she tell him about the letter? 'Well, I suppose it made me think of Charlie.'

He remained on the threshold, as if some forcefield were holding him back.

'You can't have this room, Martha. This is Charlie's, for as long as I'm allowed to stay.' His tone was stringent, resentful almost.

'Dad . . . what? No, I don't want to move in here.'

'Good. Your mother wanted it kept. Until we get her home.'

Martha looked down at her hands. 'Fine,' she responded weakly.

He cleared his throat and seemed to come to a little. 'Was it a pleasant evening?'

She could tell him now. She *should* tell him now. 'Yes. You were invited, you know. Gemma was there.'

He made a huffing noise in the back of his throat. '"I could spend half my evenings, if I wanted, holding a glass of washing sherry" . . .'

'They served champagne.' He opened his mouth and she held up her hand, suddenly terribly tired. 'Yes, I know you're quoting Larkin, Dad. I can play that game too. "All solitude is selfish."'

'You're a fine one to talk.'

'I know. But sometimes I don't think it's good for either of us.'

He came in then, and sat beside her on the bed. His chin was rough with white stubble, and there was a slightly longer patch just under his chin. He was still a handsome man. Perhaps he could remarry, then he and this house would be someone else's problem.

'Did you find anything interesting in here?' he asked. His version of an olive branch.

'Just odds and ends. She had such a busy life I sometimes wonder how she managed to get any work done. What have you been doing today?'

'Research.'

It was always research. Vague and unspecified projects that kept Gabriel in his room most of the day. He still cared for the garden, though, as the tumbling spiraea and forget-me-nots in the borders attested.

'Where do you think she is?' Martha asked, picking up a postcard from the top of the shoebox. It pictured a page of illustrated manuscript. She flipped it over. It was addressed to Charlie at Somerville. *You dazzle me*, it said. *30.iii.MMX*

A love note. Could it be from Tom, Charlie's boyfriend that summer? Probably, though she didn't think Tom was the sort of person to use Latin numerals in dates. But Charlie always had other admirers, and she had undoubtedly dazzled them all. Martha herself had been one of them. They were all still waiting for her to return and take her bow after her grand disappearing trick, stuck in the strange limbo of a moment between shock and tumultuous applause.

Gabriel got up quickly. 'Your mother liked playing "Where is she now?" games, Martha. Imagining grandchildren she'd never seen. I didn't like playing them then, and I don't have to play them with you now. I don't like . . . conjecture.'

He tugged at the belt of his dressing gown and wrapped it tightly around his diminished waist.

'Sorry, Dad. But that's not what I'm doing.'

Gabriel hesitated. 'Your mother. She liked the Facebook page. She liked to think of Charlie reading it.'

The Facebook page. It had been Martha's own profile, full not of photos but of snippets from the corners of dictionaries or novels that she'd fallen upon during her A-levels. After Charlie disappeared, Martha had posted religiously once a month, a ritual of repentance and appeal. Usually it took the form of some detail about her current life, first at university and then in Berlin, or news about her parents back in Oxford. She'd accepted every friendship request she received, just in case one of them turned out to be Charlie. She'd posted about her mother's diagnosis there too. Thanking people for their thoughts and prayers had been draining, as had been fending off faith healers and the hawkers of cancer-killing vitamins or smoothies. She'd replied patiently to the donors of platitudinous but well-meant advice.

Martha's last post had been of the bank of flowers delivered for Rebecca's funeral. If Charlie could see that and still not make contact with them, she thought, then what was the point?

'Were you doing it for Charlie or your mother? I mean, did you think Charlie might see it, or did you do it so your mother would think that?'

He was looking away from her now, a frown of fierce concentration on his face. Martha didn't know how to answer him. 'A bit of both,' she said quietly.

He nodded, a short sharp dip of his head that could have meant anything. Martha put the lid back on the shoebox and replaced it in the cupboard. When her mother became ill, she had talked a lot about Charlie and the months before she disappeared, sifting her memories for some clue, something she missed. Something to torture herself with, or some thread of hope. Had they all put too much pressure on her? She had been working so hard, and there had been many midnights when Martha would see her sister's light on over the summer. She'd be out before they woke most mornings, too, cycling to the Bodleian or the *CED*, the toast crumbs and mug in the sink the only token that she'd been there at all. And Charlie had been mysterious. Not exactly secretive, but vague about her plans and movements. Spotted in unexpected corners of town. Had she been laying plans? Having an affair? Her mother's favourite scenario involved her arranging a job abroad, as though her daughter's absence was a mere hiccup of lost time. It was true Charlie had wanted to travel more.

Each time she mentioned it, Gabriel would agree that was a possibility, and then retreat to his study until one of them summoned him for dinner.

Only once had her mother admitted the possibility that her eldest daughter was dead. It had been in the last week of her life, when she had spotted Martha wiping away tears as she sat by her bed. 'I'll be with Charlie now,' she'd said. 'Don't worry.'

Martha glanced up and saw that her father was still watching her. 'Is a hard truth better than a comforting lie, Martha?'

'I don't know, Dad. Do you have any to hand?'

Too flippant. It enraged him.

'No. Do you? Why are you actually here? Why did you come back? And don't say it was for me.'

The guilt squeezed her lungs. He was studying her, a cold clinical stare. When Rebecca was alive there had been love in this house; it felt viscerally absent now. Was that what was making the mirrors spot and the paintwork flake?

He shook his head, as if driving some thought out of his mind.

'I needed a change. And I think you do, too, Dad.'

He shook his head. 'Don't project, sweetheart.'

One of her mother's catchphrases. Her ghost flitted between them, smoothing out the connections between father and daughter, trying to make the ties that bound them more comfortable.

'Goodnight,' they said at the same time.

Martha found the postcards the next morning. Thursday's post had come while she was at work and lay uncollected on the mat; in her preoccupation she must have stepped over the bundle when she came home. It comprised a thick members' magazine from the National Trust, addressed to both her parents, and two identical picture postcards of the *CED*. She turned them over. One was addressed to Gabriel:

This young gentlewoman had a father

Martha reeled. The cruelty of it.

The other, addressed to her, had an altogether different message in neat block capitals.

Crueller still. She shoved them both in her bag and left the house, the shadows surging in her wake.

7

zemblanity, *noun (twentieth century)*:

the inexorability of unwanted discoveries

'HOT BEHIND!'

Safi and her housemates had lived together long enough to negotiate around each other like waiters in a busy café. Toast was grabbed, the kettle was on a constant boil, and milk and cereal were traded and haggled over. Different music played from different rooms, with Radio 1 the mainstay in the kitchen. Paula was usually ironing something in the living room before heading off to school where, at twenty-three, she was already deputy head of the mathematics department. Josh left later to open up the art gallery on the London Road, and Yasmin went to the shared working space in Angel Court where she ran a bookkeeping business. Which left Safi, who was currently dancing through the living room, brandishing tea.

It seemed to work. They'd all experienced roommates from hell in the past, and the house vibe was built upon relief that no one pinched anyone else's food, nor drew pen marks on their personal milk bottle. Each of them (mostly) came up with the rent on time, and only smoked in the garden out back.

They'd all been out or in bed when Safi came home last night, and she was grateful for that. She knew she would have had to tell someone eventually about the freakish letter, and how it referenced the disappearance of her slightly otherworldly boss's sister, but she also knew she'd feel bad about doing so.

She settled at the dining table and tried to clear a space for herself, earning herself tuts from Yasmin in the process, who was doom-scrolling on her phone.

'Don't just shove it about, sort it out!'

Safi dusted crumbs off her hands and grabbed the pile of fliers. A student production of Ibsen was touted on a suitably brooding background, mixed in among multiple adverts for house cleaners. Twenty pounds an hour? A better financial bet than lexicography at this point, she thought.

And suddenly there it was. A postcard of the *CED*. Safi turned it over. Addressed to her, with a neat computer-printed address label, it read:

Tis thou that must help me

'What's up, Saf? You look like you've seen a ghost.'

'Yeah, feels a bit like that. A ghost in need of help.'

Yasmin glanced up as Safi turned round the card to show her the message.

'Weird. Some sort of marketing campaign?'

Safi shrugged, but Yasmin had already turned her attention back to her screen.

Safi shoved her phone, wallet, keys and book into her crumpled teal backpack and biked into the city with a flock of fellow commuters. What a strange breed they were. London's cyclists all worshipped at the church of Spandex, testing its elasticity to the hilt as they crouched low over the handlebars of their aggressively logoed road bikes. In Oxford, by contrast, the sit-up-and-beg bike was still enjoying its moment, as if each rider had just left the set of a Miss Marple adaptation and were on their way to the butcher's for something tied up in string. Safi's bike belonged firmly to this last category; it sported pastel streamers on its handlebars, like a child's, for no other reason than they made her smile. Her cousin had gone through a wearing existentialist phase at sixteen, manifested by a combination of black polo necks, jazz, and attitude. The rainbow had been a reaction. Safi saw no reason to equate intelligence with a monochromatic wardrobe. The world was on fire, and her generation had sweet FA to look forward to, so why not at least take advantage of advanced dyes and cheap paint? It certainly made her bike easier to find among the hundreds of anonymous two-wheelers crammed into every corner of the city.

She locked it up in the modern courtyard behind the pillared façade before jogging up the wide steps and gliding through the glass doors into the offices: sleek, light spaces carved into the building's old bones.

Half the employees worked from home now – Martha's team were unusual in that they were all in most days. They each preferred coming into the office to tangle and tussle with the language together. Safi in particular liked the calm contrast to her own busy house and the small thrill of breathing in the book-scented air. She headed straight for the correspondence archives, her ruby silk jacket floating behind her.

Every piece of correspondence to the dictionary was filed and sorted. If Chorus had ever written to them before, their letter would probably have ended up in Miscellaneous, along with the hundreds of entreaties from assorted logophiles to have their word included in the dictionary immediately, simply on the basis of their say-so. 'Ipsedixitism', Safi remembered: the assertion that something is fact just because a single person says so.

She settled at a table among the stacks, breathing in the sharp scent of slowly decomposing paper, and began to riffle through the general correspondence folders, starting with 2010. There were quite a few thank-yous in there: some from writers, others from readers who addressed the dictionary directly, as though it were a living thing. A friend even, to whom they turned for solace and stability, or as a source of soothing, lexical white noise. Safi considered this as she turned over each sheet, most still attached with rusting paperclips to the envelopes they had arrived in. Some had crossed the world, their envelopes stained with travel and decorated with stamps of flowers, birds, and maps. Each February saw a great flurry of birthday greetings. Of all the things to anthropomorphise, Safi thought, the dictionary was a strange choice, but she heartily approved. It had comforted her often enough too.

She should do a thorough study of these files some day, go right back through them. Perhaps she could deliver a lecture at her old college on the thousands of narratives locked within the *CED*'s correspondence. She was half there already in her head, recounting stories of madmen and vicars, poets and astronomers, when she found it.

A postcard, the address and message written in block capitals so neatly they appeared printed.

The card was unsigned, but something about its oddness caught her eye. She turned it over, and was entirely unsurprised when the picture revealed itself to be the same as the one she herself had received.

Now she had an idea of what she was looking for, the others were easy to spot. The first had come in 2011, followed by one every year on exactly the same date. All were postcard views of the dictionary building, all were printed in neat block capitals, and all revolved around words relating to falsehood. 'Pseudologiser', read one; 'gobemouche' another. The first was an inventor of elaborate lies, the second someone who, open-mouthed, believes everything they are told, a 'fly-swallower'. Each had been sent to their former boss, Mike Orme.

Martha was the last of the team to arrive just before nine. The others were gathered around Safi's desk, and stopped talking the moment she came in.

She didn't wish them good morning, nor did she slide in behind her computer and pretend to involve herself with emails. Some things had to be faced head-on.

'Safi,' she began, 'have the others filled you in?'

'Yes.' Safi's gaze was direct. 'Did you get a postcard yesterday, Martha?'

Martha stared. 'You got one too?'

'We all did,' Simon said. 'And that's not all. Look what Safi has found.'

Safi handed her the small pile of postcards and Martha flicked through them.

'All implications of lying, or falsehoods,' Simon told her. 'Strange thing is, Chorus's letter was addressed to all of us, but these ones are just addressed to Mike.'

Alex cleared her throat. 'What do you want to do, Martha?'

Martha folded her arms across her chest and leant against the desk. 'I've been thinking about what Jonathan said, right before we worked out the crossword clue. That either the writer of these will go away and bother someone else, or they'll be in touch again and make themselves clearer. But with us all getting these postcards . . . I don't know.' She looked up at them, suddenly aware that she did, rather desperately, want their opinion. 'Oh, and . . . I haven't told my father about any of this. I think I'd rather keep it quiet for now, in case it turns out to be some sort of prank.'

'A very involved one,' Safi said. 'Finding all our addresses.'

'I haven't said anything to anyone,' Simon said quickly. 'But speaking of Jonathan, what about him? He asked us to send him the letter, didn't he?'

Martha ran her fingers through her unbrushed hair. 'Yes. I thought, perhaps, we could send it to him, but not tell him what we worked out? I know that sounds dishonest, but it's all such a can of worms, and he didn't seem particularly bothered. I'm hoping he'll take his own advice and ignore it too for the time being.'

Alex nodded, though Martha thought she saw a spasm of irritation cross her face. 'I can't see there is anything we can do at the moment, Martha. But I think you should go to the police. Who else you choose to tell is entirely up to you, but they, at least, should know.' She paused. 'What does Chorus want from us? Do you think they expect us to start interrogating each other about Charlie's disappearance?'

Simon and Safi exchanged glances behind her, which made Martha suspect that they had already done exactly that last night.

'Martha, if you decide to go to the police, you'd better take those,' Safi said, pointing at the postcards. 'And the one that came to me.' She pulled it out of the bag and handed it over.

'Yours is nicer in tone than mine,' Alex said, catching sight of the quote on the back as it passed between Martha and Safi. 'I had "I do despise a liar".'

'Well, I was, like, ten, when Charlie went missing,' Safi replied. 'What was yours, Simon?'

'Oh, er, "God keep me from false friends". I didn't bring it in, though.'

Martha concentrated on the stack of cards addressed to Mike Orme. No one asked what her quote was, and she felt a complicated curl of gratitude in her stomach for their tact.

'None of the postcards to Mike are signed "Chorus",' Safi said, curtailing the pause just before it became uncomfortable, 'but I thought they must have something to do with Charlie's disappearance. There's one a year, starting in 2011, and it's always the same picture.'

Martha shifted through them. Each postcard showed the same view. The writer must have bought them in bulk.

'Thank you,' she said quietly. 'For now let's crack on with the day, shall we?'

Alex and Simon headed for their monitors. 'Has anyone seen Mike recently?' Simon asked.

'I bumped into him at the Bodleian a while ago,' Safi said. 'I asked if we'd see him at Jonathan's party last night, but he said he was going to spend the spring at his place in France. How do people who work here end up with enough money for a house in France?'

'There's a trick to that,' Simon's computer wheezed asthmatically as he started it up. 'It's called "start working here in 1973".'

Martha half smiled, going through the postcards one more time before she began to deal with the inbox and her task list for the day. There were emails about the Forum and outreach programmes, a reminder of the staff canteen's new hours, and a bunch of requests for access to the slips from scholars – or meta-scholars as Simon liked to call them: scholars who studied scholarship. Her fingers drifted to her necklace, running the hearts back and forth as she read.

'So perhaps the cards to Mike are from Ms Wilson or someone similar who didn't get their antedating or odd quotation into the dictionary, and the picture is just a coincidence,' Safi said after a few minutes of silence. 'There's probably not a massive choice of postcards of this place.'

'No,' Martha said, more bluntly than she had intended. 'They are all about Charlie.'

'How do you know?' Alex asked, peering at her over the top of her reading glasses.

Martha picked one up and tapped the postmark. 'They were all sent on her birthday.'

8

hethensith, *noun (thirteenth century)*:
a departure or decease

THERE WAS SOMETHING LOUCHE ABOUT the word 'taphophile', Martha thought, as she nudged open the rusty gate to her favourite lunch-spot. She'd left Simon and Safi at their desks, prising open the lids of their Tupperware containers and peering inside as though their contents were a mystery. Alex was out, meeting a friend, a Friday ritual for her which made Simon grumble and wonder out loud how she could afford it, and which left Safi vocally impressed that Alex seemed to have so many friends. Martha was different. By the time the press's clock struck one she felt a familiar need to escape and to lose herself in her head once more. She needed a place to be for a little while before she could decide whether to go to the police. Today's venue was one she sought out often for she knew that its other customers would allow her the silence she craved. This was St Sepulchre's Cemetery, just minutes' walk from the office and in Martha's eyes one of the most under-appreciated spots in Oxford. A taphophile seeks out graveyards and other accoutrements of death, and she had to admit that, however unsavoury its sound, the word suited her.

The graveyard attracted few visitors these days. It had long been closed to new burials and was largely left to the devices of a devoted garden group, who sought to preserve its understated and wildish beauty. It had been consecrated in the mid-nineteenth century, when all of Oxford's twelve existing cemeteries were declared full, thanks largely to the cholera epidemic a few decades before. A wall of evergreen trees had been planted to shield the new burial place from public view.

Martha loved the higgledy-piggledy arrangement of the tombstones: some standing proudly, others teetering, and still more collapsed altogether. There were no serried ranks here: the only thing the stones shared was that they all faced east, just like every church altar, placed to look towards Jerusalem and, Martha knew, giving us the *orient* in 'orientate' in the process. Beyond this single unity was a charming haphazardness everywhere, together with an unkempt dignity and a sense of elegant decline. She noticed that the friends of the church had been clearing brambles recently, uncovering many more stones that had lain forgotten for years. Martha stepped carefully around them and relished the cool breeze that ruffled the copper beeches and heavy yews. The whisper of elves, she thought: that's how her mother had always described a breath of wind.

She sought out a spot under a rowan by one of her favourite graves, dedicated to GEORGE WAINWRIGHT, DIED 1942, AGE 61. FOR 41 YEARS ASSISTANT ON THE CLARENDON ENGLISH DICTIONARY. Wainwright's length of service was reason enough to honour him. But Martha loved him more because he had dared to do what no modern lexicographer could: to play around with definitions and even plant a fake one. Beneath the entry for 'interdespise', a nineteenth-century verb conveying mutual contempt, Wainwright had written a secondary sense: 'The relationship between a jobbing lexicographer and his critics, informed by meddlesome expectations of a language and its reality'. A dry sort of rebellion, Martha thought, but a rebellion nonetheless; resistance to the evolution of words was nothing new. But today's fictitious entries had a different motivation, planted in order to catch any copyright infringement or plagiarism by others, and known since the 1970s as a 'mountweazel' thanks to the bogus inclusion in a biographical dictionary of a woman called Lilian Mountweazel, who had 'died at thirty-one in an explosion while on assignment for *Combustibles* magazine'.

Smiling to herself, Martha took out the cheese and oatcakes she had thrown into her bag that morning and breathed out – or suspired, as she would have expressed it to her colleagues, rejoicing in yet another beautiful word that had inexplicably faded from view.

She dragged her attention to the problem at hand. Should she take the letter to the police? They might simply be the work of a crank, or prankster, a strange riddling confession that hinted at a baseless accusation. But the fact that whoever had written it had also sent postcards to their homes suggested something more serious than a cruel joke.

A cloud passed overhead and Martha's chill deepened. The letter's tangled lines hid something important, like the brambles obscuring the inscriptions on the headstones.

What was it about this place that attracted her? Probably the hidden stories of each life below the soil: the secret connections that she loved unearthing in her own work. An etymology of gravestones, perhaps. Now here was Chorus with their tantalising, uncomfortable suggestions. There was something of the melancholic in their letter, too: a pain behind the anger.

Martha thought of all the expressions in English that proved that cemeteries held sway over more than just her own imagination. The Victorians, thanks to macabre stories of exhumed coffins riddled with desperate scratches, were terrified of being buried alive ('taphophobia', she winced – one for Alex). Consequently, putative corpses would often be buried with a bell inside their coffin, lest they wake up and need to attract attention. It is this, people said, that inspired the expression 'saved by the bell', as well as 'dead ringer', and even 'graveyard shift', rumoured to involve sextons sitting by gravesides to listen out for any frantic tintinnabulation. Perfect as such stories seemed, they were all apocryphal, although even Martha herself had once been convinced by their plausibility.

She recalled relaying all this to Charlie, one sunny morning when they had both retraced the tracks of their childhood along the fairy wood their father had created for them in their garden. Retreading the paths that seemed so small now, but had felt vast to them as children, they had stumbled across a small cross at the outer boundary of the coppice of silver birches. They could just about make out some lettering running across it, spelling out the single word 'Monty'. *The grave of a beloved pet?* they wondered. Charlie had shivered and pulled her sister's sleeve to come away. 'Let's go find the sun,' she'd said.

Had they always been so different? We define ourselves by comparison with others – *I am not like them, so I am like this.* Charlie had been the fire, the limelight that transformed the ordinary. Martha was her shadow, four years younger and always following along behind. She was sister moon, the wyrd sister, the dreamer. Charlie was the driven, ambitious one who seemed to be in perpetual motion. Mary in the school nativity play, Ophelia in a production of *Hamlet*. Martha, naturally, had always been the shepherd or the attendant lord; they said she wouldn't like the attention. She sometimes wondered whether, if she had disappeared instead of Charlie, the loss would have been felt quite as keenly. Perhaps she would have simply faded away completely.

She bit into another oatcake. *There. I am real*, she told herself. *I am not just what's left behind.*

She rested a hand on Wainwright's headstone and considered how a grave is another definition of self: this person was born here, died then. Yet even in death we are defined in terms of other people. Husband, father, and grandfather. Mother, daughter, wife, sister. Good for Wainwright that he summarised himself by his profession.

Charlie's absence had no such boundaries. *Charlotte Thornhill, 1987 – ?* There had been an anthology reading in a Berlin pub one night, from a book of poems about the city by writers living and dead, and one poet had wryly pointed out to Martha the strangeness of seeing their own name at the bottom of the page with a single date *(1973 –)*. 'The gap will get filled in one day. It's an odd thing to see it there, waiting for me.'

Was there an end-date waiting for Charlie, too, or had it already been inscribed in distant stone? If her mother was right, her daughter might be buried under another name, in another country. But how could Martha, her shadow, define herself in Charlie's absence?

If the police chose to dismiss her, so be it. She had a responsibility to Alex, Simon and Safi now that they'd been personally involved, and she had a debt and a duty to her sister too. She would give the police the facts, as simple and precise as the gravestones, and they could make of them what they would.

The thought was enough to rouse her. She texted Simon to let him know she'd be late back from lunch, brushed the crumbs from her lap for the birds, and set off.

9

grob, *verb (eighteenth century)*:

to search by the sense of feeling, as with the hand in a dark place

St Aldates Police Station was quiet, and the sergeant at reception had gone to find someone to speak to her. Martha had the waiting room to herself, for a good while.

'What do *you* think it means?' the someone asked after moving them both to a chilly interview room and reading the letter in protracted silence.

Martha had spent the long minutes studying him. He was in his mid-thirties perhaps, with thick red hair, a neatly trimmed beard and broad shoulders. Put him in a flannel shirt and you'd think he was a craft brewer. She tried to remember his name; he had introduced himself but in her nervous scrutiny of him, she had failed to catch it. She peered surreptitiously at the badge on his lanyard: Oliver something.

Martha wasn't sure what she'd expected. A 'Well, that's odd' response, perhaps, followed by a form to fill in and sign. Instead the detective on the other side of the table had seemed politely concerned, and he'd let out an 'ah' of comprehension when she'd explained the clue. Now he was shifting in his chair, affording her a better view of the lanyard. Oliver Caldwell, a Yorkshire surname. Her father had long been a student of onomastics, and loved to unpack the names of people they encountered as children. Caldwell, from Old English, meant 'chill spring'.

'I have no idea. I'm assuming they'll write again, or simply go away. But these postcards addressed to our homes are worrying us.'

'Not a hard thing to look up, an address, but it does indicate this Chorus is someone who might know you . . . And I think you are right to assume the same person wrote the letter.' He rubbed his chin. 'Your sister hasn't been featured on one of these true crime podcasts, has she?'

'On what?'

He looked surprised she didn't know what he was talking about. 'True crime? Investigations into open cases? They're everywhere: podcasts, TikTok too. Virtual sleuths going over old disappearances, or unsolved murders, and recording "shocking rumours" in their bedroom. Some of them are quite good, to be fair. Others cause major headaches.'

'Why would anyone . . . ?' She tailed off.

He smiled at her. 'Gives people some sense of mission. Their followers often shamelessly contact the family or friends of people who have gone missing, and a young woman like your sister? She'd be catnip to them.'

'Catnip?' Martha said, not quite managing to suppress a shocked laugh.

'Yes, a high-flying, beautiful individual disappearing from somewhere like Oxford: they love that sort of thing. Sorry, that must sound really insensitive. But you haven't heard of anyone writing or broadcasting about her?' Martha shook her head. 'Well, good.' He pulled a manila file towards him across the table. 'If it's not just a random person who's read about the case online, then we have to assume it's someone who knows you and your team. It might be a joke, it might be malicious, but the alternative is someone who knows something. You were away at university, weren't you, when Charlie went missing?'

This explains the long wait in reception, Martha thought. He must have been reading the file. Well enough to pick up and use Charlie's nickname, too, rather than refer to her as Charlotte. She looked at the table, conscious that her heart rate was picking up. 'I was in Sheffield, yes. But I had only just arrived really.'

He nodded. 'Yes, right near the beginning of term. So I assume you'd been in Oxford over the summer?' She nodded. 'You didn't notice anything unusual about your sister's behaviour?'

'She was working very hard, but that wasn't uncharacteristic. I remember being sorry she didn't have time to hang out with me that summer. But she seemed very excited by her work, not depressed.'

He turned the pages. 'Did your parents share many details about the investigation?'

'I don't remember everything. I came down as soon as I heard she was missing, then after I went back we spoke every evening for weeks. I think they did – but how can I know what I don't know?'

'Fair point. My condolences on the loss of your mother, Ms Thornhill. Is your father still with us?'

'Thank you, and yes – but how did you know about my mother?'

He tapped the last page of the sheaf of papers. 'She called us soon after her diagnosis and asked us to have another push looking for Charlie. We did, trawled the databases and so on, but we got nowhere. Someone made a note on the file that she passed the following year.'

Martha hated the word 'passed'. Her mother had pledged to eschew the usual euphemisms as well as the martial vocabulary so many people felt compelled to adopt after a cancer diagnosis – 'she fought bravely, but lost her battle'. To Rebecca it implied the patient hadn't been strong enough. Martha had no idea her mother had asked the police to pick up the trail anew; perhaps one of the online groups had recommended it, or perhaps she simply knew her time was running out. 'Shall I run you through what we do know, Ms Thornhill? Just to refresh your memory?'

Martha felt the sweat prickle under her collar. 'I thought I'd just come in and fill in a form.'

He nodded slowly, but she caught a sharp, assessing glance too. 'Things like this – a possibility of something or someone strange in the mix, it might be best to make sure you know the facts.'

He seemed to be awaiting permission.

'Fine. Yes. Please, go on.'

'None of what I'm about to tell you is confidential. Some statements in here are, however, so I'm not about to hand over the file.' *I wouldn't want it anyway*, Martha thought, almost physically recoiling. 'So if you want to tell your colleagues anything I share with you now, you are at liberty to do so. I imagine they might be interested, given the unpleasant postcards.'

'Safi's wasn't that bad. Hers seemed to be simply asking for help.'

The detective nodded and rubbed his nose. 'Your parents reported Charlotte missing on Friday evening, September twenty-fourth. They had expected her to meet them at a party on the previous evening, and were surprised when she didn't turn up, and became more concerned when she wasn't home when they returned afterwards. Thought she might have been working. The next morning, when she still wasn't home and they couldn't reach her on her mobile, they called her boyfriend Tom, and learnt she had recently ended their relationship. They discovered that Friday afternoon that she'd also cancelled a lunch appointment on Thursday with a family friend – Gemma Waldegrave.'

'Oh, I didn't know that!' Martha said.

'Which bit?'

'Mum and Dad told me about the break-up with Tom at the time. I had no idea she was supposed to have lunch with Gemma the day she went missing.'

He sucked in his breath, his eyes flicking back and forth over the page in front of Martha. 'Apparently Ms Waldegrave was expecting your sister at her house and when she called Charlie to ask if she was still coming, she received a text saying something had come up.'

Martha tried to resist the pull of the past, but she felt it like a vortex, a sucking of wet sand under her feet. *I'm not there. That is not now*, she repeated to herself, but her mind was filling up with flashes of Charlie over that long summer, of her mother's voice on the phone that Saturday morning. 'Martha? Charlie's gone. Have you seen her? Did she come to you?'

What can you see? The formica table top. The top edge of the folder. The detective's hands. Dotted with freckles and thin golden hairs.

'You came down on Saturday, right?'

She remembered her key in the lock, how she pushed open the door and her mother and father came running out of the kitchen and saw her. Her mother's face collapsing in slow motion from hope to desperation.

What can you smell? Bad coffee. Paint and industrial cleaner.

'Yes, I got here in the middle of the afternoon. There was a policeman sitting with Mum, another going through Charlie's room.'

He nodded and turned a few pages. Suddenly Martha wanted to know what was on them. She saw the list of names of Charlie's friends and colleagues that her mother had written out, some with numbers, some without, pushed across into the hands of officialdom. She had been asked (was it a policeman or a policewoman that time? She saw only the hands round the tea mugs, heard the hushed tones) if she had any names to add to the list. She didn't. Tanya was on there already and she was the only one of Charlie's friends Martha had known. That was probably what he was paging through. The results of those phone calls.

'No information, and no red flags from the friends and colleagues we contacted. Her phone was either switched off or ran out of battery soon after she texted Ms Waldegrave. Her bank cards were last used the morning of September twenty-third.'

He glanced up at Martha again. She must have made some movement of impatience. The room felt clammy, airless.

'This won't take much longer, Ms Thornhill.'

'Yes . . . I . . . I'm sorry.'

'Then there is a question of her bike. Found in the woodland near the C. S. Lewis house.'

'She hated Narnia,' Martha said quickly. 'I know they dragged the pond there, but she always disliked those stories. Thought they were twee and pompous at the same time.'

He looked slightly hurt. 'I loved them when I was a kid. Gave them to my nephew and he learnt to read properly with them. Kept him off YouTube for the best part of a month.'

She smiled at him. 'I liked them too.'

For a strange half second they were united against Charlie's literary judgement, then his forehead crumpled into a frown. 'But why do you mention the dragging of the lake in that context?'

Martha ran her hand over her eyes, trying to get it into words.

'The bike being there was the clearest sign she'd run away, had some sort of breakdown and just left. It's near the A40, so a decent place to hitch a lift. I . . . I couldn't believe she killed herself, and when her bike turned up it was a relief. You see, Charlie would never kill herself there, not where she'd be surrounded by pilgrims gathered to worship Aslan and Mr Tumnus. Not her style.' She watched his face. 'You think I might be wrong, but I knew Charlie.'

His eyes flicked up and down. *Not well enough, obviously.*

'What do you think happened to her, Ms Thornhill?'

Maybe she should ask him to call her Martha. Maybe it was too late.

'I think she had a breakdown and left. I mean, people do disappear. They might lose their memory, or be too ashamed to come back.' The fictional jottings she'd pencilled in her mind were so well-rehearsed she almost believed them. What she didn't know she'd managed to invent.

He closed the file. 'Most people come back within a week, almost all within six months, or at least make contact. Charlie is very unusual in that respect.'

'But it happens, doesn't it?' She could hear the note of pleading in her voice. 'People do go away, reinvent themselves entirely?'

'As I say, it's very rare, and until time proves this is a prank, I think you should take this Chorus seriously. Did your sister have any enemies?' She almost laughed. How many other police drama tropes were left?

'We looked at the boyfriend carefully, given their recent break-up,' he continued, 'but I get the impression she rubbed a few people up the wrong way.'

Martha stared at him, agitated. No, that wasn't right. She shook her head. 'No, everyone loved Charlie. I mean, she was beautiful and clever and spoke her mind, so I suppose some people might have been jealous. But she was lovely. Funny. And you should have seen the crowds, the people who came out to look for her, or put up posters.'

'She had a bit of a flair for the dramatic, though?'

'Not particularly.'

Perhaps. Martha remembered when Charlie had decided to give up the violin. She had played to them one evening, a Brahms scherzo, then announced to her family she had cancelled her lessons, presenting them with a fait accompli. She had done the same thing when she got her driving licence, taking her lessons secretly and only telling them when she had passed, relishing the thrill of the grand reveal.

He put his hand out to mollify her. 'Perhaps. Look, it's possible this Chorus does know something. They might have had reasons for keeping quiet until now, and I doubt this letter turning up when you've just taken a job at Charlie's old workplace is unconnected. Is there anything you'd like to add? Anything you didn't mention to the police at the time?'

No. No. No.

'I've been here six months!'

He grimaced, squinting at the closed file as if it was a Magic Eye puzzle. 'One postcard a year, now this flurry of activity. Was there anything special about this week?'

Of course there was. 'The party you mentioned, it was for Jonathan Overton's first book. He launched his fourth this week, yesterday evening.'

He paused before saying, 'I wonder if Dr Overton got a postcard.'

'I have no idea, and I'm not going to ask the day after publication. He'll be up to his ears with engagements. But I have sent him the letter.'

'I heard him on the *Today* programme this morning, actually.'

She glanced at her watch, it was after two. 'I really should be getting back to the office. I only came to tell you about the letter, and these postcards. I mean, there's nothing that can be done at this point, is there?'

He closed the file and slowly rose to his feet. 'We can re-interview her friends and family.'

'No, please don't. Really, that's unnecessary.'

'What about the postcards sent to your colleagues, and your father?'

'They're just words. Not even threatening ones.' She tried to sound light-hearted. 'No self-respecting lexicographer should be afraid of words.'

'Maybe, but then I shouldn't have to warn a lexicographer that they can also be extremely powerful.'

Martha had turned away, her bag over her shoulder, ready to escape.

'Ms Thornhill, can I give you some advice?'

'If you have to.'

'I have no idea what happened to your sister, but perhaps someone does. Maybe she did just go away, but she'd have needed money for that. And I think she would have said something to someone. Same thing with suicide. People take time to come to that decision. It's a terrible thing never knowing, and I'm very sorry your mother never had that comfort, such as it is. But you should know. Talk to people about her. They may be more willing to speak to you after all this time, to say things they wouldn't have done when your mother was still alive. If you find out any new information in the process, give me a call and I can follow up officially.' He pulled a wallet from his back pocket and tugged out a card. 'Haven't you lived under the shadow of her disappearance long enough?'

She dug the sharp edges of the card into her palm.

'I'm used to the shadows,' she said. 'You seem to be taking a lot of interest in this case, though. Students disappear from the university all the time, don't they?'

It was his face that showed a flash of irritation this time, and he spoke slowly. 'No. They *leave* the university, Ms Thornhill. They leave Oxford and go back to their families. They don't just disappear without trace. And I am interested. I arrived here soon after she went missing. It's not something I'd forget.'

10

witship, *noun (Old English)*:
witness; testimony; knowledge

MARTHA'S DESK REMAINED EMPTY LONG after Alex returned from her lunch with a small carrier bag from one of Oxford's smarter boutiques. She noticed Safi eye it hungrily.

'A treat for the weekend,' she explained, pulling out a scarf that was gossamer-light and patterned with scarlet florals.

'Nice,' Safi said with a sigh. 'Is it for something or someone special?'

'I'm going out for lunch with my son, actually.'

'The boring one or the troubled one?' Simon asked, then looked up into the disapproving silence. 'Well, that's how *you* describe them – not in so many words, I admit, but I've lost count of the number of times you've described your eldest as "conventional".'

Alex stared at him for a couple of seconds, just to make the point, then shrugged. 'Ethan is a bit unimaginative. I admit that hearing a man still in his twenties talk about his pension pot fills me with irrational despair. But I'm having lunch with Jacob. And he's not troubled, just living in troubling times.'

'He's the novelist, right?' Safi chimed in. 'Living in London?'

'Yep. A certain amount of critical acclaim and bugger-all money. They used to be so close, my boys; now Ethan keeps telling him he needs a real job. I don't know what worries me most: Jacob blowing up at him, or him actually taking his brother's advice.'

When Martha eventually returned she looked flustered, Alex thought. None of them asked what the police had said, and until mid-afternoon discussion in the office was minimal. Alex offered to make tea at around half three, and Martha swerved the question as to what type she wanted – she always had herbal, and there was a dizzying array of brightly coloured packets in the break room. Right now she didn't care which. Instead, she asked a question herself.

'Did you like Charlie?'

Alex was so surprised she gave herself no time to prevaricate. 'Not particularly.'

Martha recoiled. She wasn't sure what she'd expected, but it wasn't that.

Alex's boys had always told her to speak her mind, and she'd enjoyed doing so more once the divorce was out of the way, when she'd regained some of her confidence. Occasionally, however, it also meant she confidently put her foot in it.

'I'm sorry, Martha, I don't mean I had anything against Charlie, and her disappearance is a tragedy . . . but if I'm being honest I didn't warm to her.'

Martha swallowed. 'Why not?'

Safi got up and headed for the kitchen to take over tea-making duties, and Alex studied the floor for a while before she answered, remembering what she'd said to Safi last night, and trying to offer Martha something more specific. 'She could be patronising. She always acted surprised that I read anything more challenging than *Vogue*. It was subtle. My boys were teenagers then, great gawky idiots, eating me out of house and home and generating more washing than I could keep up with. If I said I'd seen an exhibition over the weekend, she would express surprise that I managed to find the time, or, by implication, even left the house at all. I let it get to me. I'm sorry – I shouldn't have said anything. She was obviously a very talented young woman, and I was no doubt a little paranoid at the time. I was in the throes of divorce, nursing open wounds about my life and choices, and – well – she threw a lot of salt about.'

Martha chewed her lip. 'The detective I gave the letter to, he told me to ask people about Charlie, talk to people who knew her. I suppose I should be ready to hear things I don't like.'

Safi returned with the drinks and Martha blinked at her tea as if it had materialised of its own free will.

'It was the day of Jonathan's first book launch that Charlie disappeared, wasn't it?' Safi asked. Alex gave her the side-eye. 'What, Chorus said I should help! And it was Martha who started talking about it. Were you there, Martha?'

She shook her head. 'Uni. But you and Simon were, weren't you?' She looked at Alex.

'I was.' Alex set her cup down on the desk. 'It wasn't as grand as last night, but Jonathan knew how to make friends even then, so he pulled quite the crowd. Your parents were both there, and lots of people who had been to the *CED* seminar groups.'

'Plenty of academics,' Simon added. 'I went home early, though. My eldest was teething and I couldn't keep my eyes open.'

'I remember it being a pleasant enough party, on a very beautiful evening,' Alex said. 'My boys were with their father, so afterwards I went for a walk along Castle Mill Stream, among the canal boats, and into Jericho. Then I noticed one of the cottages in Cranham Street was for sale.'

'Is that where you live now?' Safi said.

'No. It took a while for me to sort myself out. We were still finalising the divorce, trying to sell the house. I rented for a while, saved up a bit, and I bought the next one that came on the market. So, yes, I have vivid memories of that evening.'

'So before then,' Safi asked, settling into the role of inquisitor, 'how was Charlie?'

Alex glanced at Martha. Her eyes were steady and bright, even as her colleagues discussed her family's wounds in front of her. 'I remember Charlie was very busy that summer. She'd come in tired, saying she'd been working all night, yawning like a cat.'

'Her supervisor didn't think she was working hard,' Simon added, and the women turned round to look at him. 'I was thinking back over it last night. I ran into her, Catherine Carmichael, in the middle of that term after Charlie disappeared – you remember her, Alex. We were at a conference and of course we talked about Charlie and the pressures of doing a PhD. I think mine aged me by a decade.'

'I thought you just took a decade to do it?' Safi said, fluttering her eyelashes.

'Ha ha. No, I said something about how dedicated Charlie seemed, and she raised her eyebrows. She said Charlie was brilliant, but that she seemed to be losing interest. She had been due to hand in a chapter but was late. Catherine sounded frustrated. She said Charlie had been "blithely self-confident" the entire time. Which was irritating because the self-confidence was largely justified. Still, Catherine said Charlie was the last person she expected to disappear. She said the pressure never seemed to catch up with her, and that Charlie regarded people who crumpled under it as weak.' He scratched his chin. 'That was true – I remember telling her how tough I found mine, and she looked at me like I was an alien. I was just trying to be nice, and she kind of made me feel like shit.'

Alex went home before she made her call. It was ridiculous – anyone could make a call from anywhere these days – but for some reason it felt proper to do this at home.

She made herself tea and fed Rags before sitting down at her desk under the window and finding the number. The dial tone was long and unmistakably foreign.

'Hello, Mike.' She scratched behind Rags's ears. 'Yes, good thanks. But something has come up at the office . . . No, she's doing fine. A daydreamer, but a good editor and keeping on top of things . . . I told you, I honestly didn't want the job. Too much admin . . . No, this is about Charlie Thornhill. I really think you need to come back.'

11

convent, *noun (fourteenth century)*:

a number of people meeting together
for a common purpose

THE NEXT LETTER ARRIVED ON Tuesday morning.

On Monday they had all made a tacit pact to get some real work done. Martha worked her way through her to-do list, ate her lunch with George Wainwright in St Sepulchre's, and was still at work when the cleaner came in to empty the bins.

She'd walked home, shared a largely silent meal with her father during which they both read, and actually managed to sleep afterwards. It was a relief after the strange dead hours of the weekend, when thoughts of Charlie had buzzed uselessly round her brain. But on Tuesday morning Safi paused while sorting the post, and they all turned to look at her, alert as game dogs.

'It's another one from Chorus,' she said, slitting open the envelope and taking out the letter.

Martha turned from her computer, alarm shimmering off her. 'Read it out.'

Safi cleared her throat, and Alex and Simon turned from their screens to give her their full attention.

Dear Editors,

Many might ask why you should count on me. Riddling confession finds but riddling shrift after all. But I need to make an impression. The world will pause over a pretty mystery, but hide from an ugly truth. Shall we dance? I will piece out the comfort with what addition I can, and sing in full measures. We are irrational, make me whole.

You are bound to doubt. I do, creeping in this place, this dark place between what I fear, what I know, and what is right. I am the voice of one crying out in the wilderness. I want to provoke you with what I do know, into finding what I do not. Alas poor world, what treasure hast thou lost.

Confessing sins, where a captive of the past might expect sanctuary, will help you find your level. Make a gathering together of scholars in search of mutual solace.

One person there had nothing to lose, nothing to confess. In the course of justice none of us should see salvation.

Study the pardoner's tale. When making known his identity Edgar lost the power of Poor Tom. I keep it.

Yours,
Chorus

'What the . . . ?' Simon muttered. His voice only just overcame the hum of the monitors.

Martha couldn't think about the contents of the letter yet. She noticed a shaft of sunlight break the shadows and catch the glass of a desk partition, casting a prism that danced and flickered on the wall beside her. She had been hoping, she realised, even after the postcards arrived, that Chorus would simply go away. Vanish. A trick of the light.

The door from their shared office into the corridor was open, but it took them all a moment to notice Jonathan Overton, pausing on the threshold in his slim-fitting white shirt and expensive suit, his pointy-toed shoes buffed to an unnatural shine.

He glanced between them, trying to read the room.

'Morning, everyone! What is it? New meaning of "set"?'

'Set' was the longest entry in the dictionary, one that would need to be recast almost as soon as its editors completed it. It was already twice as long as Orwell's *Animal Farm*, although the entry for 'run' was following closely on its heels. Every dictionary-maker knew that language would always outpace them, that – as Samuel Johnson had put it – they would be forever chasing the sun.

He was greeted with weak smiles. 'Or have you finally got to the bottom of "dog"?' he continued. 'That would be a coup.'

Another lexicographical cliché. 'Dog' was one of the biggest etymological mysteries in the language, arriving unannounced in Middle English with no trace of past or ancestry.

Martha forced her lips into a smile. 'Sorry, nothing new there.' She glanced at her watch. 'Are you joining us for the meeting this morning? I'll get the talking points together.'

He nodded. 'Yes, plus the BBC want to do an interview this afternoon in the Slips. How are things are going? Anything new or exciting?'

Safi opened her mouth, but Alex got in first.

'Is the Beeb thing for your series?' she asked.

Jonathan ran his hand through his hair. 'No, it's more a news item – just a bit about the programmes I have coming up.' He began to talk about filming schedules and reviews, easily diverted into his own concerns, while Martha and the others gathered what they needed and followed him across to the meeting room.

For all its reliance on hard data, dictionary work is also highly collaborative. Editors draft in pairs, swapping entries and passing them around their colleagues for peer review. They consult external advisors in the field before eventually giving their drafts to the Finalisation Team. Most of this work at the *CED* was handled informally, but every month the Revision Team would hold a meeting to discuss progress or to chat through any term that was proving particularly gnarly. One such entry, which had ended up on Martha's plate, was for 'business', a word whose existing definition had been started at the end of the nineteenth century, when it simply meant 'the state of being busy'. The plethora of modern uses – 'mind your own business', 'do business with', 'send them about their business', 'business as usual', and so on times a hundred – required Martha to wrap up a century or more of critical development within just a few virtual pages. It had taken her three months. She could no longer hear someone say 'let's get down to business' without involuntarily flinching.

For all his TV-star braggadocio, Martha knew that Jonathan had officially come into the office for an update on the Words of the Bad Quarto project, a committee that oversaw the dictionary's approach to the quarto-sized edition of Shakespeare's plays, in which the playwright's words had been pirated from contemporary performances without permission. Corruptions and manglings of the original texts were therefore inevitable, hence the rather alarming use of 'bad' in the title. Thanks largely to his academic status, Overton was consultant editor for the dictionary's overall coverage of Shakespeare, a remit bestowed on him by the chief editor.

He had been asked to sit in on today's Revision meeting because two Shakespearean antedatings were about to be put forward to the Finalisation Team, and he was highly territorial about the playwright's contributions. His first runaway success, *Think Like a Genius*, had mobilised Shakespeare's use of language into a rallying cry to aspiring writers and creatives, urging them to experiment with the boundaries of expression. The result, the author suggested, could be an intellectual fission reaction as powerful as the one achieved by the Bard.

The reality, of course, as was becoming increasingly clear, was far more nuanced. William Shakespeare had certainly long been regarded as the bedrock of all historical dictionaries, the author credited with over 30,000 first records of words and expressions, from the well-known 'it's all Greek to me' to less obvious coinages like 'under-peep' and 'crafty-sick'. It was undeniable that the playwright had been an exuberant experimenter with language, verbing furiously, dovetailing one word with another, and flipping the appearance and meaning of existing words to create something headily new. But it was also now acknow-ledged that some of his apparent inventions were almost certainly in use already, carried through the air in spoken English, where they were exchanged without ceremony or record. Shakespeare's time had been one of lexical effusiveness, when language was springy and daring, producing words as modern sounding as 'banana' and as steeped in time as 'over-morrow'. The dictionary's reliance upon his work was largely due to his unparalleled literary status at the time when compil-ation began in earnest, leading to a bias among editors, many of whom were Shakespeare scholars. Each first record attributed to the playwright had become another brick in the Shakespeare edifice. Even his *hapax legomena* – words that lasted barely a day – were routinely given full legitimacy.

The result of all this was that any discovery of an earlier record of a word currently credited to Shakespeare was held aloft as a triumph of word detection. Alex, in particular, much to Jonathan's annoyance, would share each find with an email headed 'Fakespeare'.

Martha had no doubt that Jonathan could feel the sand shifting beneath his feet, for all that he seemed to accept each antedating with good grace. She was aware of his subtle attempts to shift the argument, of his assertions that neologisms were just one measure of the great man (undeniable), and that his lexical brilliance was unmatched by anyone then or since (dodgy, Martha thought – she had heard some linguists maintain that, if anything, Shakespeare's vocabulary range placed him bang in the middle of his contemporary pack, and no more). But she could still summon empathy for a man whose career was being slowly chipped away by an army of readers who relished the chase, knowing they would win over the bardolaters in the end.

It was Alex who opened today's discussion, welcoming those who joined the meeting by Teams, projected onto a screen on the nondescript wall like the lexicographical equivalent of *Celebrity Squares*. She began by listing those revised entries that were near completion, and those that were taking longer than expected. One of the editors, Imogen, spoke about watching the entire series of *The Wire* to locate the earliest mention of 'burner phone', only to find her colleague had pipped her by finding it in a rap song from a year earlier. Saki, an editor with a passion for unearthing obscure evidence of use, announced that one of the dictionary's readers had found in a chatroom exchange from 1992 an earlier example of *meh* before *The Simpsons* got hold of it. Someone had used it in response to something 'far too Ken-doll to me'. *How our icons fall*, Martha thought.

Various other new finds were duly shared. Targets sent down by the chief editor were tabled and noted. At times Martha was aware of Jonathan stirring impatiently in his chair or throwing glances at his phone. It was only when Alex turned to the word 'arch-villain' that his head snapped up suddenly. In neutral tones she explained that there was now an earlier record that significantly pre-dated the *CED*'s first user, Shakespeare. The same word, she continued, had in fact been used over twenty-two times in other texts of the period. Martha listened without looking at Jonathan directly, but she was all too aware of his body language, which bristled with irritation. She sensed him playing for time as he spoke the lines 'You that way and you this, but two in company; each man apart, all single and alone, yet an arch-villain keeps him company'. He looked around the room and said, 'That's amazing news. I'll add that to the edits for *Genius.* Excellent work.' As he concluded, his shoulders gave a faint shrug, and Martha sensed another brick falling from the tower.

12

mathom, *noun (Old English)*:

a precious thing; a valuable gift

THE MEETING CLOSED AT LUNCHTIME. Jonathan left quickly, thanking them again for their work then murmuring something about lunch with his publicist. Martha, Simon, Alex and Safi returned to their desks and produced sandwiches and Tupperwares from their bags. For once Martha resisted the temptation to flee for the churchyard, choosing instead to stay with her colleagues who seemed to have forged a tacit pact of secrecy, since no one had mentioned the letter or postcards to Jonathan. Hanging in the air was a sense that Chorus, for now at least, belonged to them.

Other than the snap of plastic and the tear of cellophane, the room was silent for a few minutes. It was Simon who broke it at last, swallowing a mouthful of a dismal-looking sandwich and wiping his mouth with the back of his hand. 'The letter,' he said, although he barely needed to. 'So much for our hopes of a little clarity. But lots of Shakespeare again, I note, one way and another.'

Safi put down her salad fork and came out from behind her desk, then dragged the whiteboard they sometimes used for meetings into the middle of the room. She started copying the letter on to it. The squeak of the red marker grated on Martha's nerves as she watched each word form, looking for signs of Charlie. 'Alas poor world, what treasure hast thou lost!' That must be her sister, surely. The missing golden child.

'A paragraph-by-paragraph acrostic doesn't work this time,' Safi said as she wrote. 'Many . . . You . . . Confessing . . . One . . . Study . . .'

Alex watched as Safi finished transcribing. 'Still *a riddling confession* must mean more clues.'

I want to provoke you with what I know, into finding what I do not. Martha shoved her lunchbox away from her. The Tupperware looked ugly, cheap.

'Martha? Are you OK?' Safi asked. 'Does any of this mean something to you?'

'No!' she exclaimed. They were all looking at her with confused concern. 'Who the hell is doing this? "Shall we dance?" Fuck! Turning my sister's disappearance into a parlour game?'

The explosion came from some other place, some other person. She heard the words spill from her mouth, but they felt alien and alarming. It was as though language had broken down, lost the conjunctions linking time and place, cause and effect. Anger and grief didn't care for whole sentences. She pushed her hair away from her face, her hand shaking a little. 'Sorry . . .'

'Don't be,' Safi said quietly, setting the marker down at the bottom of the board. 'You're right. It's not a game, so why should we play along? We could just shut it down, send this to your detective. Do nothing else.'

Martha shook her head. 'I . . . he'll probably just ask what it means too. I just don't understand though: why is Chorus doing this?'

'The postcards they sent the *CED* before didn't work,' Simon said. 'And so they're telling us, aren't they, quite explicitly this time? Trying to tempt us all in with this "pretty mystery".'

'There is nothing *pretty* about it,' Martha said. Her mobile, sitting on her desk, began to buzz. She picked it up and saw that the caller was her godmother, Gemma. She'd normally avoid taking personal calls during the day, but in this moment Gemma was an excuse to walk out, to avoid looking at the monstrous puzzle on the board. She accepted the call and moved into the waiting area near the lifts.

'Hi, Gemma. Is everything OK?'

'Darling!' Gemma's voice boomed through the speaker, making Martha wince. 'Come for supper at my place on Friday. You are a funny old thing.'

Martha was feeling anything but funny.

'Am I?'

She didn't want to go anywhere. She wanted to read in the shadows, wander through her own thoughts beyond the mire of people and conversation. She remembered what she had told her father, that isolation wasn't good for either of them. And Gemma – perhaps she could tell her about this. An old family friend who knew them all, knew her.

'You are, and I'm dying to see you.'

'Yes, I'd like that,' Martha said.

'It'll be just us, darling. Don't bring wine, I have some marvellous whites in the cellar. Six-ish. Buy a cake or something we can have for afters? Bye-ee!'

She rang off without waiting for a reply.

Martha stared at the phone in her hand. *This dark place between what I fear, what I know, and what is right.* The words sounded a sympathetic echo inside her. She didn't recognise that as a quote, so perhaps here at least Chorus was expressing their own feelings directly. Her anger at their correspondent was crosscut with a sudden sense of fellow feeling. But why? Begrudgingly, she knew that answers would only come from playing the game.

She walked back into the room. Alex, Safi, and Simon were all talking at once, but they fell silent when they saw her.

Martha sighed. 'I don't feel like I have a choice – let's try and work this out. What are you all thinking?'

Her colleagues visibly relaxed.

'There are numbers in here somewhere!' Simon exclaimed. '"Count on me." That's too modern an idiom for Chorus. And there's addition in the first paragraph too.'

'What about "full measures"?' asked Alex. 'That's in the same paragraph. Sounds a little maths-adjacent.'

'The key to finding the clue should be upfront. Measures . . . the Americans use that as a synonym for a bar of music, don't they?' Simon added. 'Maths and music, counting . . .'

'Whisht!' Safi said, holding out her hand, her smooth forehead creased with concentration. 'Full measures, dance, singing, and numbers. What about a time signature?'

Martha stared at the letter transcribed in Safi's neat and even handwriting. She remembered Charlie, her violin under her chin and the music on its stand – the numbers of the time signature balanced on top of each other. Three over eight, four over four. Looking like a fraction. *I am irrational.*

'Here.' She took the marker from Safi's hand and stepped forward, underlining the first word of the first paragraph, the second two words in the second. The marker squeaked and shook.

'It's a whole – one – expressed like a fraction, a theoretical time signature. And we count on in each paragraph.'

'That's working!' Alex said excitedly.

Many . . . are bound . . . where a captive

'Four in the next line – "there had nothing to" . . . no!' Martha wiped out the line under 'there' with her thumb. '"Had nothing to lose" . . .'

Simon scurried out from behind his desk, pointing. 'And in the last line start from "when" – that's the fifth word. "When making known his identity."'

Martha stood back and read out the underlined words.

'Many are bound where a captive had nothing to lose when making known his identity.' She turned round and looked at Simon.

'That certainly sounds like a clue to me,' Alex said, tilting her head to one side and crossing her arms. 'These quotes and fragments must mean something too . . .'

'I'm sorry . . .' Simon said. 'I know I'm supposed to be the crossword expert, but that's tough. Nothing to lose? Take out a zero, or the letter "o" from a word?'

Alex picked up another of the markers. 'We know Chorus puts these letters together with real precision.' She tapped the second line of the second paragraph. 'Look at that repetition of "place".'

'So you think the clue might indicate a location?' Simon asked.

'Perhaps. What else? This captive . . . Where might he be? A prison? A castle?'

'Chorus does like his history,' Martha said. The pretty mystery was reeling her in. She tried, briefly, to resist it, to hang on to her anger with the writer. But she knew she couldn't turn away now, that to do so would be to snip away at the ties that tethered her to Charlie. 'People were kept captives all over the place in the early modern period. Watch houses, courts, colleges, houses, even churches.'

'"Crying in the wilderness" . . . that's a phrase used in the Gospels about St John the Baptist,' Alex said. 'A Baptist church?'

Safi yawped. 'A church! Alex, remember that talk we went to on church graffiti last year? The man was talking about local examples.'

Alex shook her head. 'Not really . . .'

Safi was fizzing excitably, waving her arms, making the loose sleeves of her iridescent top quiver like butterflies. 'There was someone, a captive in the Civil War: he wrote his name in a church. Too early for Baptist churches, so is there a St John the Baptist around here? A church older than the seventeenth century?'

'There's one by Merton College!' Simon said after a pause. 'And another in Abingdon.'

Alex had returned to her computer and started typing. 'And Burford! Safi, you're right!'

She turned the screen so they could all see. It showed a page of images, a variety of close-ups on a patch of lead, a name scored into a baptismal font: ANTHONY SEDLEY 1649 PRISNER.

'Nothing to lose . . .' Safi said. 'Simon, you were right too. Sedley missed out the "o".'

'Sixteen forty-nine . . .' Martha underlined 'level' in the second paragraph. 'Was he . . . ?'

'Yes, he was a Leveller, imprisoned in the church during the Civil War.'

'I keep forgetting there was a civil war in England,' Safi said. 'Let alone that there was a whole bunch of early modern social justice warriors mixed up in it.'

'Three of the Levellers were executed in the churchyard,' Alex added, reading from the screen. 'Bleak.'

'OK – so the church in Burford. That must be the place. Was Charlie part of any protest movement or anything?' Safi asked. 'Or was she religious?'

'No,' Martha said, shaking her head. 'She was an atheist, and I don't think I ever heard her talk about politics.'

Safi took the marker back from Martha, and underlined 'pages', 'gathering', 'scholars'. 'The "impression". "Many are bound". Look, printing and bookbinding terms. I know that Charlie was a scholar, and of the early modern, but is there anything that links the church in Burford to books particularly?'

Alex and Simon exchanged glances, and spoke as one.

'Brin.'

'Who?' Safi asked.

'Brin Edwards,' Martha said. 'He's a book dealer in Burford. Charlie used to work there too.'

13

ert, *verb (fifteenth century)*:

to irritate, disturb, or poke

ALEX STARTED PUTTING HER THINGS in her bag. 'We can take my car. It's a Mini, but it's got five doors so there'll be none of that undignified clambering over the seats to get into the back.'

'It's the getting out again that messes me up,' Safi said, packing her lunch container in her backpack. 'I end up jammed in some sort of screwed-up yoga position with my arms everywhere and no purchase.'

'What are you doing?' Martha asked. She looked between them, horrified by the sudden shift to the banal. 'We're still at work.'

'We're going to Burford, of course,' Alex replied, 'to see whether Brin can shed any light on all of this and why Chorus is sending us his way.'

Simon was hurriedly chewing the last of his sandwich. 'Gorgeous place, Burford.'

Martha couldn't believe it. 'We can't just leave!'

'Why on earth not? What etymological emergencies do you think are likely to turn up on a Tuesday afternoon?' Alex scoffed. 'Most of the editors are working from home anyway, so it's not as if anyone will miss us.'

Safi held up her phone. 'And I get work emails on this. Come on, Martha, we'll make up the hours.'

Simon was peering at his screen. 'And Brin's shop closes at five, so we can't wait until after work.'

They paused, staring at Martha. 'I don't know why we're just dropping everything to go chasing after whatever breadcrumbs Chorus is feeding us.' Martha heard the querulousness in her voice.

'It's a quest,' Safi said with unnecessary relish. 'You can't refuse the call.' Alex glanced at her, and Safi blushed. 'Sorry, Martha. I just mean, we've got this far, shouldn't we take the next step?'

Her mother wouldn't have hesitated, Martha thought. Her mother would have snatched the car keys out of Alex's hand. She closed her eyes for a second.

'OK. Fine. As long as we do make up the time.'

Alex was out of the office before she'd even finished the sentence. 'Give me ten minutes to fetch the car!'

'I'll just run to the loo,' Safi said and swept off down the corridor.

Martha slowly got up and gathered her things: her glasses, the book she'd meant to read at lunchtime. She shut down her computer.

'Martha, would you rather not know what happened to Charlie?'

She looked up. Simon was frowning at her, but his expression seemed more concerned than judgemental. He had opted for another of his Hawaiian shirts today. Tiny surfers raced over his broad stomach and chased waves across his chest.

'I don't know if it will help, that's all,' she said. Then, meeting his gaze: 'I'm sorry Charlie was unpleasant to you, Simon. It's been playing on my mind.'

His smile was fleeting, and she felt a shiver of disconnection. 'Hardly your fault. And as far as making me feel bad goes, she wasn't a patch on my ex-wife.'

They walked together down the wide staircase into the sunlit foyer, where Martha avoided the eye of the curious receptionist as they signed out. They found Alex at the gate in her sky-blue Mini.

'Come on! Before the wardens catch me . . .'

Martha climbed into the passenger seat, while Safi and Simon sat in the back. Seatbelts were clunked and clicked, indicators ticked.

What are we doing? Martha thought, looking up at a sky that had turned an industrial grey.

'Anyone remember *The Pardoner's Tale*?' Alex said, pulling smoothly out into the traffic and raising her hand to a SUV that had slowed to let her out onto the main road. 'It's one of Chaucer's *Canterbury Tales*, but that's the sum total of my knowledge. Chorus must have mentioned it for a reason.'

Martha had a Pavlovian response to mention of Chaucer. She could see the opening page on her desk at university under the glow of her reading light, hear the laughter of other students passing in the corridor outside.

Whan that Aprille with his shoures soote
The droghte of Marche hath perced to the roote,
And bathed every veyne in swich licour,
Of which vertu engendred is the flour

'It's one of my favourites,' Safi said. '*Radix malorum est cupiditas.* Greed is the root of all evil. It's the one where three young men go in search of Death to kill him because he's taking so many of their friends. They're told they'll find him under a tree, but when they get there there's a big pile of treasure instead, and they end up killing each other over it.'

So unwittingly they find what they were originally seeking. It played out in Martha's mind. *The mysterious tree and the pile of gold, the youngest of the three bringing poison to the others, then being killed by them. The wages of sin is death.*

'Ah yes,' Alex said. 'Betrayal, avarice. There's that mention of treasure too. Although,' she glanced at Martha, 'that might mean Charlie.'

'I was thinking of Edgar and Poor Tom in the letter's last line,' Simon said quietly. 'It's *King Lear*, isn't it, with Edgar disguising himself as poor mad Tom? Why does he do that?'

'To hide in plain sight, I think,' Martha replied.

They lapsed into silence, and Martha glanced down at her hands. The red marker on her thumb looked like pooling blood. She tried to wipe it off, but it refused to budge. She turned and looked out of the window.

14

philobiblist, *noun (twentieth century)*:

a lover of books

THE MEANING OF RITUAL, SOMEONE once said, is to remember something that must not be forgotten. Martha ritualised many things, from the order with which she got dressed to the silent kiss she blew her mother's photograph by the front door each time she left the house. But by far the most important habit in her life, stretching as far back as she could recall, was her weekly visit to a second-hand bookshop.

Pequod Books in Berlin's Neukölln district had been one of the least prepossessing buildings on its street. Its fresco of zebras and lions in the savanna had been graffitied over more than once, splodged with the street artist's signature and unapologetically displaying the word 'BEER' across a red-tinged sky. A springbok now sported a comical eyemask. But those who knew, knew. To enter the shop's doors was to leave all sense of sparring identities behind. For inside was nothing but books – hundreds of them, in dozens of languages, stacked high from ceiling to warm oak floors. The shop's only punctuation was a collection of lime-green velvet sofas to which the customer could take a book and study its contents without pressure or scrutiny. Inevitably many of those same books found their way back onto the shelves, becrumbed and coffee-stained, but Martha had relished the spirit of it all.

'You'd think it would be a busman's holiday,' she had commented to her colleague Sabine when she shared the details of her weekend, not long after she'd moved to Kreuzberg and started at Hartmannsverlag. She worked among books every day, after all.

'What's a busman?' Sabine had asked. Her English, always excellent, would occasionally stumble when met with yet another of the language's eccentricities. Martha would explain the idiom and then invariably follow up by asking for the equivalent in German. Unsurprisingly, there often wasn't one. Not that German didn't have its own idiosyncrasies, of course. Martha knew that whenever any lexicographer was asked why English failed to have a word for X, Y, or Z, the questioner's very next comment would be 'I bet German does'.

And they'd be right. German usually did. Famed for its Lego-like constructions, it generously bent over backwards (sometimes literally) to fill a linguistic gap. Martha's favourite, without doubt, was the *Verschlimmbesserung*: an attempted improvement that ends up making things worse. She knew all about those.

Her Berlin weekends, often spent solo, would almost always include a trip to Pequod, where she would pick up a second-hand novel or poetry collection in either language before catching the train – or, on a fine day, making the fifty-minute walk – back to Kreuzberg, sometimes stopping in a café or picking up a schnitzel sandwich to demolish in Viktoriapark.

The memories milled around Martha's head until a sharp brake of the car shoved her thoughts back to the present. Alex cursed a driver who had stopped suddenly to let out their passengers onto the crest of a hill that swept majestically down to Burford's High Street, towards the river Windrush. After a furious session of tooting they made fitful progress to the free car park, behind the church that had once held Anthony Sedley and his fellow rebels.

Besides sharing a first syllable, Burford and Berlin were worlds apart. Not just in the obvious: their geography and ethnography and the people they attracted. It was what they *made* of people too. Martha never ceased to marvel over the distinct personalities she assumed in different places. Berlin had allowed her a whole new level of freedom; it was as though she could march off the edge of her map and relocate her personality as well as her physical self. Burford, on the other hand, was an album full of old snapshots of who she used to be. Just half an hour away from Oxford, its soul was colder but more straightforward. It bore both its current and ancient wealth with pride. An important trading centre for the Anglo-Saxons, it had gone on to become a prosperous wool town during the Middle Ages, funding a stunning architecture in the form of timbered framing or Cotswold stone. Charlie and Martha had been brought here often as children, usually to be rewarded with ice cream after a long walk. In the years that followed, Charlie would scour the town's quaint independents for tiny trinkets, many of which ended up in the treasure hunts she would organise for Martha on special occasions. Now, Martha looked down the road, half expecting to see herself as a child coming the other way.

The Cheshire Cat antiquarian bookshop was in the middle of the High Street, with a gallery on one side and a coffee shop on the other.

'Anyone know this Brin guy?' Safi asked, scanning the road around them, and raising an eyebrow at the genteel artwork in the window of the gallery.

'Yes, Simon and I do. He was a member of the *CED* Forum for some years,' Alex said.

'The what now?'

'It was mainly a series of seminars.' Simon got out of the car and bent backwards, stretching his spine and exposing a round curve of hairy belly, before straightening up with a middle-aged groan. 'One of Mike's initiatives, and it ran for a few years.'

'Oh, yeah, I remember you saying. Why did it stop? It sounds great.'

'Just ran out of steam, I think. Your father was on it, wasn't he, Martha?'

'Yes. He used to go to them all and stay in the pub afterwards, until Charlie disappeared. That was almost the point of the Forum in the end – like minds plotting lexical adventures over a few pints.' It had been unusual for Gabriel to do much socialising without his wife, but Martha remembered how he had come home late those evenings.

They strolled towards the shop, as if having got this far they were all reluctant to go further.

'Yes, I enjoyed them too. I never got to stay, though, had to go and look after the boys.' Alex paused, her hand on the door. 'Martha, you should do the talking when we go in.'

'Fine. Yes, I suppose so.'

Alex pushed open the door and Martha entered first, the others trailing behind her like recalcitrant children. A bell rang somewhere in the distance, a tuneless brassy jangle, but there was no one behind the desk. The four of them dispersed, all heading instinctively for the shelves. Brin evidently had a rather eclectic way of arranging his stock, mixing old titles with new ones and only vaguely paying attention to their subject. Martha would enjoy browsing here, she knew: it was a place to linger; a place whose shelves might not yield exactly what a person was looking for, but delivered something far more interesting. And, of course, there was that scent. Vellichor: the musty, musky, and utterly beguiling smell of old books.

'I've just found a dictionary in the fiction aisle!' Alex said, slightly offended.

'Dictionaries *are* storybooks in their own way,' Safi countered. She had pulled out one of the older volumes and was turning its pages; Martha could hear them creaking in her hands, the whisper of thick, old paper. She imagined them drinking in the attention, revelling in it.

'Good lord, it must be rush hour!' A tall figure shambled out from the depths of the building to stand behind the cash desk, blinking at them in amiable surprise. He spoke with a rolling Welsh accent. Martha recognised him now – he'd been at her mother's funeral; they'd shaken hands. He reminded her then as now of Shaggy from *Scooby-Doo*: all lanky limbs and mussy hair. He might be in his late fifties, his shoulders slightly stooped as though in permanent resignation. He half smiled, tilting his head, trying to place her.

She stepped forward. 'I'm Martha Thornhill. Gabriel and Rebecca's daughter.'

'Ah, of course you are!' He took her hand warmly. 'And you're at the *CED* now, aren't you? Which explains what Alex and Simon are doing with you.'

He shook hands with them, too, reaching out over the greeting cards and bookmarks stacked by the till. 'I'm sorry the seminars stopped, but I still read the blog from time to time. And I've been thinking of you lot these last few days. Are you with this gang too?' he added, smiling at Safi.

'Yes, I'm Safiya Idowu. You have a copy of the letter from the Young Shepherd to his friend in Borrowdale!'

'I do – is it the vernacular you enjoy, then?' Safi nodded eagerly. 'I have a few things I should look out for you in that case. There's a very lovely PhD a woman wrote on Cumbrian folk songs, set me off buying a few nice oddments.' He tilted his head again. 'Is this a field trip? You fellows run out of things to read at the office?'

Martha steeled herself. 'No, Brin. This is going to sound very odd, but it's about Charlie.'

She ran through the story as best she could: the letter with the crossword clue pointing to the year Charlie disappeared, then the one that brought them here today.

'Well, that's all bloody peculiar,' he said when she had finished. He walked over to the door, flicked the store sign to 'Closed', and ushered them towards a circle of armchairs around the fireplace. Not quite Pequod's level of comfort, Martha thought, but inviting nonetheless. 'I could do with a beer,' Brin announced. 'Anyone joining me?'

He took some bottles out of a small fridge near the till. Safi and Simon took one, Martha and Alex asked for water.

'So,' Safi asked, once they were all settled, 'have you received any strange postcards recently?'

Brin blinked at her as if she'd just performed a mesmerising magic trick.

'I did, as a matter of fact. How on earth did you know?'

'It's just you said you'd been thinking about the dictionary team over the last few days and I wondered why,' Safi replied. 'And last week we each had postcards delivered to our homes, too, with Shakespeare quotes on them, so . . .'

'Whoa,' Simon interrupted. '"Curiouser and curiouser," said Alice.'

Martha felt her focus pulse in and out. *What do you want, Chorus? What do you want of me, of Brin, of Safi?*

'Apt.' Brin grunted and poured his beer into a glass with care. 'Mine came Thursday, and a funny quote it was too. I had to look it up. *What traitors have we here?* That's all it said. With a picture of the dictionary offices on the front.'

'Charlie worked for you for ages, didn't she?' Martha asked, trying to stay grounded in this room by gripping onto the arms of the chair, half expecting the world to grow or shrink around her. 'I remember her coming here while she was doing her A-levels.'

Charlie had decided to become a weekly boarder at that time. Twelve-year-old Martha had missed her terribly, and resented her a little too. Her mother had started taking her to art galleries; her dad had spent more time in his study.

'Yes, eight years she worked for me, on and off,' Brin said. 'Started at sixteen and quit in the April of 2010, the year she disappeared.'

'She quit?' Martha said quickly. 'Charlie told us you didn't need her anymore. That was why she went to work at the *CED*.'

He sighed, his shoulders sinking a little lower. 'Is that what she said? No. She quit. Came in for her wages and expenses for the last couple of buying trips she'd done for me, then said she was off. I could have killed her, it was Easter and one of the few really busy weekends in the year. But I couldn't hold her to anything. I'd paid her cash, off the books, all those years.'

'Was that the last time you saw her?' Safi asked. Martha noticed to her surprise that her colleague was taking notes between sips of her beer, the pompom bobbing furiously at the end of her pencil.

'Are you doing shorthand?' Brin exclaimed, delighted. 'I didn't think people your age had those skills!'

'My mum's a journalist. I begged her to teach me when I was little. It seemed such an exotic private code. But I ended up getting banned from using it at home because I kept referring to my notes during family arguments to quote people's words back to them. My brother was convinced I'd end up in the police.'

Brin laughed loudly. 'I'll bet! For that story, Safi, I give you that copy of *The Shepherd's Letter*. My gift to you.'

Martha looked between them. *I bet Mum liked him*, she thought. Brin was like her. Expansive. Why would Charlie give up working here and then lie about it? Her mind went into overdrive with possibilities.

'Thank you!' Safi looked delighted.

'Was it the last time?' Alex pushed.

'Blimey, like being interviewed by Cerberus, this is.'

'Except Cerberus was a three-headed dog,' Simon said, shifting in his chair. 'There are four of us.'

'Well, it's like being snapped at by a hellhound,' Brin said quickly, his mood shifting fast. 'I just haven't worked out which of you is holding the leash yet.' Safi's face fell, and he noticed. 'Oh, don't mind me, Safi, love. You can have the book still and I mean nothing by it. It's just a thing I'd rather forget, and if I do have to remember it, I'd rather not have to tell you, Martha.'

He sat forward, his knee jiggling up and down.

'If it's something unpleasant about Charlie,' Martha said, 'go ahead. You won't be the first person to tell me something I don't like.'

She tried not to look at Alex. Brin glanced at Martha, assessing if she meant it or not, and she straightened her back. The small patches of wallpaper visible between the bookshelves were off-white, busy with swooping leaves and tendrils of vine.

'Well, you know for a few years I took Charlie to sales with me. House clearances, that sort of thing. We'd look through the notices for the county and we'd go to the ones that looked promising.' He jutted his chin at Safi. 'She was like you. Had a nose for the good stuff, and she was enthusiastic. Always urging me to go to places farther away on the off-chance, and often as not we'd find something interesting. Then she'd chat with the auctioneers and the sellers. Charm their socks off, so we often got a keener deal than we might have done.'

She was there in the room with them again, brushing the hair off her face, laughing eagerly. A living absence.

'I taught her everything I knew. Wasn't much, but she sucked knowledge out of you like a sponge, and I was happy enough to do it – I mean, you all know what it's like, the pleasure in talking about the trade. The joy of the hunt and finding something a bit unusual: it's rare. When she started doing her PhD, I thought she'd give it all up, but she was still keen to go. "Don't you waste your Sunday," she'd tell me. "I'll go searching." And it was nice to be able to mind the shop or be around my wife and kids; then she'd come in the day after and we'd go through what she found. Honestly? I was hurt when she quit on me like that. I mean, she was only a kid, but I thought we'd become friends.'

'And then?' Alex asked. 'What happened?'

He jumped to his feet and started rearranging the greeting cards on the cash desk. 'A dealer I know popped in a few months later. Must have been June, July. He knew Charlie from the sales and asked after her, and when I said she'd left, he asked me if I knew she'd been dealing herself. *For* herself for the last year.'

'Oh.' Alex sighed.

'I don't understand,' Safi said. The pompom on her pencil stopped its dance.

'I was paying her to go to sales, paying for her petrol and her time, and I gave her a commission on anything she got which we resold,' Brin mumbled. 'It turned out she'd been buying the best lots for herself and flogging them elsewhere. Keeping the profit for herself.'

The pompom resumed its movement.

'I . . . That's pretty low,' Simon said slowly. 'On antiquarian websites?'

'Not under her own name – she had a made-up handle, but the dealer had seen her buying, then saw what she'd bought coming up on various selling sites, but not our shop. He put it together.'

'Do you think she regretted it?' Martha asked. 'Is that why she quit?'

No one answered her. She followed the sweep of the wall-paper pattern to the edge of a shelf. A slim volume of poetry by Christina Rossetti, published at the end of the nineteenth century. '"Remember me when I am gone away" . . .' Martha closed her eyes.

'Did you challenge her about it, Brin?' Alex asked, staring at the water glass in her hand.

'I did. I was angry. I went to the house. She was on her own, your mum and dad were out. She just laughed. Told me it was my own fault for opting out of the sales and ushered me out.'

'Ouch,' Simon said with feeling.

Brin raised his glass. 'Yeah. It was humiliating. I mean, worst thing is she was right.' He glanced at Martha. 'I never told your mum and dad. I was embarrassed. Truth is I was dreading seeing her at Jonathan's launch a couple of months later. I was glad she wasn't there. Felt horrible about that later, of course.'

He crossed the shop and turned the sign back to 'Open'. 'I occasionally get a bit of an after-school crowd, this time of day. Don't want to put them off.'

It was a clear signal that the discussion was over. Martha thanked him. 'If you get any more postcards, or you think of anything else . . .'

'I'll let you know, Martha. I promise. If you want to have a browse through some more of the vernacular treasures, stick around, Safi. I've got some rarities. And we have some Boer War correspondence somewhere. There's a tin of Victorian chocolate to go with that, though I wouldn't recommend eating it.'

'Oh God, yes, that would be brilliant. I'll get the bus back, Alex,' Safi said, putting away her pad and pen.

Brin looked pleased. Martha hoped Safi's enthusiasm would be some sort of recompense for the unpleasant memories of Charlie.

'I might hang round, too,' Simon added. 'And I'll do the same.'

Alex pulled out her car keys and bounced them in her hand. 'Did you work out which of us is holding the hellhound's leash, Brin?'

He shook his head. 'Seems like this Chorus is yanking all our chains, don't you think?'

15

oberration, *noun (seventeenth century)*: a wandering about

EVERY HISTORICAL DICTIONARY HAS ITS singletons, words recorded only once before they slipped away into the shadows. Wordrobes, motivated as much by fashion as by value, have little room for outliers. Dictionaries of current language consequently neglect them, their compilers intent only upon the words their databases suggest people use. The rare, the obscure, the untested and the uninvited are left behind.

Whenever Martha came across such abandoned words in the course of her work she found herself wondering about their creators, questioning whether they had looked on with hope as 'their' word enjoyed a brief moment in the light, or whether they had even cared at all. Few of them would surely have predicted that their voice would be quoted in the greatest of all lexicons, one that uniquely preserved every entry ever made within its pages – once a word went into the *CED*, it never came out. Yet it was precisely the unsung words that were the most beautiful in Martha's eyes. 'Apricity', the warmth of the sun on a winter's day, she had found mentioned in just a single source from the 1620s. And then, nothing. 'Respair', sketchily defined in the dictionary as 'a recovery from despair', apparently lived for just one day, like a linguistic mayfly, before it vanished into the recesses of a word-hoard so vast that its tiny footprint lay buried beneath the tread of words more ordinary, yet inexplicably more popular. *Just like people*, Martha reflected, not for the first time. She felt a strange affinity with such words, understood both the risks and pleasures of a life below the radar. She'd had her share of boyfriends and anonymous lovers, but had never felt comfortable enough with any of them to share herself fully. Better to stay in the shadows than risk being melted by the sun.

Yet just at this moment she felt a throbbing need for some apricity in her own life, some warmth on her skin to shake off the chills. *What chance respair now?* she thought.

'Martha?'

'I'm sorry, what did you say?'

'I asked what you thought. Why did Chorus send us to Brin? Is he suggesting Brin might have hurt Charlie in some way?'

She was in the Mini with Alex. Driving along the A40 back into Oxford, a blur of green hedgerow outside the passenger window, a steady ribbon of tarmac ahead.

'I don't know. He did say he could have killed her.'

'I noticed that, but if he had, it would surely be the last thing he'd say. He could be drawing attention to their disagreements as a sort of double bluff?'

'Perhaps,' Martha said, focusing on the traffic in front of them. Alex drove well, with a mix of confidence and care that made Martha, always a nervous passenger, relax. 'I can't believe

Charlie did that. Told him she was going to buy for him, then took the best things for herself.'

Alex shrugged, tapping her fingers on the steering wheel. 'We only have his version of events. Perhaps he suggested she went on her own, and that irritated her into thinking, "Sod him." The "sad naive teacher betrayed by the ambitious student" trope can hide a lot of laziness and inertia on the teacher's part.'

'Is that a trope?'

'Definitely. So where next?'

'Back to the office, I suppose.'

Alex let out an exasperated sigh. 'Oh, come on, Martha! Chorus, the police, *everyone* is telling you to find out more about Charlie. Are you really just going to sit there and wait for another letter? Let's go and ask some questions. Who do we need to talk to?'

'Is that really a good idea?'

'It's a necessity. God, I've just realised, this wool-gathering habit of yours. It's your portable escape hatch, isn't it?'

'What?' Martha said, snapping her head around to look at her.

Alex slapped her palm on the wheel, looking amazed, as if she'd just unlocked a puzzle. 'You're a bolter. You ran away to Berlin when Charlie disappeared, and maybe something has made you run away from Berlin to come back here.' Her voice became gentler. 'I get it; I've been there. Whenever you are threatened, you flee, or you disappear into your own thoughts. I mean, really disappear into them.' Martha held her breath as Alex continued. 'You're like a kid climbing into the attic and drawing up the stepladder behind them when they hear their parents arguing. And that's what you do when you go into your reveries. You're running away from life.'

'I'm *thinking* about life!'

'Try experiencing it instead,' Alex said firmly. 'Eat a pie. Have sex. Go for a run.'

'Alex, this is a totally inappropriate way to talk to your boss.'

'I'm still off the clock. Fire me if you want,' she laughed. 'Though I'd love to see the write-up. While helping me investigate the disappearance of my sister, Alex Monroe strongly advised me to eat a pie.'

That surprised Martha into a laugh. The outward cruelty of Alex's words came, she knew, from a place of solicitude. 'Honestly! I like thinking. It's not the worst vice, is it?'

'I'm a great believer in vices, never met one I didn't like, but it's just like drinking, or gambling or whatever: if retreating into your thoughts is getting in the way of your *actual* life, maybe you should think about cutting down a bit.'

Martha studied the hedgerows. They were threaded with the curved thorns and pallid pinks of dogrose, like untidy stitching on a patchwork quilt.

'Habits of a lifetime are hard to break.'

'I know. But it's possible. Believe it or not, ten years ago I didn't have a lot of faith in myself. Too many bad voices in my head parroting my ex-husband. I was a bad wife, a bad mother, a bad writer. Hardest thing I've ever had to do was get them to shut up long enough for me to prove them wrong.'

Martha sighed. 'I hate this, Alex. I know I can deal with the not-knowing. I've done it for years. I just don't know if I can live with the truth.'

'I do get it, Martha. But we all have to face the truth in the end. Messiness, pain – they are teachers. A necessary part of life – like pie.'

Martha considered. 'Fine. I suppose we should go and talk to Tom. Charlie's ex-boyfriend.'

'He's still in Oxford?'

Martha nodded slowly, remembering. 'Yes. Works at the John Radcliffe. My mother mentioned seeing him there when she was getting chemo.'

'So who would have his phone number?'

'Charlie's friend Tanya might. They all lived on the same corridor in their first year, and stayed in touch. I met her in town – God, years ago now – and she gave me her number. As long as she hasn't changed it.'

Alex nodded pointedly towards Martha's bag. She fished out her phone and scrolled through the contacts. The lists of German names made her stiffen. She hadn't called any of them since she came back. *It's not like Charlie*, she told herself. *I told them I was going. They knew I was coming back to Oxford*. That image, of clambering into the attic, pulling up the ladder, and snapping the door shut came back to her. Was that what she'd done?

'Here . . .' She pressed dial and put her phone on speaker as Alex turned off the Woodstock Road and pulled into the kerb.

'Yes?' The voice on the other end of the line was far from warm.

'Hi, Tanya, this is Martha Thornhill.'

'I can see who it is, Martha. What do you want?'

Alex grimaced as she looked ahead.

'I'm sorry to bother you. I wondered if you had a number for Tom. I need to talk to him about something.'

'Oh really, Martha? You'd like to speak to him? Fascinating. I do have his number as it happens. We've been married seven years.'

'Oh, I didn't . . . congratulations,' Martha said, sharing a pained look with Alex.

There was a long pause, and the sound of a murmured conversation in the background.

'OK. Fine. You better come over.'

16

umbrage, *noun (seventeenth century)*:
a feeling of suspicion, resentment, or doubt

THE ADDRESS TANYA GAVE WAS in Staunton Road in Headington, close to the hospital. The road was an eclectic mix of 1930s villas, rebuilt and restored over the decades. Most of the narrow front gardens had been sacrificed to cars, but the street was still dotted with conifer hedges and Japanese maples in various degrees of untamed exuberance. The house was at the far end, before the road curved to a stop at Headley Way. The bend had given it a larger garden, accommodating both car and grass.

'Nice,' Alex said as she got out of the car and admired the bay windows and white-painted stone. Martha closed the passenger door, feeling the reassuring crunch of gravel beneath her feet. 'What sort of doctor is he?'

'He'd just started his general surgery training when Charlie disappeared.'

There was movement behind them. Tanya stood framed by the doorway, older now but still athletic, her glossy dark hair tied up in a ponytail. She was squinting in the bright sun.

'Was it you? Did you send those bloody postcards? If it was, I swear, I don't care how grown up and civilised we are now, I'll knock you into next week.'

Her voice had kept its Midlands twang. Whatever Martha was expecting, she hadn't for a minute considered that Tom might have received a postcard too. Chorus was reeling in a lot of actors.

'No! I got one as well. And some other things. Can we come in, Tanya? This is Alex, my colleague from the *CED*.'

Tanya looked Alex up and down and said nothing, but her expression became, if anything, more hostile.

'Come in, then,' she said, pushing the door wide. 'And shoes off, please.'

The hallway felt dark after the spring sunshine. She led them through into the kitchen, where peppery worktops and wood-finished cabinets had settled into a professional kind of homeliness. A long kitchen table edged out a huge fridge smothered with magnets, timetables, notes, and jumbled plastic letters. Photos of two children in a series of professionally taken poses had been mounted in a long beechwood frame above the table. Martha guessed they were of primary school age, owners of the small shoes in the rack in the hall.

'Tom's taken the kids round to their friend's house for a bit. I didn't want them here while . . . Those postcards. It brought it all back. Bloody Charlie, still fucking things up.'

Martha was too stunned to respond.

'I'm sorry,' Alex said, swooping in to fill the silence, 'but you'll have to catch me up. So you are married to Tom? Charlie's ex-boyfriend?'

Tanya waved vaguely towards the table and filled the kettle. 'Yes. We'd been friends for years, and all the shit around Charlie disappearing, it brought us closer.'

'Are you a doctor too?' Alex asked.

'No. I read PPE and now I'm in Marketing.' She lifted a quartet of nostalgically floral mugs out of the cupboard and set them on the table. 'So, what gives, Martha?'

Before she could answer, the front door opened and closed. 'We're in here, Tom. She says she didn't send them. She and . . .' she waved her hand towards Alex '. . . this lady got one too.'

A man walked in and dropped his keys on the side. He stared at each of them for a long beat.

'My name's Alex,' Alex said. Tanya shrugged as if this information was of little interest, and retreated to sullen silence.

Tom was as handsome as ever. Dark-haired, with high cheekbones and a strong jaw. The sort of surgeon one expected after watching too many years of *Grey's Anatomy*. Martha had developed a madly inappropriate crush on him when he and Charlie first got together, to which he had responded with brotherly affection. It had been both delicious and terrible.

'Good to meet you, Alex,' he said, looking her in the eye, then glanced at Martha. 'Hey, Martha.'

'Hi.' Martha was surprised to find her voice was even audible.

'So these postcards are nothing to do with you? Really?' He folded his arms and leant against the work surface.

Tanya tutted and returned to making the tea, warming the pot first.

'No. You're not the only ones to have got them. And there's more,' Martha said. 'We had some strange letters.'

By the time she had finished explaining, the tea was made and poured and each of them had found a chair around the table. She told them about Burford and Brin, and all the while Tom stared at the table, his hand clenched round the mug's handle. Strong hands, Martha thought, finding it impossible not to picture them holding a knife.

'So why come here?' Tanya said, sitting back and folding her arms. 'You didn't get a letter about us.'

'I persuaded Martha it was time to seize the initiative, rather than wait for more choral compositions,' Alex said evenly. Tanya glanced at her and nodded reluctantly.

'And the police seem to think that after all this time people might be more willing to talk honestly about Charlie,' Martha added.

'I've never had any problem saying what I think about Charlie,' Tanya said.

'I think we all know that,' Tom said sharply, looking up for the first time.

'And? The shit she put us through, Tom!'

'I told you I shouldn't work in Oxford! It's always waiting for us round the corner in this bloody city. It was you who wanted to stay here.'

The exchange had the rhythm and ritual of a well-rehearsed argument. Martha looked between them.

'I don't understand.'

'Everyone thought Tom had killed her, of course!' Tanya said, spitting out the words. 'The police questioned him for hours, searched his rooms—'

'Tanya, for God's sake, I can tell them that myself,' Tom interrupted. He breathed in carefully, then looked at Martha. 'She dumped me, what, a fortnight before she disappeared. I was still crazy about her and so I was mad with worry when your mum called, wondering if she was with me. I was confused as hell, too, especially as she hadn't bothered to tell your parents we were over, and when the police first called, I thought they wanted my help. I spilt my guts to them, about the summer, the break-up. I thought something, anything might be significant. Then I realised they were looking into me as a suspect.'

'I never thought you had anything to do with it, Tom,' Martha said. She remembered the interview with Oliver Caldwell on Friday; the room, the smell. What would it have been like for Tom? Not the solicitous chat she had enjoyed. She imagined those walls, the atmosphere thickened with accusation and fear.

'Did you tell your parents that?' Tanya asked. 'Because they certainly believed it. It was their turning up and asking to talk about Charlie that wiped out Tom's first year of surgical training.'

'You missed a year?' Martha asked.

'Yes, you never noticed that, did you? Your parents basically hounded Tom out of the city. He had a breakdown, and when he did come back, everyone was looking at him sideways. Then ten years later, just when we think we're settled, the police are on the phone again. Dredging it all up.'

'Oh, for God's sake, Tanya, I didn't mind. Rebecca was dying. She had every right to try again. Whatever I've been through is nothing compared to what Charlie's family has suffered.'

None of us were ever questioned in one of those foul little rooms though, Martha thought.

Tanya wiped her eyes, thumbing away tears with a quick angry gesture. Martha tried to remember what she had looked like a decade ago without the thin network of lines around her eyes. Martha's mental picture of Charlie – the one which her subconscious mind compared to every stranger she glimpsed, that sent alarms of cortisol through her body when it thought it had found a match – shifted slightly. Charlie married, Charlie after six or seven years of interrupted sleep. Her new picture of Charlie acquired those same lines, and her sister's laugh became less throaty and full – sharper, as if forced from her lungs with a punch of surprise.

'You were in hell again, Tom. You think I didn't notice the 5 a.m. runs and snapping at the kids?'

He put out his hand. She hesitated a beat and then took it with her own, and her expression softened.

'And now what? Now there's some mad poison-pen person in the game,' she said, her thumb stroking her husband's knuckles.

'I have no idea,' Martha admitted. 'Chorus seems to know something, but it's all dark hints and treasure hunts.'

'Did you both get postcards?' Alex asked the couple. They nodded, a united front again. 'What did they say? We all had ones with Shakespeare quotes. Even our colleague Safiya at the office got one – she was ten and living in London when Charlie went missing.'

'What did yours say, Martha?' Tanya asked. Martha remembered how clever she was. Charlie was not someone who liked to shine among a group of lesser minds. She wanted to outblaze the cleverest people she knew.

Martha swallowed. She could hardly refuse to say after blundering into their lives again, but it hurt her to form the words. 'It said, "Where have you been sister?"'

Alex reached out and put a hand on her shoulder, a brief touch, grounding her. Keeping her in the room, just.

Tanya flinched, a twinge of sympathy, swiftly covered with a frown. 'I can't remember. Mine was something about fake friends. Tom's was about faithfulness, which is just ridiculous – he worshipped Charlie! I knew I was never going to measure up but . . .' He shook his head slightly and squeezed her hand, quick to cover an old wound. 'Anyway, I tore them up and threw them in the bin.'

'How did you know it had something to do with Charlie?' Alex asked.

'The postcards were pictures of her,' Tom said. 'Yours weren't?'

Alex shook her head. 'We got ones of the *CED* building.'

'It was the picture they used in the "missing" posters,' Tom went on, 'maybe they thought the *CED* would be a bit subtle for us.' His face twisted into something between a smile and a sneer, 'but I think we could have got it from the quotes. Mine was "Wilt thou betray thy noble mistress thus?", and Tanya's was "God keep me from false friends".'

'Can you imagine doing that?' Tanya's voice cracked slightly. 'Sending us pictures of her, just landing on the doormat with the broadband bill and council flyers? I actually thought for a moment . . . I thought they were from Charlie herself, that she's still out there somewhere.' She looked at Martha. 'I'm sorry. I think she ran away, without thinking what it would do to Tom or me, or you and your parents.' Then she looked at Alex: 'Did you know her?'

'Yes, I did. And I once thought the same as you. Depression can make people incredibly selfish, and Charlie could be thoughtless. But she didn't seem to be depressed, she left her passport behind, hasn't used her bank account since the day before she disappeared. I think something happened to her.'

'Well, if it did, it has nothing to do with me or my husband. She hardly hung out with us at all that summer. I think she lost interest in me when I began working in business rather than academia anyway.'

'But you were still living in Oxford, then?' Alex asked.

'No, London. But I seemed to spend most of my weekends here. I didn't move back permanently until Tom and I got together.' She half smiled. 'It was hard being in London at first. I was already nostalgic for my university days.'

'Did Charlie ever come and see you?'

'Always said she was too busy.'

Martha stood up suddenly and the others looked at her in confusion. 'We shouldn't be here. I don't want to play this Chorus's games. If he knows anything, let him go to the police. This is just making everything worse.'

She was out in the hall, thrusting her feet into her boots.

'But as we are here . . .' Alex began.

'No.' Martha held up her hand. 'Enough. I've had enough. Whoever Chorus is, he has no right to put us through this, to put Tom and Tanya through this.'

'You think it's a man?'

'Oh, of course it's a bloody man, Alex.'

She opened the door and strode out to the car, yanking at the door handle until Alex pressed the fob and she was able to get in.

Alex followed at a more leisurely pace, her back straight, and Martha heard her saying goodbye to Tom and Tanya. She climbed into the driver's seat without comment and was beginning to back out into the road again, radiating disapproval and mild disappointment, when Tom rushed out, skipping awkwardly over the gravel in his socks. He tapped on Martha's window. Alex pulled on the handbrake and lowered the window. Martha couldn't look at him. Why had she never considered what he might have gone through?

'Look, Martha, I was infatuated with Charlie, but it was a romance, not a real relationship. I love Tanya, and when she's not wound up about Charlie she knows that, she does. And the kids are amazing. I have a good life and I'm grateful for it. I don't want you to think her disappearing ruined anything, not in the long term.'

'I'm glad, Tom. You were always very kind to me.'

'You were sweet, Martha.' He remained stooped by the window, studying the stones at his feet. 'I don't know what was going on with her that summer, but I thought she might have been having an affair. I don't know.'

Martha felt the blood pounding in her ears. An affair, no. But she had been giddy, Martha was sure of that. And not because of Tom.

'You thought she'd met someone? Who?' Alex asked, leaning over. Martha felt the muscles in her legs tense as if for flight.

He shook his head. 'Someone older, I think? Someone who could help her with her career? Sometimes when I asked her where she'd been, she'd say "forging my golden future", or something like that. I saw her getting on the London train one day when she'd said she was going to the library, things like that. Nothing more concrete.'

'Did you tell the police that?' Martha asked.

'Yes. And your parents eventually. Your mother said Charlie would never have had an affair behind my back, and the police just thought me paranoid and jealous, like I was planting distractions.'

He lowered his head. Martha could smell his cologne, something oddly citrus, and underneath it a faint smell of hospital.

'Charlie was exceptional, and she knew it. Tanya and I both worshipped her for a long time. And I did take it hard when she dumped me, but I think part of me was relieved. It was getting too much. She liked a bit of drama, being the centre of things. You know that, Martha.'

She only nodded.

'Are you sure you didn't suspect who she was seeing?' Alex pressed.

He was silent for a long time. 'I did think it might be someone she was working with. I came to pick her up at the house once, in that beaten-up old Volkswagen you thought was cool, Martha.' Martha found herself blushing slightly. He'd let Charlie borrow that car when she went on buying trips too. 'She was in the garden, on her phone and arguing with someone. I don't know what it was about. She just sounded angry and whoever was on the other end kept interrupting her. Anyway, she ended it with "Forget it, I'll see you at work."'

'When was this?'

He frowned. 'In the summer, I think? Maybe spring.'

'Can you remember which? She worked in different places that year.'

He shook his head. 'It was over a decade ago.'

They said their goodbyes again, and Alex drove them back to the *CED* office so that Martha could pick up her bike. As soon as she parked, Alex pulled a notebook out of her pocket and wrote the date in the top right corner. An Arabic numeral for the day, lowercase Latin for the month, uppercase Latin for the year. Martha knew she'd seen that recently. On the postcard from the British Museum that she'd found in Charlie's shoebox: *You dazzle me.* Alex glanced up, realised she was being observed.

'Safi's got the right idea. No use us going round asking questions if we don't remember the answers. I can't do shorthand, though, so I thought I'd try and jot everything down now, while it's fresh.'

'That's a cool way to do your dates.'

'The compulsive habits of an archivist,' Alex said, still scribbling. 'I picked it up from my husband. It stuck even if the marriage didn't.'

Martha felt as if she was drifting away, untethered, a balloon disappearing off into the spring sky. 'Was he a book person as well?'

'Still is. He's been at the British Library almost twenty years now. Shall I tell Safi and Simon what Tom said?'

Martha blinked.

'Yes, of course.'

Alex put away her notebook and restarted the car.

17

videnda, *plural noun (eighteenth century)*: things deserving to be seen

SAFI SPENT A VERY HAPPY hour in the bookshop, sitting on the floor in a far corner where Brin kept obscure dictionaries of regional English, and a smattering of texts in which some eighteenth- or nineteenth-century writer had attempted to catch accent and idiolect in type. Safi knew and loved many of them. *Kything*, she thought: *the recognition of old friends in a crowd.*

Brin's after-school rush came and went. It consisted of a dozen or so customers, the children flopping down around a low table to open splashily coloured books plucked off the shelves, their parents browsing the latest book club offerings or Moleskine notebooks.

They all seemed to know Brin, and as Safi sat cross-legged between the second-hand stacks, turning the pages of the *Dictionary of Obsolete and Provincial English* on her lap, she listened to him flirting pleasantly with some of the mothers as they looked around. *Everyone has to make a buck*, she said to herself, turning over another page. One of the women chuckled gleefully and her concentration broke. She remembered her colleagues' descriptions of Charlie's throaty laugh. She had looked up a picture of Martha's sister online, finding the reports of her disappearance in archives of newspapers and social media posts. She was undeniably beautiful: what tabloidese would class as an English rose. Her image seemed to force its way through the crabbed black print of the book in Safi's hand. Beautiful, but flawed, she reflected, remembering what the others had said of her: superior and even a little cruel.

Safi thought back to one of the popular girls at her school, who had sought her out at various times as a target for bullying. Safi's bookishness had cast her as an oddball, a geek whose love of her own company unsettled those who flourished only in the gaze of others. She'd met the girl five years later. She had wanted to apologise for any hurt or distress she'd ever caused Safi, who had responded quite sincerely that she had not been bothered then or now. Safi recalled the disappointment in the girl's face, and realised that her former classmate was sorry that she hadn't made her mark; any regret over her teenage cruelty had failed to outweigh the disappointment that she would never be a main character in Safi's story.

She turned another page. The world needed another dictionary, one for London English in its entirety. It should capture and codify this moment in time: the chat of the city's kids, their mouths full of the riches of Bengali and Punjabi, Yoruba and Tamil, Akan, Arabic, and Turkish and so many more – over three hundred languages, each given a new, homespun dimension. It would document the lexicon of Peckham, where a new sociolect was slipping effortlessly into the mainstream, wrapping itself around existing language to become a uniquely anglicised hybrid of itself. 'Multicultural London English' was too soulless a term for such wealth, Safi thought. But it did need to be lexicalised, otherwise in fifty years' time the scholars of tomorrow would be puzzling over grime lyrics in the same way students today grappled with *Beowulf*.

She set the dictionary back on the shelf, her fingers lightly stroking the cracked leather volumes that flanked it. What had Charlie found and sold? She must have chanced upon some real rarities to make it worth her while. Safi wondered whether there was any chance of finding Charlie's old accounts, or of contacting the dealers she'd sold to. Brin must have some leads on the sales she'd visited, or remember where he had seen the listings he had confronted her over.

The shop had fallen quiet again and the children's books lay discarded on the table. She looked at her watch: almost five. She got to her feet. She'd buy *A Glossary of the Essex Dialect*, first compiled in the nineteenth century. The entries for 'belly-wengins', meaning 'small beer', and 'dallop', a 'patch of ground missed by the plough', had swung it. Besides, it was a lovely edition and keenly priced. She'd also taken a few screenshots of a copy of the *New Dictionary of the Canting Crew*, a romping collection of the slanguage of rogues and vagabonds in the seventeenth century. *The language of crime always pays*, she thought, as she tucked her phone into her pocket.

She emerged from the stack to find the main body of the shop deserted. She was about to call out when she heard whispers, urgent-sounding ones, coming from the back room.

'Of course I haven't . . .' a voice was insisting. 'No reason to think that, unless you . . .'

Brin and Simon were in the office behind the desk, silhouetted by a window that looked onto the back yard.

The shadows and low voices made it hard to tell who was saying what.

'Ancient history . . .' one of them hissed – Brin, maybe. 'I did you a favour! Don't you dare drag all that up again.'

'A favour . . .' Simon said. She was certain it was his voice cracking from a whisper to a bark. 'You did nicely out of it.' The figures shifted, and Simon glanced around, realising he'd raised his voice. He saw Safi, and abruptly stopped.

Brin moved hastily from the back room, rubbing his hands, his twinkling smile slapped back in place. 'Safiya! Almost forgot you were there. Find anything interesting?'

'Yeah, thanks,' she said, setting the book down on the counter and getting out her purse.

Brin picked it up and checked the flyleaf. 'No charge, you can have that one for free too. Lovely to have some scholars back in the place.'

The forced heartiness was almost painful. Safi smiled. 'Wow, thanks. Appreciated.'

He slipped the volume into a paper bag, added a bookmark advertising the shop, and passed it back to her.

'Brin, what sort of things did Charlie sell? From the sales you went to. I was just thinking, she must have got very lucky to make it worthwhile.'

The twinkle dissipated. 'Luck was part of it, I'm sure. But I think she made most of it by picking up volumes of prints and selling them individually. Razoring them out and plonking a "Rare" sticker on the back. From what I can remember of the listings.'

Safi shuddered. She knew people did that, and for the most part the volumes they cut up were not particularly rare. Still, taking a sharp blade to a volume felt like an act of violence. 'Oh,' she managed. 'I see.'

'Lowest of the low,' Brin said, and looked sideways at Simon. 'As good as thieving. But she had an eye for true rarities too. I only saw some of it when it ended up on the usual websites, but I wouldn't be at all surprised if she went to specialist dealers with other finds. I'd introduced her to enough of them over the years.'

'Right,' Safi said, falteringly. 'I'm going to get the bus back into town.' She paused, expecting Simon to say he'd come with her, but he didn't. 'Well, OK, then. Really nice to meet you, Brin, and thanks so much for the books.'

He replied with the usual niceties and Safi left, deep in thought, her backpack slung over her shoulder. It was half an hour until the next bus, and rather than wait at the stop she headed in the direction of the church spire to have a look at the inscription that had brought them here.

She walked up Lawrence Lane, passed the side of the school from which Brin's customers had emerged, and headed towards the ornate, faintly hubristic porch of St John the Baptist Church. *What are you up to, Chorus?* Was he watching each of them now, assessing whether they were up to the challenge he'd set them? She thought again of Shakespeare's Chorus in *Henry V*: a professional storyteller who moved the story's action on, urging the audience to participate in the performance, engage their 'imaginary forces' and 'piece out imperfections' with their thoughts. What imperfections had this Chorus discovered?

With little agenda other than to keep thinking, Safi stepped through the entrance, picked up a leaflet, and made a slow tour of the building, exchanging smiles with an elderly man who was gathering up hymn sheets from the pews. The church's interior was labyrinthine, a mix of confusing angles and different levels that, according to the leaflet, one architectural guide had described as 'an illogical agglomeration of parallelograms'. Safi liked their style.

She moved through a maze of interconnected spaces beneath a ceiling studded with elaborate sculptures, and on towards the east side of the church. The inscription on the font, covered by protective glass, was hard to see with the naked eye, but Safi experienced no flash of revelation on deciphering it. She could picture its author, dirty with the road, resentful of the present, working at the lead with his knife. ANTHONY SEDLEY 1649 PRISNER. Perhaps he did so in a fit of defiance, perhaps he wrote out of despair. Were the other prisoners sitting around watching him, she wondered, or were they too troubled by their own uncertain fates to notice what he was doing? Sedley had been lucky, Safi thought. So many people wanted to make their mark, yet so few were remembered beyond their own generation. This man's small act of vandalism had given him a permanent place in history, a remembered instance of a human soul in the undifferentiated mass of the past. What of the rest?

She looked up and saw other markers of time, from the art of the scattered memorials to the stone floors tempered by generations of worshippers. But even though, unlike Sedley the 'prisner', their legators remained anonymous, their touch was still perceptible. Their christenings, weddings, burials and all the prayers in between had left their impression upon the stone. The country church: a repository of time and a bulwark against its depredations.

Safi paused at the large seventeenth-century tomb in St Katherine's chapel and glanced at her pamphlet. Two local dignitaries, their hands in ruffs of carved velvet and clasped in prayer, lay side by side beneath a stone canopy, an effigy of their grandson praying at their feet. Sir Lawrence and Lady

Tanfield had enjoyed the means to make a surer bid for immortality, far more so than Sedley, scoring the lead with his knife.

Below the entombed pair, like a kid on a lower bunk, lay a stone skeleton. Safi glanced back at her pamphlet and her eyebrows shot up. Although the composition of this memento mori was mostly stone, it told her, one of its femurs was 'of human origin'.

'Horrible pair,' a voice said behind her. The elderly man had paused in his collection of hymnals. 'They haunted the village for ages.'

'Really?' Safi said. She'd have to tell Alex.

'Yes. Foul to their tenants. Lady Tanfield said she would like to grind the people of Burford to powder beneath her chariot wheels. People heard them driving their ghostly coach across the rooftops of the town for years after their deaths. In the end a priest bottled up her ghost and hid it under an arch of Burford Bridge.'

'And did that work?' Safi asked with a half laugh, not sure if the man was as serious as he sounded.

'Yes. But it needs to be kept wet. I worry in these long dry summers we've been having, she'll get loose. You can't disturb ghosts, you know. Let the air get to them, and they'll be back to cause all sorts of trouble.' He winked. 'Though I trust that fellow in here to keep an eye on the bones themselves.'

Safi followed her gaze. One of the corbels at the top of the pillar was carved into the face of a man with flowing hair and beard, casting a sideways look across the church.

'He looks worried,' Safi murmured. But her informant had already moved away.

18

velleity, *noun (seventeenth century)*:

the act of wishing or desiring, without any accompanying effort

SHE SHOULDN'T HAVE COME, BUT the realisation only came to Martha in the microsecond after she'd pressed the doorbell. Instant regret for an act taken: there must be a German word for that. She wished she could ask Sabine, and felt a familiar stab of guilt; her friend hadn't understood why she'd been so keen to leave Berlin as soon as she could. The thought of her face, sympathetic but also baffled and confused, made Martha wince.

'Hello?'

Olivia Overton had opened the door. Her hair fell in soft golden waves around her face and her make-up was characteristically flawless. Both made a strange contrast with her outfit: a thick white towelling robe.

'Olivia. I'm so sorry to disturb you, but I need a word with Jonathan, is he here?'

Olivia didn't hide her irritation. Nor did she reply, but shouted instead over her shoulder into the depths of the house.

'Jonathan! It's Martha!'

He emerged from one of the back rooms into the hall with a small boy in his arms. Father and son were both laughing, and the boy's cheeks were pink. Olivia's frown deepened.

'God! I asked you not to get him riled up tonight. He'll give the babysitter hell now. We leave in twenty minutes.'

Jonathan nodded in her direction. 'Understood, and you'll be good for Maggie, won't you, Eddie?'

The little boy half nodded, suddenly shy as he buried his face into his father's neck. 'Is Maggie here yet, Liv?'

'Yes, in the nursery room with Miranda.'

He set the boy down and tapped his bottom. 'You go and find your sister.'

Edgar zoomed up the stairs, and Olivia tutted.

'Twenty minutes, remember!' she admonished her husband, then climbed quickly up the stairs after her son. Even in a fluffy robe she managed to be coltishly graceful.

'Come through, Martha.'

Martha stepped into the hall and closed the front door behind her. Jonathan's house was as polished as its occupants; its open spaces were naturally lit and flowed organically between one room and the next. The hall was more akin to a lobby, sweeping past a riser-less staircase through high, wide doors that led into a dining and drawing room on the right, and an expanse of kitchen and living rooms at the back. The walls were dominated by enormous abstract paintings and a large, staged photograph of the family, which had them examining flowers together in the Oxfordshire countryside. A marble sideboard bore an equally curated arrangement of spirits on a tray, alongside a pedestal vase of dried flowers. Martha could see it was tasteful, acknowledging the way the ochres and ivories of the bouquet complemented the wood and the canvas, but it all looked utterly dead to her. Too controlled, too spiritless.

She had not been here before. When her family had first met Jonathan, he was living in rented rooms in the middle of town. As she followed him through the hall she wondered how much of this money had come from his book sales versus his wife's trust fund. Surely even his level of success couldn't buy all this.

The kitchen and dining area at the far end of the house consisted of one long room. Bifold glass doors looked out onto a large lawn backed by mature copper beeches and oaks.

Jonathan went over to the marble sideboard. 'Can I offer you a drink? You're a G&T woman, aren't you?' His hand had automatically reached for a balloon glass.

'Yes, thank you, if you have time.'

Jonathan smiled, a complicated little grimace. 'Olivia will need a bit more than twenty minutes, I'm sure, and all I need to do is put on my jacket. One of the many advantages of being a man.' He glanced at his watch. 'Though I don't want to be late tonight. My publishers have organised a dinner with a few journalists and reviewers. Supposed to be a "thank you for your support" event, but really it's about coercing them into mentioning the new book at all.'

On the silver tray were an ice bucket, silver tongs, bottles and decanters. An antique tea caddy turned out to hold individual cans of tonic. He didn't even need to go to the fridge.

Martha turned away and went to the sliding doors, looking out over the garden. You'd think you were in deep countryside. Still, all this glass. She wasn't sure if the house felt like a sanctuary or a fishbowl.

'There you go.'

She took the drink from him, careful not to touch his fingers.

'Thank you.'

'So what did you want to talk to me about?'

She breathed in, wishing she'd rehearsed this moment. 'Do you remember that odd letter we showed you at your launch?'

He took a slow sip of his own drink, head tilted, a concerted attentiveness in his gaze. She couldn't do this while looking at him. She concentrated instead on the way the evening light was softening across the garden, and began. First, their deciphering of the letter, its clue which led to the year Charlie went missing, then the arrival of the postcards and her own visit to the police. Finally, the second letter, and Brin.

She glanced sideways at him, afraid she had lost him, and found he too was staring out across the garden, concentration puckering his forehead.

'I wish you'd told me about this sooner,' he said sharply as she came to a halt. 'This second letter arrived today? Before our meeting?'

'Yes, but—'

He cut her off. 'I mean, I know I'm not as involved with the day-to-day at the dictionary anymore, but I do think you should have consulted me or someone in senior management before running off to the police.'

Martha was stung. 'Charlie was my sister, Jonathan. And I didn't "run off to the police", I'm not a child. I reported some disturbing letters to the proper authorities.'

He let his shoulders drop. 'Of course. Sorry, that was a stupid thing to say.' He turned towards her and offered a smile that was finely balanced between apology and sadness. 'Contristation', Martha thought, processing emotions the only way she knew how.

'I just hate the thought of you having to deal with this on your own,' Jonathan continued, 'especially when I could have been offering you some support.'

He put his hand on her upper arm as he spoke: a warm, firm pressure that she was tempted to lean into. She shouldn't bristle at him now. She remembered his frantic activity in the weeks after Charlie went missing, sitting with her parents, posting flyers around town. He'd urged Martha to go back to university and, she suspected, talked her parents into doing the same.

'So this Caldwell, he thinks you should start asking everyone about Charlie again?'

'Yes, that was his suggestion, though he didn't push it. I can't say I'm keen. What is there to find out after all this time?'

'Yet it seems like this Chorus knows something we don't,' he said. 'Who the hell could it be?'

The glass was chilling her fingers. 'I honestly have no idea. It must be someone connected to the dictionary – or perhaps he wants us to think that way. Those dark comments about poisoned fountains are ridiculous.'

'Every institution has its scandals.' The smile was scornful now. 'Ours have mostly been about injudicious tweets and the occasional definition someone has deemed either offensive or offensively woke.' He hesitated. 'I'm sorry, Marth, this must be bringing up memories of a terrible time.'

He had never called her 'Marth' before. That had once been the exclusive right of her sister. It seemed to signal an adjustment in their interaction. She shook her head.

'Those memories never went away. I see her everywhere,' Martha replied simply. 'You were very kind to my parents. I haven't dared tell Dad about this yet. I suppose I must.'

His hand hadn't left her arm. 'I can see why you'd want to avoid doing that. How is Gabriel?'

'Jonathan?' Olivia was standing in the doorway in long silk trousers and a floral shirt, her hair pulled up into a half bun, its casualness offset by a thick rope of pearls around her neck.

He dropped his hand from Martha's arm. 'Darling, you look spectacular. Martha's just been telling me about some funny goings-on at the dictionary. I'll explain in the car, but we haven't had any odd postcards, have we?'

'Postcards?' Olivia replied, though she was still looking at Martha. 'I don't think so.'

Jonathan nodded, picked up his jacket from the back of one of the dining chairs and shrugged it on. 'Thank you for coming to tell me, Martha. Let's catch up later in the week.' Martha set down her gin and tonic on the table, its ice now melted to a few tiny shards. 'In the meantime, if you could email me scans of the letters, that would be wonderful. I'll see you out.'

'Goodnight, Olivia,' Martha said as she was shepherded back out into the hall, Jonathan's hand on the small of her back. Olivia gave a minuscule nod as she passed.

'Always stressful getting out of the house when there are young kids,' he said, opening the door. 'Chin up, Martha.'

'What *do* you think happened to Charlie?' Martha said, turning back to him on the doorstep.

He looked startled; the door was already half shut behind her. 'I . . . I hope very much she left Oxford and made a life for herself elsewhere. I didn't know her that well. A little from the dictionary, and as you know, she was interested in my work.'

He offered her another, complicated, smile.

'I thought she was in love with you,' Martha replied. 'Obsessed, even. You said as much to me at the time.'

He had no time to disguise his shock. 'No! That wasn't . . .' He stopped and looked down; a faint blush creeping up his throat was just visible in the crack of light. 'She . . . I thought perhaps her interest in my work wasn't purely intellectual, I admit.'

'No, it was more than that.'

It was strange, seeing him look so unsure of himself. For most of their acquaintance, if that was what you could call it, Martha had been the one prone to stammering. 'For a while I wondered whether it was something more, and whether the fact my romantic interests lay elsewhere had something to do with her running off. I was an arrogant sod, I admit that.'

'So coming to see my parents after she left. That was guilt?'

He had regained his poise, leaning against the doorframe. But there was a rueful, world-weary look in his eyes.

'Such an important motivation, guilt, isn't it? I sometimes envy sociopaths their lack of it.'

'Jonathan!' Olivia called from inside the house.

He became brisk again. 'Sorry, Martha. Duty calls – time to do the publicity dance.'

He closed the door on her, and Martha returned to her bike, a raw chill wrapping itself around her. A memory came into view, of Charlie helping her with her bike helmet, playfully chiding Martha for getting the straps twisted again, and apologetically stroking her younger sister's cheek when she realised the teasing had gone too far. When had she decided to shut her heart away?

Halfway home Martha stopped, fished her mobile out of her bag, and rang Caldwell. It went straight to voicemail. She left a message.

19

xenium, *noun (eighteenth century)*:

a present given to a guest or stranger

ALEX PUT IN A COUPLE of hours at the laptop while Rags dozed on an armchair behind her. She couldn't manage anything creative – her head was too scrambled – but she spent a couple of hours collating notes on a potential entry they'd discussed that morning, double- and triple-checking her footnotes before turning the dossier over to the Finalisation Team. The entry was for an old word from Cumberland dialect: 'rackups', which Alex had broadly defined as 'the consequences of ill-doing'. 'Let every man stand his awn rackups,' read one of her accompanying citations. The irony wasn't lost on her.

When she checked the time it was after seven, and she went through into the tiny kitchen built onto the back of the house to cook. Her sons claimed she was at her witchiest when it came to cooking. She enjoyed the ritual of it, appreciating its gift of communion with past generations. *There is alchemy in turning raw ingredients into a meal*, she thought, adding a pinch of sea salt. *What luxury we live in, where this everyday commodity that once held up the Roman Empire can be delivered to us in neat little jars for pennies*. Salary, salad, silt, sausage, salsa, sauce . . . the lexicon of salt whirred through her brain as she turned the stew down to a simmer. The story was richer still, she knew. Salt was once believed to ward off the evil eye, to cure anyone considered fairy-struck, and to defend against witchcraft, demons, and sprites – for witches, and the animals they bewitched, were unable to eat anything salted. *That rules me out then*, she thought.

She picked up her phone and messaged Safi and Simon.

We went to see Charlie's ex on the way home. He's married to an old friend of hers. I took notes, but mostly felt sorry for them. Police obviously gave him a difficult time when Charlie went missing. He thought Charlie might be having an affair. Illicit trips to London.

The three little dots appeared almost immediately; Safi was replying.

:-(Any chance you're around tonight? Could do with a chat.

Alex glanced at the pot in front of her.

Come for supper.

The light in her father's study was on when Martha arrived home, casting a yellow halo onto the grass. The plate in the sink meant that he had already eaten, so she went straight upstairs to Charlie's room.

If Charlie had been going to sales, and reselling the books and ephemera she found there, why had Martha spotted no sign of that here? She turned on the ceiling light, its paper lampshade carefully cut to cast onto the walls silhouettes of birds taking flight. A relic of their childhood, Martha thought. She found its shadows menacing. A murder of crows: a collective noun from the Middle Ages that had dipped below the radar for centuries before English speakers began to seek out such Gothic fragments and swooped upon the brooding coinage.

She returned to the built-in wardrobe. No ancient volumes here, just the same rows of shoeboxes. She lifted the lid of the one dated 2010 again and took out the postcard. An archivist's habit, Alex had said. Martha brought the card closer so that she could read the copyright notice in the corner: the British Library.

Shit. Could it be from Alex's husband? She chided herself, of course not. These postcards were available everywhere. But he could have met Charlie via Alex, and he did work in London. Tom had said he'd seen her taking the train to the capital. But then she could have been taking volumes she'd discovered while supposedly working for Brin to specialist dealers in the city. That was far more likely.

Her mind fought with itself for several minutes. The questions built themselves into great heights, like gathering waves that towered above the shoreline before smashing into nothing on the sand, only to build again.

Martha took the card and put it in her pocket. Better to just ask Alex if she recognised the handwriting and risk looking like an idiot than fret over it.

Had some of the older volumes above Charlie's desk come from house sales? Why had she told Brin she was stopping? Too busy working on her PhD, probably. Surely Simon must have misremembered what her tutor had said. Martha had seen for herself how focused Charlie was that summer. There had been a shimmer of intellectual heat about her, the energy people give off when they are working at full capacity. Something had excited and absorbed her, of that there was no doubt. Martha felt the sudden scorch of her own excitement a year before, when she had stumbled across a rare volume in a shambling Berlin bookshop. She had only dived under its rickety awning to avoid a sudden rain shower, but had lingered for over an hour. She'd spotted the book's faded blue-green cloth and gilt lettering under some old maps, and instantly knew she'd chanced upon something special. A first edition in English of *Madame Bovary*. She'd felt a momentary guilt for not sharing its true value with the bookseller, but any misgivings vanished the moment she shared her booty with Sabine, unwrapping it carefully from her woollen scarf as though it was the most sacred of talismans. The two of them had talked in hushed tones about their mutual love of the story, and how the translator of this edition, Karl Marx's daughter Eleanor, had killed herself in exactly the same way as the novel's heroine. By swallowing arsenic.

She sat down on the edge of the bed and stared at her sister's photograph.

'What were you up to, Charlie?' she asked it.

They'd thought of using that photograph of her for the 'missing' posters, but the police had gently pointed out that she was squinting slightly against the sun, and asked if there was perhaps another option that better showed her face. They picked one Martha had taken in the garden that spring, of Charlie smiling widely, as though she held some secret and delicious knowledge that she had no intention of sharing.

Martha leant forward and picked up the rejected picture, looking at it properly for the first time in a decade. The police had been right, she was squinting. Strange that Charlie had chosen to frame this image from the myriad photos the family had of her. Had she ever put one of Tom here? Or of Martha and their parents? Martha didn't think so. Charlie claimed not to care about her looks, and it was true that she'd never been the type to linger in front of a mirror, but everyone has a touch of vanity. Whenever wallets of photographs were brought home from the developers Charlie would go through them systematically, tearing up ones she didn't like: a precursor to the instant deletion of unflattering images from their first digital cameras.

So why this picture?

Martha looked at it again, broadening her focus to the backdrop behind Charlie. A low wall, above it the gable end of a large house in white painted brick. Grass. A happy day out with Tom? Charlie had broken up with him, so it's unlikely she'd want that reminder, surely? So if the house or the day had no romantic association, perhaps it had a professional one. Charlie went to country houses to collect things, maybe she had found something particularly interesting the day this photograph was taken. Martha took a screenshot of it on her own phone, angling it so that the murderous crows didn't obscure the image, and sent it to Brin.

Do you recognise this place? Maybe a sale Charlie went to?

The answer came back almost immediately.

Sorry, no.

'You didn't take long to think about it, did you?' Martha said to the glowing screen.

Perhaps Charlie had written on the back of the photograph. Their mother had always done that, adding names, dates, and locations on the shiny backs. 'For future historians,' she had told them.

Martha turned the frame over and bent back the metal clasps before pulling off the backboard. It came free with a jerk, and something that had been placed behind the photograph fell onto the floor. A bank card.

'Of course you have to tell Martha about it,' Alex said, picking up Safi's plate and taking it to the sink. They'd eaten in the kitchen, and Alex had enjoyed Safi's evident pleasure in the meal. She delighted in feeding people, and now the boys were grown she rarely had the opportunity. Not that they'd appreciated it much when they were young. Her enjoyment of their praise whenever she fed them now was slightly tempered with resentment. Memory had recalibrated their childhood so that they genuinely believed they had savoured every dinner she had prepared for them – before, no doubt, settling down to a board game or embarking on a country walk. Alex never attempted to disabuse them, but couldn't forget the slammed doors and week-long sulks, the coruscating, all-consuming mood swings of adolescence.

'Really? I could just ask Simon, couldn't I? Drop it in – "By the way it sounded like you were having a fight with Brin, what was that about?"'

Alex rinsed off the plates and put them into the dishwasher as she considered. She felt the severing of that communion with past generations as she set it going.

'I'm not sure that would do any good. He'd probably just deny it. It is interesting, though.'

Safi refilled their water glasses from the jug. 'So I get the feeling there are things you're not telling me: Charlie, Brin, Simon.'

Alex wrinkled her nose and sat down again, ignoring the water in preference for her wine. 'That makes it sound very clear and definitive, and it's really not. I have a suspicion that something happened over that summer at the dictionary, but the senior management sorted it all out between themselves as far as I can tell.'

Safi looked confused.

'God, I know I'm not making any sense, I just remember that Mike and Jonathan and some of the others went around looking miserable and serious, even angry for a while. I kept walking in on conversations where suddenly everyone fell quiet. There was a lot of sudden HR interference: questions about our job satisfaction levels, that sort of thing. I honestly thought the dictionary was going to be closed down or something. Then Charlie disappeared, and for a while everything was about that.'

'And then?'

'And then nothing. Time passed, and we had the December updates to finish. There were a lot of bio-something ones that year, so we needed specialist advice. "Bioelectrochemistry" took me forever to finalise. Whatever had spooked the horses higher up had fizzled, so we returned to peaceable intellectual grazing.'

Safi's eyes flitted round the room. 'You've worked at the dictionary a long time, haven't you?'

'Fifteen years, and yes, before you ask, I still enjoy it very much. I have my own particular interests, but I like the variety, truffling after old words, unwrapping new ones.' She paused. 'But I did call Mike yesterday.'

It felt strange to say it.

'Our old boss? Really?'

Alex nodded. 'Chorus obviously thinks there is something rotten in the state, and if there is, it happened on Mike's watch. I keep thinking about those interrupted meetings, so I called to tell him I think he should come back and explain.'

'Wow! Will he come?'

Alex twirled her wine glass. It was a lovely vintage, full of autumnal fruits. She would put the cork in it and send it back with Safi; it would be sacrilege to let this turn to vinegar on her sideboard.

'He tells me he's booked the Eurostar for next Thursday.'

20

sardonian, *noun (seventeenth century)*:
one who flatters with deadly intent

THEY GATHERED IN THE OFFICE the following morning. The warm weather had, today at least, been replaced by persistent, squally showers. They shook off umbrellas, hung up raincoats to dry, then fetched coffees before turning on the computers and going through the motions of beginning the working day. Alex arrived, her Chanel bag over her shoulder, looking for all the world as though the Oxford she had walked through had been one of sunshine and zephyrs rather than pavements slicked with rain. Only a drop or two of water lingered on her long Burberry mackintosh and her hair was as sleekly styled as ever. Martha touched her own hair reflexively; it tended to go wild and springy in the damp. Alex tucked herself in at their desk.

'So,' she said as soon as she sat down. 'You told Jonathan.'

'I did. Last night after I left you.' Martha frowned. 'But how did you know?'

'I got a rather curt text from him asking why I hadn't told him myself.'

Simon put his hands behind his head and stretched his shoulders. 'I had the same. Sent one back saying it was up to Martha to tell him as a) she is our boss, and b) Charlie is her sister.'

Alex smiled at him. 'Good. That's exactly what I said. His message came through after ten; I assumed he got worked up over his last whiskey of the evening.'

'I'm sorry,' Martha said. 'I didn't think for a moment he'd be annoyed with both of you.'

'That's not all,' Safi added. 'I got a text asking for scans of the letters. I guess I'm too junior for him to be pissed off with me.'

'No doubt your time will come, Safi,' Alex said dryly, putting on her reading glasses as she began tapping through her emails. 'But I'm going to struggle to concentrate on anything today other than Charlie, Martha. Did Jonathan have anything useful to say?'

'No. He and Olivia were going out, so we didn't have long. Olivia said she hadn't noticed any postcards.'

'Did she say anything about the night of that first book launch?' Alex asked. 'I'm sure Jonathan was too busy soaking up the adulation to notice anything, but Olivia would have kept an eye on everyone in his orbit.'

Simon looked confused. 'Would she? I didn't know they were a couple then.'

'They weren't,' Alex said smoothly. 'She was an eager young student helping out. I mean, she did always seem to have eyes for Jonathan, and a watchful stare for everyone else.'

Martha frowned. 'Olivia was at the launch?' Alex nodded.

'Well, he didn't say anything, but like I said, we didn't have a chance to talk in any detail.'

Alex took off her reading glasses and twirled them unconsciously between her fingers, looking up at the ceiling. 'Judging by his messages, Jonathan seems to want to get involved now, so we can ask. Chorus obviously meant us to discover something by sending us to Brin, and I suppose we did – that Charlie hadn't behaved very well towards him. But I don't see how that makes a liar of anyone at the dictionary, or gives any good reason as to why she disappeared.'

They all looked at Martha. 'I'm not sure. Charlie had one picture of herself in her room. There's a corner of a country house in the background, and I wondered if Brin might recognise it, so sent him a screenshot. He said he didn't. But I did find something else: a bank card in the frame.'

'A bank card?' Safi asked rhetorically, writing in her notebook. 'Not an emergency credit card? I have one of those, but I keep it the freezer to make sure I don't use it for drunken internet shopping again. I call it "pregret": knowing you're going to regret something but going ahead and doing it anyway. Maybe Charlie was trying to avoid the same thing.'

Martha smiled briefly, watching the pompom on Safi's pencil dance as she made her notes. She had somehow become their recording angel. 'It was a debit card. Not the bank our family normally use, and in her name.'

'Charlie had a secret bank account?' Simon asked.

'I have no idea if it was secret or not,' Martha replied. 'I sent the details to Caldwell to compare with his records.'

She hesitated. Should she parcel out her secrets, or share everything? The idea of keeping track of who knew what seemed utterly impossible. Whom to ask what question? Whom to suspect and whom to trust? She thought of her mother, living her life with her palms outstretched.

She took the postcard out of her bag and took it across to Alex. 'The way you did your dates, Alex. It reminded me of this. I found it in Charlie's things.'

Alex glanced at the picture then turned it over and read the message. Her expression didn't change, but it seemed to freeze for a moment.

'I don't understand. What is this? It's my husband's handwriting,' she said finally.

'Your husband's? What does it say?' Safi asked.

'It says, "You dazzle me,"' Alex replied, her voice strangely hollow.

Safi flushed and the pompom stuttered.

Simon slapped the table with the flat of his hand. 'Tom said he thought Charlie was having an affair! You said so in your text! So she was seeing Alex's ex?'

'Shut up, Simon. Dear God, have you even seen George?' Alex said angrily.

He puffed out his cheeks. 'No need to use that tone. You're fine speculating about Charlie until it hits a bit close to home, are you?'

'Simon,' Martha said sharply. 'Just give Alex a moment, will you? I'm sorry, Alex. I thought it was unlikely to be your husband, but I should have asked you privately.'

'Yes, you bloody well should have,' Alex said, then shaded her eyes with her hands. 'God, now I'm sorry too. Simon's right. We've been speculating about Charlie and solving Chorus's clues and acting like you should thank us, Martha. Perhaps this might teach me to be a bit more sensitive.'

'But are you sure it's your ex's handwriting?' Safi asked tentatively.

'I'm sure. You better tell Caldwell about this, too, Martha,' she added, handing back the card and getting to her feet. 'Excuse me, I'll call George right now.'

She picked up her phone and moved stiffly into the corridor. Martha returned to her own seat.

'Bloody hell!' Simon burst out as the door shut behind Alex. 'So George was shagging Charlie? Didn't think he had it in him. Thought he was out of his league looks-wise with Alex, but Charlie! That changes things a bit, doesn't it?'

'You don't need to look so gleeful,' Safi retorted, before realising that Simon's smile was, in fact, more sardonic than joyous. She allowed herself the memory of that word's history – how its definition of grim mockery was born out of associations with a Sardinian plant, the eating of which was believed to produce facial convulsions resembling horrible laughter. And death.

'I just got Alex Monroe to apologise to me,' Simon replied. 'I'm savouring the moment.'

'She said sorry to Martha, and said you were right – which is *not* the same thing as apologising,' Safi replied crisply. 'And I don't think we should leap to conclusions. I mean, even if George was having a fling with her, and even if he knew something about Charlie's disappearance, that still doesn't seem to have anything to do with the dictionary, or with Brin. Actually, Simon, while we're at it: what can you tell us about Brin? I get the feeling you were quite close.'

'Brin? I hardly know him,' Simon said quickly, and turned his attention back to his screen.

Martha looked between them; there was something of the strike and parry in that last exchange. Simon and Brin hadn't seemed close to her, but then Safi had stayed on at the bookshop. Safi didn't pursue the question, turning to her own screen instead.

Alex returned and sat back down without looking at them. 'No answer. I left a message asking him to ring me.'

Martha put the card back in her handbag, trying to imagine Charlie having an affair with a middle-aged archivist in the throes of a painful divorce, ditching her handsome doctor to be with him. It seemed unlikely – unthinkable, almost – but the same thought had obviously occurred to all of them.

How could she have just dropped that postcard in front of Alex in the middle of the office? She felt a spasm of anger at her own insensitivity, and as she read the morning's crop of emails her mind offered up a range of choice epithets from the lexicon of self-flagellation. Humicubation wouldn't be excessive at this point, she thought: lying prostate on the ground in penitence.

The atmosphere in the office seemed to thicken. Simon looked affronted, Safi seemed unsettled, and Alex's face was a mask. Martha realised she hadn't taken in a single sentence from the emails she'd been clicking through, and returned to the top of her inbox. The quarterly update to the dictionary was only a month away now and the list of additions was still growing, bulging with new words or senses related to cryptocurrency or AI. Even cricket was getting a look in, thanks to the recent success of Bazball. Whatever else was happening, the dictionary still needed to be tended, the messiness of language given a semblance of order within its virtual covers.

A Teams message from Safi popped up on her screen:

What was the date on that postcard from George?

Martha replied, and on the other side of the room Safi took out her notebook and flicked through a few pages before typing again:

That's three days before she told Brin she wouldn't be working for him anymore. Remember he said it was the

Easter weekend. Shall I tell the others? Might help Alex pin him down or something.

Martha hesitated.

Sure.

Her phone buzzed and she glanced at the message. Caldwell would like to meet at lunchtime, in town.

21

addubitation, *noun (sixteenth century)*: a suggestion of doubt

MARTHA DUCKED THROUGH THE IRON gates of Oxford's Covered Market, escaping the dirty spray from cars as they whooshed down the rainy High Street. The Market had been designed in the eighteenth century to house the traders who had once occupied pitches on Fish Street, now St Aldates, before being unceremoniously forced by the Oxford Mileways Act to vacate their 'untidy, messy and unsavoury stalls' for the building of new roads. Their principal wares had been vegetables, herbs, fish, and – above all – meat, and when the new premises opened, it housed over forty butchers' shops. Today only a few remained, and the Market's stalls now drifted eclectically from barbers to cheesemongers, pie shops to cobblers, and soft toys to overpriced menswear.

The Market had four avenues running north to south, crossed by three long aisles of shops. Open-fronted stalls selling fruit and veg ran along the flanking walls. Martha had noticed visitor numbers waning during her visits home, but each Christmas the old place would come into its own again, the rafters of its polygonal roof decorated with twinkling lights and brightly coloured piñatas. It also became a hellscape for vegetarians. The surviving butchers would ritually hang out haunches of venison and heads of pigs, whose watery gaze seemed directed at row upon row of pheasants and dangling rabbits. All of them were suspended perilously low. It was pure retail theatre.

Now the market was preparing for the summer season and the same butchers were angling their wares towards customers wanting to fill picnic baskets for lunches by the river. The window counters heaved with Scotch eggs and pies, platters of cheese and ham, sourdough breads, half bottles of rosé and expensive cordials, seltzers, cocktails in cans, and miniature tarts.

Martha loved to wander through the Market's mazes alone. Whenever her meandering walks around Oxford took her in this direction, she'd tuck herself into a space by the entrance for a while and observe the people passing between the timber shop fronts. She'd surrender to her imagination, picturing every aspect of their lives – their family, friends, and obsessions, their tastes in food and films, their dreams and nightmares. It was her own take on the concept of 'sonder': the realisation that other people have rich and complicated lives that we will never know.

Walking between the stalls today on her way to meet Caldwell, it was Alex's life Martha was thinking about. Her colleague moved through the world with such self-assurance, but after Martha had stupidly ambushed her with that postcard Alex had spent the whole morning staring fixedly at her computer screen, shooting covert glances at her phone. She seemed such a model of successful middle age, her children out in the world having given her new energy and the freedom to spend it. But Martha was worried that in passing her that postcard she had triggered some charge beneath the foundations of Alex's life, had altered the story of her marriage and divorce, destabilising it and everything built upon it.

Martha watched as a harrowed-looking mother listened to her silk-skinned teenage daughter shouting and swearing at her. The woman looked trapped, helpless, unable to comprehend how a child she had once wrapped up in her arms could turn into a foul-mouthed stranger. She caught Martha's eye and looked pleadingly back at her with heavy-lidded eyes. Martha could offer nothing but a sympathetic nod as she walked past. Had she ever sworn at her mother? Probably. But time had softened the bumps and papered over the cracks, so that the only texture of her memories now was smooth.

She passed a narrow-angled counter at the end of one aisle, home to the best cookies in the world, and breathed in the chocolatey fumes. She'd bought them for her mother during those last months of her illness. Chemotherapy had stolen Rebecca's appetite, but those cookies always pleased her, and the buying of them had become another soothing ritual for Martha. She'd liked to take her time choosing, tuning into the decisions of those in front of her and weighing up their preferences against her own. The last time she'd opted for two white chocolate cookies that were fresh out of the oven, their velvety-sweet aroma temporarily outperforming all the others. Her mother had enjoyed the few nibbles she took, and they'd reminisced together about Charlie, who as a little girl would pounce on the cookies whenever Rebecca had brought them home, her thick blonde ponytail bouncing up and down as she tucked in, closing her eyes and nodding with joy.

Someone coughed. Martha realised she had stopped dead, blocking one of the exits. She apologised and turned back into the recesses of the Market. Caldwell had asked her to meet at Brown's café, a frowzy space whose four walls lived up to its name, but which served one of the best fry-ups in the city.

She found him already halfway through one of their signature English breakfasts, and noted with surprise that she was very glad to see him. On spotting her he hurriedly wiped his mouth and got to his feet with an old-fashioned, slightly self-deprecating politeness. His pale grey suit was immaculately pressed.

He asked her what she'd like, and by the time she had settled into the chair opposite him a waitress was setting a pot of tea down in front of her. Caldwell seemed to know the staff here, calling the waitress by her first name.

'Are you sure you won't eat?' he said. 'I'm sorry I'm almost done.'

'I'm fine, thank you. But please don't rush on my account.'

'Thanks, if I try and eat and talk I'll get egg on my notebook.'

The food on his plate seemed to diminish almost magically, vanishing in huge forkfuls. He put his knife and fork together and sat back.

'Did I get beans on my tie?'

She smiled and shook her head. 'You look very smart,' she added, dropping the tea bag onto her saucer and mentally kicking herself for such inanity.

He didn't seem to notice her discomfort. 'I'm in court today,' he said. 'We get training, you know, on what to wear. Smart, but not flash. Conservative, but not too conservative. And that's all before you actually get to say anything out loud.' Martha recalled her mother telling her about the dress code at her old school, where girls were instructed to dress 'attractively but not provocatively'. She had listened with a mixture of mirth and horror.

Caldwell wiped his fingers, edged the empty plate aside, and took out his notebook. 'I've put in a request for details about the account the bank card was issued for. It wasn't in our records, and it will take a few days for the information to come back, but tell me about this latest letter. You said it led you to a bookshop where your sister used to work?'

She explained as best she could: the arrival of the letter, the working out of the clue, and the decision to head straight to Brin. Caldwell interrupted only occasionally to clarify a particular point, before asking her to carry on. She glanced at his notes: the confusions and conclusions of her team, Chorus's hints and obfuscations, all reduced to a series of neat bullet points. He had good handwriting. Clear, fluid and precise. 'Safiya took shorthand notes of our conversation with Brin,' she finished.

'Did she now? She sounds an impressive woman.'

'She is,' Martha replied, feeling vicariously proud.

'Anything else?'

Martha sipped her tea for a few seconds, then told him about her visit to Tom and Tanya, and the postcard to Charlie from Alex's ex-husband.

His eyes became serious as he added to his bullet point list. 'You better give me all the contact details of everyone involved so far.' Martha scrolled through her contacts and read out the names and numbers of all the characters on the increasingly crowded stage, whereupon Caldwell flipped the notebook closed again and tucked it into his jacket pocket.

'I talked to my super this morning,' he said. 'We went down quite the rabbit hole. The letters and postcards don't contain any actionable threats, although if we found out who was sending them we'd want to speak to them, warn them of the dangers of harassment, and try to get them to stop playing games and tell us what it is they think they know about your sister. The boss is in favour of adding anything you receive to the file, but there's not too much to go on at the moment.' He scratched his freckled nose absent-mindedly. 'Though who knows what will turn up in the bank records, and the fact that Charlie was dealing in books is interesting. A bit underhand, perhaps, going behind this Brin Edwards' back, but hardly illegal.'

'No. Not even that unusual,' Martha said. She found it unexpectedly calming, talking to him.

'Just to reiterate, Martha: we did do a thorough review of the case when your mother came to us. Made sure we hadn't missed anything in that first flush of inquiries, any physical evidence from your home that remained untested . . .'

'You searched the house?'

He nodded. 'Yep. It's standard procedure. We do an immediate search of the house and outbuildings, then if nothing has turned up, we come back to do a more thorough fingertip search. In the event of foul play. Neither search turned up anything significant.'

Martha's imagination had never allowed the possibility that her parents' house might be a crime scene. The idea shook her and brought with it a brief sweeping sense of vertigo as though her feet had missed a step. She felt a rash impulse to reach out and take his hand so she could stabilise herself.

'It's very interesting that Mr Edwards was sent a postcard too. I'm beginning to think your Chorus has his own suspect pool.'

'Suspect for what?' Martha said, still trying to recover her balance. 'Charlie either killed herself, ran away and had an accident, or is living under a false name. Why she did any of those things – what led up to it – I don't know. Isn't that what

Chorus is trying to find out?' She remembered the last line of Chorus's first letter. But no, that was only a quote, there was nothing literal about it.

He didn't answer her directly. 'The ex-boyfriend's alibi was solid. I'm sorry he felt hard done by, but there's a good reason we look at intimate partners first.'

'I know crimes of passion happen . . .'

'That's not how we describe domestic violence these days.'

That brought her up short. She nodded, acknowledging the point. 'But if Tom didn't harm her, no one else had any reason to!' She reminded herself of the teenager from earlier: hot-headed, deaf to reasoning and logic.

He didn't reply at once, just looked at her with those sympathetic grey eyes and an understanding half smile. 'You think I'm naive,' she said in a dejected tone.

'Perhaps a bit,' he said, breaking eye contact and straightening his tie. 'But I live in a darker world than most.' *The many-worlds theory*, she thought. *Parallel universes. We all live in different realities, but occupy the same space and time. The doctor sees illness everywhere, I see words. Caldwell sees what? Depravity?*

'Murder is such a terrible crime,' he went on, 'we all try to control it, you know, by imposing some logic on it. Make it a puzzle to be solved. Work out the whos and the whys, tidy it up as though that gives us permission to move on from it. And when we can't wrap it up into something comprehensible we turn to talk of evil or madness. The thing I've learnt is that murder might make sense to the killer in that exact moment, but even they may not be able to understand it later. The rest of us rarely even get that glimpse of logic, can never impose any reason or larger meaning on it.'

'I'm sorry, but are you really saying you think Charlie was murdered and Chorus knows something about it?'

'I'm beginning to think that's a distinct possibility, Martha, even if Tom had nothing to do with it. I wouldn't have said that when she first went missing; murder is not that common – a mystery like this even less so – but all this time with no sign of her? No indication of depression before she went missing? Now this Chorus with their dark hints . . .' He expelled the air from his lungs, a quick, sharp exhale. 'We aren't yet in a position to reopen this as a murder inquiry, not without more to go on than Chorus's insinuations and my own gut feeling. But yes, Martha, I'm beginning to think Charlie died in 2010. I am so very sorry to say so.'

The laughter of strangers in the café, the hiss of the coffee machine, every sound was suffocated by the ringing in her ears. She held onto the weathered edges of the table, focused on the slight warmth retained by her china teacup. 'Is that why you wanted to meet? To tell me that in person?'

He nodded. 'But not just that. When we last spoke I suggested you ask people about Charlie and about her disappearance. I'm not going to reverse that advice now, but I do want to add a caution. If someone did kill Charlie, and has got away with murder for more than a decade, they'll be clever. To do something like that – it suggests a level of self-control, of planning that not many people have the capacity for. They might have been lucky, of course . . . But you should be careful.'

Martha shook her head. 'I honestly have no idea what to do.'

'It's a very unusual situation,' he said softly. 'Try to be as honest as you can. Don't keep secrets, however uncomfortable they are.'

It's funny, Martha thought, retreating into the safety of her head. *I spend my life uncovering secrets*. Her job was to carefully dismantle language like a Russian doll until its very core was revealed, then put it back together to preserve its mystery.

Words were defined by what they hid. Sometimes in plain sight, like 'breakfast' or 'freelancer': a knight free to use his lance for anyone that paid him. But the etymologies she adored most emerged from far below the surface, like the unexpected findings of an archaeological dig, their stories layered beneath centuries' worth of sediment. Lexicographers sought out the thrill of the chase as much as detectives did. She remembered her linguistic fleshment, when she'd discovered as a student that 'thrill' itself, in medieval times, had meant to pierce someone with a sword; only later did the 'piercing' move to excitement.

Secrets beyond the safety of the dictionary were something else entirely. Martha feared them. 'We dance round in a ring and suppose, But the secret sits in the middle and knows.' Robert Frost, she seemed to remember. *What secrets sit in the middle of us now?*

'I better get back to the office,' she said at last and reached for her purse. He waved it away.

'It's on me. Thank you for coming and please, call me if anything happens, or even if it doesn't, call me anyway.'

His kindness was both welcome and unbearable. She managed to smile, briefly, then left him.

The office phone rang. Simon had gone to 'get some air', Martha was still out, and Safi, who usually answered the phone, was enjoying a mouthful of sandwich. Alex picked up the receiver and pressed on the blinking red light.

'Alex Monroe here.'

The caller cleared his throat. 'Hi, yes, I'm calling from the *Oxford Daily*, we've been told that the dictionary has been receiving some strange letters containing . . .' she heard a rustle of paper, 'crossword clues? Allegations of dark dealings? I'm calling to follow up.'

'Where did you hear that?' Alex said after a shocked pause.

The man on the other end of the line laughed. 'Can't reveal my sources! It's true then?'

'Let me see if I can find someone who can help you,' Alex said sweetly then muted the call. '*Oxford Daily* asking about the letters,' she said to Safi.

'Shit!' Safi wiped her mouth with a scrunched-up napkin. 'What are you going to say?'

'I've no idea! Do I lie?'

Safi shook her head sharply. 'No, play for time.'

Alex reconnected. 'I'm sorry, there's no one here who can help you at the moment. Perhaps you'd like to leave a name and number?'

'Is it true they're connected with a missing woman? What does Jonathan Overton think about it?'

'You'd have to ask him,' Alex snapped. 'And perhaps it would be best if you emailed.' She hung up and stared at the phone as if it were toxic. 'Dammit. I shouldn't have said that about Jonathan. I'll email him myself.'

'Better to text,' Safi said. 'You know Jonathan. If a newspaper calls, he'll pick up without thinking twice and they might catch him on the hop.'

She was right, of course. Alex fired off a message then took off her reading glasses and rubbed her eyes. 'I'm rattled, Safi. That postcard this morning . . . Honestly, I don't think for a second George was having an affair with Charlie. But I'm rattled.'

'Why did you get divorced?'

A pause. 'You can be really blunt sometimes, Safi.'

Safi shrugged and took another bite of her sandwich, the question floating in the air between them. 'So can you.'

That was true.

There wasn't an easy answer. The marriage had lasted for fifteen years, and Alex usually told anyone who asked – men who wanted to date her, women who wanted to justify staying in their own unhappy marriages – that they had simply grown apart. It had been more than that, of course. She had grown frustrated by George's lack of ambition, for one. Not in terms of his career, and Alex didn't particularly care about his salary – though bringing up two young children in Oxford certainly meant she could have done with a little extra income – but it was his dispassion towards life that ate away at their marriage. He stopped wanting to travel, to learn, to explore. The moment he hit forty he had steered clear of new foods, begun to sneer at the latest music, fashions, even art. A mistrust of all that was untested or challenging became George's default, and Alex had felt smothered by it. When she tried to explain this to him, he had grown wary and resentful of her too.

'A total absence of joy,' she said in answer to Safi's question, then sighed at her younger colleague's puzzled look. 'We only have this one life, so I want to celebrate existence while I can. George wanted to be safe, I think. It doesn't sound like much but it led to a rift. He was very hurt, and that made the divorce bitter in the end.'

'And are you more joyful now?' Safi asked.

'Oh, yes,' Alex responded instinctively, before remembering the confusions of the last few days, the terrible fact of Charlie's disappearance spreading like an inkstain across her life – the inexorable movement of it. 'Well, most of the time. God, I'd better tell Martha. As soon as they realise she's Charlie's sister, they'll be on to her too.'

22

induratise, *verb (sixteenth century)*: to harden the heart

MARTHA RESOLVED TO TELL HER father that evening about the letters and her conversation with Caldwell. The news that the local papers had caught wind of something was forcing her hand. As she chained up her bike outside the family home, a breeze caught her hair and ruffled the spring leaves of the bay tree by the porch. 'Caught wind of something'. The metaphor felt right: a mysterious breath of smoke from a distant fire.

Gabriel was weeding the flower beds behind the house, using his wife's old kneeler. Martha paused, watching him for a minute before approaching, and taking comfort in the susurrus of the silver birches and the scrape of the trowel as he turned the dark earth.

'Dad? I have to talk to you about something.' He looked over his shoulder and shielded his eyes, as if he couldn't make out at first who it was, then got slowly to his feet.

'Very well. Tea?'

They entered the house through the French windows and he moved to the sink to fill the kettle. Not for the first time since she'd returned from Berlin, Martha found the silence of the house oppressive. Her mother used to love it: 'Such peace,' she'd say in a sort of purr. For Martha the quiet was like holding a seashell against her ear. Her thoughts, accustomed to skipping rapidly among the noises of the busy road outside her German flat, its clatters of conversation and movement, felt hemmed in by the silence of Oxford. She found it hard to focus beyond the rushing chirr of her own blood.

Her father flicked on the kettle and reached up for the pot and mugs.

'We received a strange letter at the dictionary last week,' she said to his back. 'It was a sort of puzzle, and it seemed to be about Charlie.'

There was a momentary pause in his movements, then he lifted down the teapot.

'Go on.'

She did, describing both letters while he made the tea. He didn't turn round until she had finished the whole story: the postcards, the visit to Brin, the bank card, the postcard from Alex's husband, even the meetings with Caldwell, although she stopped short of sharing the officer's suspicions about Charlie's fate: the irony was she simply didn't have the words.

Eventually he took the tray and carried it outside onto the patio, setting it down on the table. He said nothing until he had given her a mug. Her mug. A Christmas present from Charlie, as it happened, cumbersome and slightly awkward to hold, emblazoned with the word 'procaffeinate'. 'It's putting everything off until you've had enough coffee, Marth,' Charlie had declared, delighted, as her sister lifted it out of the wrapping paper.

'What was happening between you and Charlie when she disappeared, Martha?'

Martha felt a cold lurch in her stomach; she glanced up and found he was watching her.

'How do you mean?'

'I mean, you're asking other people questions, but you were sent a postcard too. What was going on between you two?'

'Nothing. That is . . . I'd hardly seen her over the summer.'

'I remember you complaining about that,' he said, sipping his tea. 'Grumbling that she had no time for you and wasn't interested in your course.'

'I was hurt, Dad,' Martha protested. 'I was proud of my results and excited about uni, and it didn't seem to matter to anyone.'

'We'd all moved on a bit from A-levels by then.'

'I hadn't! I got the same results she did in her exams. You threw her a party.'

He raised an eyebrow. 'We took you out for dinner.'

'And spent the whole evening talking to Charlie,' Martha snapped. She felt her cheeks flush. *I am thirty-two*, she thought, *surely this shouldn't still hurt this much?* She hadn't thought about that bloody dinner for years: the quiet humiliation of picking over her pie in the other, smarter Brown's in Jericho, while her parents hung onto Charlie's every word. Suddenly the injustice felt as fresh and important as it had that evening. And she'd thanked them for it, she remembered that. Thanked them for dinner, and then cried herself to sleep.

'So you did resent her? I thought so.'

'Of course I did! A bit. It didn't stop me loving her too. But why are we even talking about that? I've just told you some insane person is sending us letters about her disappearance, and you're asking me if I resented her. What has that got to do with anything?'

'It might have quite a lot to do with it,' he said, his voice thick with frost. The sort of frost that snaps dry branches in the forest, sending out echoes like a pistol shot.

Martha was shocked into silence again. *Is this what we've come to? Is this all that's left?* Sabine had tried to teach her visualisation techniques in Berlin. Ways of picturing feelings and parcelling them up, like setting them on an imaginary leaf on a river to float away downstream. She inhaled, trying to picture this strange explosion of emotion being folded up into itself like an origami box until it was totally contained. Something to be put on a shelf and unwrapped, cautiously, another time.

'What do you remember, Dad, of the day she disappeared?'

He crossed his legs and drank his tea, looking out across the garden.

'Your mother and I were going out. She wanted to go to the garden centre and we thought we'd have lunch at the Plough. Charlie was at home when we left. The last time I saw her she was sitting at her desk, working on her laptop, books everywhere. I told her we were off, asked her if she wanted anything. She said she'd be going out for lunch and then on to the library later, and would see us that evening at the launch.' His expression shifted subtly, as if the evening light was moulding it moment by moment into a different shape. The hardness and anger were moving by degrees into a softer blanket of deep and abiding pain. 'It was such a nothing conversation, the sort one has a dozen times a day.'

'Did Mum spend time with her that morning?'

'She'd taken her a cup of tea a little earlier,' he said. 'I'm glad of that. We didn't have a fight, there was no tension or upset.

They were just very ordinary moments, the last ones we ever had with our daughter.' His voice dropped to a murmur, as though he had forgotten Martha was there and was talking only to himself. 'We tried very hard, your mother and I, not to talk about what might have been if we'd stayed at home, but of course we both thought about it constantly. It was a routine day, full of the unspoken give and takes of a long marriage. Lunch was my idea, the garden centre hers. We shared the guilt. What if I'd said we didn't need any more plants? Or she'd said she'd already got something out of the freezer for lunch? The what-ifs are the least bearable. They're still there even if you don't speak about them. They killed your mother in the end. I don't want that for you.'

He took off his sunhat and ran his fingers through what was left of his hair. His face was hollowing out year by year, his cheeks sucked inwards, his eye sockets deepening.

'When we came home the house was locked, and her bike and laptop were gone. We assumed she'd gone to the Bodleian and we got ready for the party. You know the rest.'

'Who do you think Chorus might be, Dad?' she asked after a long silence.

'"Thus far, with rough and all-unable pen, Our bending author hath pursued the story,"' he said, quoting Chorus from *Henry V*. 'Some crank with a buried sense of mission and a guilty heart would be my guess.'

'But what is he hinting at?'

The softness disappeared again, and he set down his mug with a heavy clang on the metal table. 'I don't know, Martha, and in the end it doesn't matter to me. I don't care. Charlie is gone – the hows and the whys of it are of no help to me. But perhaps they might be to you. You can't run away from things forever. And one thing: she should never be forgotten, that I won't tolerate. I know you want me to leave this house, Martha. Put it up for sale and get myself something smaller, but her room and her possessions are the only sign Charlie ever existed at all. I can't give that up. You'll have to wait until I'm dead, too, or too far gone to protest over being shuffled off into a home. Don't worry, it will come. Then you can finally wipe the slate clean of both of us.'

The familiar burn of injustice. 'Why would you say that, Dad? Why would I want to do such a thing?'

'Really? Are you sure you weren't sometimes secretly glad that Charlie was out of the way?'

Martha stood up. The neat origami box had burst open and was spilling its contents over the both of them.

'She wasn't out of the way! She was more here than ever. I couldn't compete with Charlie when she was here, and I had even less of a chance when she was gone. She's still ever-present, like the holy fucking ghost!'

Gabriel looked at her coolly. 'That must be very hard for you,' he said, flatly. 'I hope Chorus prompts you into finding some answers, for yourself. Now, I want to finish the weeding before it gets dark.'

Martha watched as he returned to his kneeler and lowered himself slowly down to the earth. The scrape, scrape of the trowel began again.

23

broggle, *verb (seventeenth century)*:

to poke with a pointed instrument

'CHEERS!'

Safi clinked her beer bottle against Josh's and took a long swig. The garden of their shared house wasn't huge, but Paula had made every effort to keep it tidy, and Josh had placed some of his abstract, colourful sculptures among the sporadic herbage. Safi's father had contributed his old set of lawn furniture together with a gift of rum punch – a flagon of it. The memory of the hangover still made her shudder.

Josh had the free Oxford newspaper open on his lap; reading it was part of his campaign to spend less time staring at screens. Safi wasn't sure his attention span was properly trained as yet: he somehow still found time to send endless anti-capitalism memes to the house chat even as he was reading.

'Your overlord is in the paper,' he said, and Safi looked up from her phone. Had the *Oxford Daily* published something about the letters already? He was showing her a picture of

Jonathan and his wife at some event the previous evening. She peered at it closely.

'"Bestselling author celebrates success of his new book",' Josh read. 'God, his wife is overdoing the devoted spouse look a bit, don't you think? I mean, it's not 1950 anymore.'

'Yeah, I noticed.'

'Is he the massive creep I think he is?' Josh asked. Finding nothing more of interest, he threw down the paper on the table.

Safi leant one elbow on the table and considered. 'Jonathan? I wouldn't say that. I mean, he's a bit smooth and patriarchal, but no. Encouraging about my work without getting creepy.'

'Must have cleaned up his act, then,' Josh replied yawning, picking up his beer again. 'I heard he had a reputation for picking a favourite student every year. That's how he met the heiress.'

Safi smiled. 'So since when do you hear English department gossip?'

'Oh, it's amazing what posh boomers will say to each other in the gallery in front of me. It's like they think I'm furniture or something. His wife's parents are part of the art crowd of Oxfordshire too. In fact, he's a regular topic of conversation – well, he was when all the #MeToo stuff was trending. Lots of comments about how he was lucky it hadn't been a thing ten years ago.' He started picking the label off his bottle. 'I know for a fact that he took a fancy to a girl just a couple of years ago, and his wife made *her* life hell rather than his.'

'And they talked about that in front of you?'

'No, the girl was a friend of mine. He got her a design job on one of his TV programmes, then she found out Olivia was spreading nasty rumours about her.'

'What did she do?'

'Her girlfriend is a solicitor. They wrote a stiff letter and the rumours disappeared. But Jonathan never spoke to her again.'

He smoothed his beer label onto the plastic table. 'We should cover this with labels. Upcycle it a bit. You still OK to help with the thing next week?'

'The thing' was a party and print sale that Josh and a couple of his friends were putting on between the May bank holiday and the Coronation. It was happening at their studios, a messy sprawl of cheap rooms on an old light industrial site. Flyers for it were stuck around the house and had been thrust through half the doors of Oxford.

'Yeah, course I am. I've booked the week off.'

'Invite your colleagues. Jonathan, too, even, if he'll come. Need to have some people there who might be able to afford to buy something.'

Safi considered. She couldn't see Martha liking the loud and political pop-art prints a few of the artists made, but Alex might like some of Josh's slightly dreamy abstracts. Simon might go for a bit of colour on his walls too: his wardrobe certainly suggested he wasn't afraid of pigment. 'Sure. Will do. Though I don't think it's Jonathan's sort of thing. He's more black tie and champagne than beer and jeans.' She considered something for a few seconds. 'So you think he's dodgy?'

'This is only gossip, Saf. I don't think anything. But I mean, handsome forty-something-white guy thinks it's his God-given right to shag anyone is not exactly breaking news, is it?'

The printed smiles of Jonathan and Olivia were beginning to distort rather grotesquely as they absorbed the water from the tabletop. If Charlie, from what Safi had heard of her, was going to have an affair with anyone, wouldn't she be more likely to choose the charismatic up-and-coming Jonathan over poor joyless George, as she now thought of Alex's ex-husband? Safi picked up her phone. She could text Alex, and Martha. Her finger hovered over the screen. Should she send it to Simon too? Maybe, probably even, but he'd irritated her today, and had then brushed her off about Brin. Sod Simon. Let's keep it among the girls for now.

Bit of gossip about Jonathan.

She hit Send, and waited. Neither of her colleagues replied.

24

ireful, *adjective (fifteenth century)*:
angry, stormy, inflamed

Alex said nothing about George or the postcard the next day, and Martha didn't press her. She told them what her father had said about Charlie's movements on the day she vanished, and left it at that. She began to read an article Alex had written about the linguistic roots of various May Day celebrations. It was excellent: scholarly and precise without overloading the reader with jargon. She suggested, via email, that Alex should forward it to the Communications Team in case they wanted to share it over the bank holiday. Alex agreed and cc'ed her into a note to Pippa, the head of that small but apparently influential department. Martha had a sinking feeling that she should message Pippa about the letters, as well as the call from the newspaper. She knew that simply hoping a journalist would forget about something was a failing strategy. She set about composing an email that would be truthful, lucid, and professional. No need to mention Tom, or their visit to Brin. She sent it off before muting her notifications so that she could dedicate herself to the editing of the adjective 'parasocial', her next target.

Martha found the word neither memorable nor friendly, but she had to admit its usefulness. Coined in 1956 by two American sociologists, parasocial described the false intimacy people often feel towards a celebrity. It gave voice to the sense that you *know* the person you see on your screens, might even assume them as a friend, or – at the extreme end – believe them to be the fictional character they portray.

There was another reason Martha enjoyed her work on it. This was one of the rare instances when the *exact* moment of a word's appearance was known. In most cases a lexicographer had a good idea of a word's chronology, pieced together from dated records collected over time. But any timeline was usually an approximation of a year or decade, one that might well be antedated in future as more evidence was gathered. In their midst was a sliver of words and expressions whose coinage was so well documented that it was possible to record a precise moment of creation. Of these, Martha's enduring favourite was 'stealing someone's thunder', whose time and place of birth were as solid as the leather covers of her first dictionary. On 5th February 1709, a critic named John Dennis saw his own play open at London's Drury Lane theatre. The rather turgid drama had one surprise: Dennis had perfected for the stage a machine that reproduced the sound of thunder. But despite its dramatic sound effects, the play closed after only a short run. Not one for grudges, Dennis decided to attend the premiere of the production succeeding his, *Macbeth*. As the witches' scene began, the sound of thunder filled the auditorium: its reverberations booming out, Dennis quickly realised, from his own sound-effect machine. Accounts from members of the audience that night relayed how Dennis stood up, his face as louring as the darkened stage, and shouted, 'Damn them! They will not let my play run, but they steal my thunder!'

Surely an urban myth, people would say to Martha whenever she shared her delight – nothing could be that literal. Her answer was so well rehearsed that she felt like she knew John Dennis and shared his pain. *Maybe I have a parasocial relationship myself*, she noted wryly.

She continued in this perfect, precarious state of work, her mind stretching into the business in front of it. Before she was aware of time having passed at all, her notifications switched back on automatically. Pippa had already prepared a press statement. *The editors of the* CED *have received a series of anonymous communications*, it began. These communications related to the disappearance of Charlie Thornhill, a part-time assistant on the dictionary who had disappeared in 2010. The information had been duly passed to the police. Anyone with any information should contact DS Caldwell at St Aldates station. The Thornhill family asked for privacy at this time.

OK? Pippa had added at the end. *And my sympathies, Martha. This must suck.*

Martha felt a wave of relief.

This is perfect. Thank you. And it does.

It was the following day, the Friday before the May bank holiday, that the next letter arrived.

'Oh hell,' Safi said. Martha looked up as the adrenaline-in-waiting swamped her body again. 'There's another one.'

Martha swallowed hard. 'I'll text Jonathan.'

Safi opened the envelope and smoothed it out. 'OK, it's got some strange line breaks.'

She began to read:

Dear Editors,

Search for that lost treasure. I'm no rhymer, but in rhyme resides the truth.
That's the journey I have set you on. I am perhaps a Freudian, though few think his work worthy of a
Psalm of praise now.
Does that grieve you, as it does me? He thought that the pattern of language on

The mind is important. Who can speak truth, after all
Without understanding somehow the living history of words – the time in our mouth.
For an answer to appear, we must look back.
I trust you to unpick rotting threads

Of memory. Search amongst the early scholars
Who made paths through the universe of English and
Came back with treasures. Find something remarkable in their scraps of linguistic loot.
Traces of unfamiliar footsteps in the newly turned soil.

Be eager, know that those too thirsty for glory are dangers to themselves and others.
Although they may be that poor creature the scholar, and inks and reputations fade in sunlight.

Yours,
Chorus

Alex made a noise that hovered somewhere between admiration and exasperation. After that, silence, which drifted on until Martha's phone buzzed and she glanced at the screen.

'Jonathan's nearby, he'll be here in ten minutes.'

'Lucky us,' Simon growled and pulled at his beard.

'Do we wait?' Safi asked.

Martha shook her head and stood up. 'No, could you write it up on the whiteboard, Safi? I'll put the coffee on.'

'If we work it out before he turns up, I suppose we could all pretend to be befuddled until he arrives at the solution and explains it to us,' Simon suggested semi-cheerfully.

'Excellent idea. Might pre-empt more snippy texts,' Alex said.

Martha pulled down some mugs and went through the process of making coffee for the others, her mind as blurry as the dust-furred windows of the office's kitchenette. Now that the relief of her work had gone and Chorus had re-entered the stage, the conversations she'd had recently with Caldwell and her father began to return in waves, and each one made her flinch. Sentence by sentence her thoughts slowly cleared until they became needles: bright metal slivers that punctured the fog and were impossible to swerve.

'Dammit!'

She'd spilt the coffee, of course. The hot liquid seared her skin and she felt tears prick her eyes. There it was again, the flickering of time. Her father's questions came thudding back. *What was happening between you and Charlie when she disappeared?* Martha would give anything not to have to answer that question. She didn't even really know what the answer was. That Charlie – even distant, busy Charlie, who, like her dad, had moved on from A-levels – had still exerted some magnetic force over her that summer? That Martha had wanted, just for once, to have something first, something Charlie wanted? That she had taken it and felt a sharp, bitter sense of triumph? Then Charlie had disappeared and the triumph had gone with her, leaving Martha with nothing but an aching guilt that had been her companion now for more than a decade. Her last memory of Charlie wasn't ordinary, as it was for her parents. It was decisive, the dividing line between Martha's before and after. And now, thanks to Chorus, she was going to have to follow its path again. What had Tanya said? *Bloody Charlie, still fucking things up*. There was a truth in that.

She mopped up the mess with paper towels, but the inky coffee dripped down the cabinets and pooled on the floor.

'Stupid, stupid . . .'

'Are you OK, Martha?' It was Safi, peering through the door of the kitchenette. 'I wondered if you needed any help.'

'I spilt the coffee,' Martha offered by way of explanation.

Safi grinned. 'You sound like you've just wiped the database or something.' She put out her hand. 'Here, give those to me and I'll finish wiping up. The master has entered the building.'

Jonathan had bought his own cappuccino. He cradled it in one hand as he picked up a chair from the edge of the room and placed it in the middle of the horseshoe formed by their desks. He now sat facing the whiteboard, one leg crossed confidently over the other.

'Hi, Martha!' he said breezily as she came in with the tray and handed out the coffees. 'I was just telling the team I've spent some time on the first two letters. They are a fair old hodgepodge, but I can see how they got you to Charlie and to Brin. I'll email you a list of the words he uses that are either coinages once held to be Shakespeare's, or a handful that are still thought to be his. Did Brin have anything interesting to say?'

Safi clinked her spoon nervously around her mug. Martha found, again, that she didn't really want to look at him, so left it to Alex to explain Charlie's sideline in rare-book dealing. Martha noticed that she didn't say anything about their visit to Tom. Neither did Simon or Safi, and she felt a pulse of gratitude towards all three of them.

He leant forward, his hand on his chin, and stared at the whiteboard with a studied nonchalance. Each of them followed his gaze and read the letter again. The odd paragraph breaks in the first letter had nothing on this. Lines seemed to be cut willy-nilly, sentences interrupted in a way that irritated as much as they intrigued. Each of them tripped over its oddities as they reread the text.

A snort from Jonathan broke the silence, but he looked ill at ease. 'Freudian? I'm at a loss.'

'Did you get a postcard, Jonathan?' Safi said. Her notebook was open, poised.

His eyes suddenly locked on hers. 'Oh, yes, it turns out we did. I found it among my fan mail yesterday.'

'No wonder it got misplaced, then,' Alex observed, walking a tightrope between plausible politeness and sarcasm. 'What was its quote?'

'Does that matter?' he replied abstractedly, still staring at the board.

'It might.'

His features rearranged themselves into their usual bonhomie. 'It said, "Thou art a scholar, speak to it!"'

Hamlet. Martha's mind filled with the image of a mist-shrouded battlement, a group of frightened men summoning the courage to communicate with a ghost.

Jonathan deftly switched direction and pointed at the whiteboard. 'There's no Shakespeare at all in this missive. The first two letters were stuffed with quotes. Did you see the release Pippa put out, by the way? Nicely done, I thought. I had a chat with the journalist, too, on my way here.'

No one seemed to think it necessary to reply.

'Did you notice anything on the day of your launch, Jonathan?' Simon asked, sitting back and draining his cup. Jonathan turned away from the whiteboard again.

'You mean last week?'

'No,' Simon said. 'The day Charlie disappeared. Or had you spotted anything about her in the previous days?'

Jonathan looked vaguely confused. 'I came here to talk about the letter.'

Simon sighed theatrically. 'We are aware, but you also got a postcard. As did we. What with all of Chorus's poky comments about secrets and lies and cover-ups, we've been trying to put together a sort of timeline.'

He glanced at Safi, who turned back through the pages of her notebook.

'Martha's mum and dad saw Charlie working at home on the morning of the twenty-third of September. The next thing we know is that Gemma, your agent, got a text saying Charlie couldn't make lunch. Her parents seem to have been the last people to have seen her; she didn't come home that night.'

'That would seem to imply the crucial window of time was late morning, not the evening,' Jonathan said.

'Maybe. Or the afternoon. But Chorus seems to have sent postcards to a lot of people who *were* at your launch. So it might be significant.'

'I was here all day,' Simon said, 'as was Alex, and we went together to your launch. I went home early because Chloe was teething. Alex stayed until the end then went for a walk in Jericho. Martha was away at uni, and Safiya was at home in Peckham, dreaming about S Club 7 or something.'

'Before my time,' Safi murmured.

'I was at the launch, clearly,' Jonathan said irritably, 'then we finished up and I went home. I was exhausted.'

'Did you go home alone?' Alex asked.

'Christ, that's none of your business!' Jonathan exclaimed, standing up and turning to look at them now, his face no longer pressed into the service of civility.

'Of course it's none of our business,' Martha said, surprised by the sharpness in her own voice, 'but Chorus is pushing us to talk about things we'd all rather keep quiet.'

Jonathan met her gaze, his eyes still blazing, then picked up his jacket. 'Olivia came back to my rooms for a drink, and I put her in a cab at some point in the early hours,' he said unevenly. Martha's eyes were wide. 'The next day I had a couple of radio interviews. I went into the studio of BBC Oxford for those, then some signings in town. After that I was mostly at your parents' home, trying to be of use or putting up bloody posters.'

The pompom bounced. His answers seemed well rehearsed, Safi thought, but then so did everyone else's. The result no doubt of endless interviews by the police.

'So you got a postcard too?' Jonathan said to Safi. 'You can't have had anything to do with it, which means Chorus isn't just sending cards to people he suspects of some strange sin or other.'

'Maybe he didn't want me to be left out,' Safi said.

Jonathan scowled, then glanced back at the board. 'Well, if there aren't any Shakespearean references in this one, I'm not sure how I can help. Let me know how you get on.'

With that he swept back out of the office, taking out his phone as he did.

'Before his cappuccino even had a chance to cool,' Alex said.

'Yes, almost skittish,' Simon added.

Safi looked round at them. 'Were we out of order not saying anything about the number of lines? But . . . I mean he's a Shakespeare scholar! Supposedly one of the best. He must at least have realised there are fourteen.'

25

quaesitum, *noun (Latin)*:

the answer that is looked for

THE ATMOSPHERE EASED CONSIDERABLY NOW Jonathan had left.

'Are you all right, Martha?' Alex asked, before continuing tentatively: 'We face the usual question: try and work it out, or let Chorus go hang, pass it on to the police and get back to work.'

Martha emerged from behind her desk and picked up a marker pen.

'I honestly don't know what I want anymore, Alex. But here we are.'

'He hasn't called me back,' Alex said quickly, and Martha noticed a new sadness in her voice. 'George, I mean. I tried again last night.'

'Thank you for that,' Martha replied, tensing her stomach for the next stab of guilt. At least Simon had the sense to keep his mouth shut this time. She turned back to the board, and tapped the marker in her palm. 'I wonder if it would help to have a Shakespeare sonnet next to it. I can't see that Chorus is pointing at any particular one, though. Anyone got a favourite?'

'116,' Safi said immediately. 'It's my dad's favourite. He quotes it to my mum whenever he's in trouble. Works every time.'

Martha smiled, and wrote it up on the other side of the whiteboard:

Let me not to the marriage of true minds
Admit impediments. Love is not love
Which alters when it alteration finds,
Or bends with the remover to remove.
O no! it is an ever-fixed mark
That looks on tempests and is never shaken;
It is the star to every wand'ring bark,
Whose worth's unknown, although his height be taken.
Love's not Time's fool, though rosy lips and cheeks
Within his bending sickle's compass come;
Love alters not with his brief hours and weeks,
But bears it out even to the edge of doom.
If this be error and upon me prov'd,
I never writ, nor no man ever lov'd.

She contemplated the words. A poet's hope for immortality, and for the immortality of love. A plea and a prayer for every marriage.

There was a long pause while they read Chorus's disjointed lines next to it.

'Well,' Simon said at last. 'Chorus is no Shakespeare.'

Safi snorted. 'No. His lines don't scan at all. No attempt to put it in iambic pentameter.'

When Martha had first come across iambic pentameter, her mother had explained it as a heartbeat in poetic form: ti-dum, ti-dum, ti-dum. You could force the rhythm reading one of Shakespeare's lines, and hear it sound plodding and heavy, or speak the line naturally and let it become a frame on which the poetry could hang: the elegant, invisible bones of verse, like those in a bird's wing – light and delicate, but allowing the words to soar.

'He does say he's no rhymer,' she said. 'But that in rhyme resides the truth. That sounds like it has to be the key somehow, don't you think?'

'Stick up the rhyme scheme, Martha,' Alex said.

She did. Minds/finds, love/remove, mark/bark. The classic Shakespearean form that he stuck to throughout his published sonnets. Abab, cdcd, efef, gg. Three quatrains and a couplet.

Then she stood back, looking between Chorus's work and Shakespeare's.

'Do you think we're looking for another hidden message within the plain text?' she said.

'God, I hope there's some hidden sense in that nonsense,' Alex drawled. 'There are other hints, too, though, I think. He wants us to search among the work of previous scholars. Here that can only mean one thing, surely? The slips.'

The word 'slip' has a specific meaning in lexicography, another tribal code that Martha had quickly mastered. According to her predecessor Mike, crowdsourcing began with dictionaries. Martha remembered him talking about it as he gave her the tour, shortly before she started work at the *CED*. Part of the handover. Any scholarly or historical lexicon, he had continued, relies on evidence in the wild of a word's personality: how it behaves, the friends it keeps, the environment in which it thrives and, if you're lucky, the one that created it in the first place. Lexicographers gather this information in different ways. Some rely on the data behind existing dictionaries, where the legwork has already been done, but others start the hunt anew.

The *Clarendon English Dictionary* certainly belonged in this last category, the ongoing result of a mammoth logistical operation involving evidence submitted by thousands of volunteer readers. Astronomers, novelists, vicars, suffragists and housewives, philosophers and palaeontologists, and even a few convicted criminals, had collectively built the backbone of what had come to be regarded as the highest lexicographical authority in the world.

The clues amassed by this curious and eager army of readers were submitted on strips of paper – slips – comprising 4- x 6-inch biographical records of language. They amounted to thousands, submitted in such numbers after a public appeal by the dictionary's editors that the lexicographers had trouble finding enough space to house them. Slips libraries – or scriptoria – had been created for them; in reality, they often amounted to nothing more than an editor's front room. Martha always relished the fact that a significant proportion of slips from the letters M-ME had once fallen behind an old piano, their corners nibbled away by mice who cared little for the value of these precious witnesses to history. Today, those same battered slips were stored in oak card-cases atop steel filing cabinets, where they remained available to the dictionary team as old entries were revised and new ones drafted.

'Got it!' Simon said, so loudly that all the women jumped.

26

inquilinate, *verb (seventeenth century)*:
to dwell in a strange place

'It's fiendish: the key is the rhyme scheme!'

'Go on, Simon,' Alex said.

Simon was bouncing with excitement in his ergonomic chair. 'OK, so in the last letters we've had to nail down the significant words in the plain text. The first one let us in easy, just using the first word in each paragraph. The second one was much trickier, using measures of music to point to the right words in each paragraph. This time neither of those would work – and as we've said, it doesn't have a rhyme pattern of its own, nor is there any apparent rhythm. The opposite, if anything. But there *is* a key there, and it's laid out like a sonnet. The rhyme scheme of a Shakespearean sonnet is the key.'

'So the last word or syllable in each line?' Safi shook her head. 'But that's nonsense!'

Simon waved his hands in the air, as high on revelation as a revival preacher. 'No! We use the most basic numerical substitution code: a is one, or vice versa, and b is two . . . Which gives us the first word in the first line, the second in the second, the first in the third . . .'

Martha circled the words in the first quatrain. 'Search the psalm that . . . no, then it doesn't work after that.'

Simon shook his head. 'No, remember the form: abab, cdcd, efef, gg. Those rhymes are the c and d in the sonnet scheme, so take the third and fourth words alternately in the second quatrain.'

'Is . . . the . . . answer . . . to . . .'

Safi applauded. 'Si! You've got it!'

He grinned, a faint blush of pride appearing above his beard. 'Next quatrain, fifth and sixth words . . .'

Martha spoke it out loud as she carried on. '. . . "the universe find the", and then the seventh in each line of the final couplet: "thirsty creature".'

'Search the psalm. That is the answer to the universe. Find the thirsty creature.'

There was a collective congratulatory murmur as they each took in the solution.'Which psalm, though?' said Alex. 'Does anything in the letter hint at that?'

Simon shook his head. 'I just can't see it. Fuck.'

Safi leant over the desk and offered her palm for a high-five. 'Man, you took us all this way, though. Better than Jonathan managed.'

They turned away from the whiteboard in the end, but as the day rolled on, they each cast glances towards it while its puzzle churned away without let-up in their heads. Safi could see the twitches of irritation and confusion in everyone's faces. Twice when she looked up, she saw Martha staring at the whiteboard, playing with her necklace. Each time she'd eventually chew her lip and return to her monitor. Simon kept staring out of the window and frowning, as though he might find the solution etched upon the spring sky. Late in the afternoon Martha got a call from Caldwell.

'The secret bank account,' she explained to their expectant faces after hanging up. 'It had just under five thousand pounds in it. Caldwell is tracing the transactions, but most of the income seems to be from legitimate book dealers in London, and the withdrawals were in cash.'

'So, we need the date of the last one,' Safi said, ignoring Simon's automatic tutting over her 'So' habit.

'Last withdrawal was just before Easter, though some payments were coming in right up to when she disappeared.'

'That fits with her buying on her own account at sales, then selling off her stock but not buying more.' Safi tapped her pencil on her notebook. 'Did he say anything else?'

'He wished us luck with the clue,' Martha said, and all three shot a look at the board.

Towards the end of the day, their glances shifted from befuddlement to something verging on resentment. By the time the clock eventually passed five, deflation had taken over. Simon left first, then Alex, wishing them a pleasant bank holiday, leaving Martha and Safi in the settling gloom, still staring at the whiteboard.

'Staying late, Martha?'

'Off to have dinner with Gemma in a minute,' she replied. 'Have a great break, Safi.'

Safi mustered a cheery goodnight, but felt unsettled leaving the office, twitchy and tired. She was sure that if she went home now, she'd have a spat with one or other of her flatmates. Moving from the enclosed space of the office to the four walls of her room felt impossible, so she changed into her running kit in the loo, fetched her spangly bike, and rode to Folly Bridge and the path along the bank of the Thames. She'd just have to run herself into a good mood – or a different mood, at any rate.

Oxford was as much an Elysium for runners as for cyclists, with miles of towpaths and tracks away from the city's maddeningly congested roads. Safi passed between brightly painted canal boats on the water, some fluttering with bunting for the impending Coronation, and followed the path alongside thick banks lush with clover and meadow foxtail. Rowers sculled across the river like water boatmen, their ripples radiating silently across a surface still flushed by the sun. She jogged slowly for a couple of minutes, then began to push, counting her strides to keep her breathing regular, and bouncing lightly on her toes. She'd read up on the benefits of silent running, and whenever she heard other runners thudding past her on the Oxford streets she would wince for their knees, but she was alone in the twilight now, her flow interrupted only by the occasional dog walker.

She listened to her muscles and lungs, checking and refining her posture as she ran, occupying her conscious mind with the physical mechanics and letting her subconscious throw up fragments of memory, music, random snapshots of life. Books she had read as a child, her political passions, her fears for the future: all of them swirled through her mind like the leaves on the river. *What do I want to do with my life? Is this enough? What* is *the answer to the universe, Chorus? A stray psalm?* She thought of one of her aunties plucking a Bible verse at random as a sort of personal divination tool. 'The Lord will tell me.'

Well, Lord, got any hints?

She had found her stride now and fell into an easy lope that could take her for miles if she wanted. Her mind returned to the latest puzzle, glancing off it and away. It worked better if she shifted her focus to something else, let the thing she needed to resolve whirr away in the background like an app updating itself on a phone. How strange these letters were. Had Martha loved her sister? Safi thought she had, but was beginning to sense that their love had been a complex one. Siblings . . . puzzles. There had been a book she'd loved when she was little, unearthed in the Peckham library that had become her second home. She had loved the building's solidity: it was brash and huge, a great slice of glass resembling a playful upside-down L. What was that book called? She could see the cover. Yes, *Minnow on the Say* by Philippa Pearce.

Its cover illustration of two children in a boat was like nothing she'd ever seen in London. It could easily have been Oxford: one of the puntable channels of slow-moving brown water, overhung by greenery. The librarian, a kind woman who wore armfuls of silver bracelets and never brushed her hair, had recommended it because Safi had lapped up *Tom's Midnight Garden* by the same author. Its puzzle had been a poem, too, although, unlike Chorus's, this one actually rhymed. And the solution had been hidden in plain sight . . . all about . . .

She stopped, feeling the answer hovering on the edge of clarity.

The comma.

The solution in that book had rested on where the comma in the poem was. It had changed the sense of the line and led to the hiding place of the treasure.

'Search the psalm that is the answer to the universe . . .' she said out loud. And there was the librarian again, this time with a book from the grown-up library with an exciting neon cover. 'There's fun in life, too, Safiya,' she had said. Douglas Adams' *The Hitchhiker's Guide to the Galaxy*.

She pulled out her phone and rang Alex.

'Forty-two!' she blurted as soon as Alex answered.

'I'm sorry?'

'The clue. We messed up the punctuation by putting in full stops. What if it reads "Search the psalm that is the answer to the universe"? The specific psalm we need is the one "which is the answer to the universe".'

A short beat. 'Forty-two! Of course! Hang on, Safi, I'm looking it up now.'

'You recognise the reference, then?' Safi asked, shivering slightly as her clammy skin began to cool.

'Of course I do. *Hitchhiker's Guide*. The most advanced beings in the galaxy create a super-computer with one task, to solve the answer to life, the universe and everything, and after a million years or something, it announces the answer as forty-two. Still makes more sense than most established religions in my book.'

'So is there a thirsty animal in Psalm 42?'

Safi heard a tiny intake of breath at the other end of the line. 'Indeed there is. It's the first line: "As the hart panteth after the water brooks, so panteth my soul after thee, O God."'

'A hart?'

'Yes, adult male deer. Germanic origin, I believe.'

'I know what the word means, Alex. But what do we do now?'

'I suggest going back to the office and searching the slips for "hart". I suppose we could wait till Tuesday . . .'

'No!' Safi protested. 'Now!'

'Fine. Let me call Simon and Martha. We'll see you there.'

Safi did the return run at a personal best.

27

engouement, *noun (nineteenth century)*:
an irrational fondness

GEMMA'S HOME LAY ON THE gentle curve of Holywell Street, a long and narrow medieval lane in the heart of the city, close to the expansive thoroughfare of Broad Street and the winding alley of the Turf. Hers was a tall, three-storey townhouse with a Georgian façade, its double-sash windows in mullioned frames flanked by Victorian lampposts that looked perfectly at home in the gathering twilight. The house belonged, like most of the street's buildings on the north side, to Merton College, to whom Gemma was more than happy to pay a substantial rent in return for one of the coolest postcodes in Oxford. The College allowed her to redecorate at regular intervals, and Martha was only now seeing it in its latest incarnation, which leant heavily on the mid-century modern.

'Pecan pie!' Gemma gushed, as she ushered Martha into the hallway. 'What an excellent idea. I'm guessing you can't buy

German cakes here, not like New York. Is it true they're to die for? I did love Schwarzwaldkuchen in my youth.' Gemma mangled the pronunciation so thoroughly that it took several seconds for Martha to decipher it.

'They are good.' Martha smiled, handing over the bag from Nash's in the Covered Market. 'There was a wonderful bakery in Neukölln that I used to visit every weekend.'

'And then you probably didn't eat anything the rest of the day. We're having roast chicken, by the way, so I hope you've an appetite. There's white wine in the cooler on the table.'

They swapped small talk for a few minutes until Gemma invited her into the sitting room. There were fresh flowers – gladioli – in a large Chinese vase on a table behind the sofa, and the mantelpiece above the open fire was lined with multi-coloured invitations to various book launches. A small bowl of olives sat on the table.

Martha remembered something an MP had said in Parliament about olives and 'posh people'. She'd seen it on Twitter and laughed, prompting Sabine to ask for an explanation, whereupon Martha had found herself mired in the complexities of the English class system for over twenty minutes.

'Gemma, why did you say I was a funny old thing when you rang?'

Gemma settled into one of the armchairs by the fire and set down her wine glass, beaded with moisture, on a glass coaster. It was the same green as the necklace she wore, carved out of seaglass and wrapped in intricate silver chains, manifesting some queen of the underwater caught in a magical net.

'For sending that postcard, of course. You always were a sweet, strange girl.'

Martha shook her head. 'I didn't send you a postcard. Was it of the *CED*? With a Shakespeare quotation on the back?'

'Was it Shakespeare? I only know what Jonathan quotes in his books and half of those go in one ear and out the other. "A figure of truth, of faith, of loyalty". You mean it wasn't from you?'

'No.' Martha picked up her wine and sipped from it; it was a Gewürztraminer, and for a moment she was in Leipzig, drinking the same wine from a glass with a twisted green stem at a bar just outside the cathedral. She could almost taste its warm smokiness, hear Sabine laughing.

'But I got one too. So did quite a few other people.'

Gemma said nothing, just tilted her head to one side and waited for Martha to continue.

'It's about Charlie.'

'About *Charlie*,' Gemma repeated. 'Oh, goodness. Not again. First, there was the ten-year anniversary, then your mother's push to have it all reopened. And I've had to squash a rabble of chancers already.'

'Chancers?'

'Oh, there was a journalist who wanted to do a book a few years back, and another one who read your mother's obituary and thought the whole story would make a great podcast. Ghouls.'

'How did you stop them?'

'Martha, darling, I may just be your mum's old friend to you, but I do have some sway in the industry. Particularly after Jonathan's success. They both went away with deals for other projects.'

Martha stared at her glass, feeling instantly ashamed. How did she not know any of this? 'And why did you stop them?'

'Because they were vultures,' she said firmly. 'Worst of the true-crime rubberneckers. I might have reacted differently if they'd been serious people. But they absolutely weren't.' Martha remembered what Caldwell had said about the ascension of true crime, about families being harassed. 'I was also quite sure you and your father would hate it. Was I wrong?'

'No. No, of course you weren't.'

'Good.' Gemma drank and then set her glass back on the coaster with a clink. Martha noticed a small still-life painting on the wall behind her chair, of a delicately striped jug in front of a deep velvet curtain. It looked very much like a Ben Nicholson. But why buy something so exquisite and put it behind your chair, where you yourself couldn't see it? She instantly comprehended: the point was for the person sitting in the other chair to see you and it together. It was part of the arrangement, the framing Gemma had created for herself, like the flowers and the necklace.

'These postcards are probably a warm-up for another attempt,' she continued. 'God knows, there's been a true crime book about every killing in the country in the last hundred years, so they'll keep coming after Charlie, I'm afraid. It's a huge market.' She reached forward to take an olive and popped it in her mouth, savouring it for a few seconds. 'Actually, the postcards are a rather clever idea.' She nudged the bowl towards Martha. 'Have you told your father yet?'

'Wednesday night.'

Gemma paused, waiting for her to elaborate, and Martha took an olive to signal she had no intention of doing so. 'Not a fun conversation, I take it. No judgement, darling. I'm fond of your father, but I admit what I liked about him best was how much he loved your mother. Appreciated her from the day they were married to the day she died, and that is a remarkable, rare thing. In both my marriages we obsessed about each other's failings more than our virtues. What's that thing psychologists say? The salience of negative stimuli. But I suppose everyone has their faults.'

The olives were good. They tasted of thyme and sunshine and long days of reading with a glass of wine and a view of the Adriatic. 'What was Charlie coming to see you about, the day she disappeared?'

'What makes you think it was about anything in particular?'

'It was always something in particular with Charlie.' It felt strange saying it out loud, a betrayal, but it was also strangely empowering.

Gemma was quiet for a while. 'She didn't say. But I always assume that if someone suggests lunch with me out of the blue, they probably want to write a book.'

'You didn't ask her?'

Gemma frowned. 'I saw her in town. She was sitting outside the printers' bar with a friend, and I had the feeling she was showing off for them a bit. I was walking past, and she called me over. She said she had "something exciting" to talk to me about. I was having a bad day, everything was so frantic with Jonathan's book, so no doubt I said something foolish like, "Oh God, you haven't written a novel, have you?" Her friend laughed, and that made her bristle a bit. She said no, it wasn't a novel, but it was something special and she wanted to give me the chance of first refusal as I was a friend of the family.' Gemma shook her head, the seaglass around her neck casting watery shadows over her skin. 'I remember thinking how wearing the young can be. I thought it was probably about turning her PhD thesis into a book, and that's not really my thing. If it doesn't have a chance of ending up in Waterstones, I'm not really the person for the job. But Charlie was insistent. Phones out, let's make a date. So I told her to come over on that Thursday for lunch.'

'What did you think when she cancelled?'

'I was annoyed. It was a busy day. I suspect she'd realised she'd just make a fool of herself if she came. She was . . . well, it was always the Charlie Thornhill show at your house, wasn't it? She liked a drama, getting a reaction out of people. When she failed to show I assumed the whole face-saving thing was more serious than I'd thought. She was so used to being the golden girl. It's dangerous to build your sense of self on the adoration of others.'

Martha felt disorientated. She longed for the repose of her old flat, its welcome recesses and faint smell of tobacco, the puddled wax beneath the candlesticks on the scarred table. Above all, its distance from here. In all the years since Charlie's departure, it had never once occurred to Martha that others saw her sister as she did. Her assumption had always been that Charlie would be forever frozen in a state of perfection: the one who shone, who pleased, who ran at life with an unwavering gaze of china blue and lived as though an invisible camera was trained on her every minute. Was this all the projection of a jealous mind? The realisation brought no relief; instead, Martha felt an immediate, illogical need to defend her sister.

'But she made life brighter,' she said quietly.

The chicken was excellent, and Martha let herself feel revived by it. Gemma was very good at making the person she was talking to feel interesting, at least when she tried, and she was trying now. Martha was grateful. She found herself talking about Berlin, Sabine, her old flat and the new job. For a moment Chorus and Charlie retreated and she felt an unfamiliar sense of being cared for, but she also noticed an incipient discomfort from talking only about herself.

'How is Jonathan's new book doing?'

'Pretty well, really.' Gemma pushed her plate aside. 'It's a difficult time of year for hardbacks, so I wasn't surprised it didn't break into the top ten this time. And as it's a tie-in the newspapers tend not to review as heavily. There was a rather snippy paragraph in the *Literary Review*: I had to tell Jonathan to contain himself. No sock-puppeting this time, I warned him.'

'Sock-puppeting?'

'Yes. There's a term for your dictionary pages. You didn't hear about *that* episode, then? Good. That shows I'm doing my job. It was three years ago. Jonathan got angry about a review in *The Telegraph*, went on Amazon and gave the reviewer's own book a one-star rating and a nasty review. Under a false name.'

'Oh, that was reckless.'

She'd counselled enough authors in Germany herself to avoid doing anything like that. Although one had refused to listen and became embroiled in a tussle of review and counter-review on Goodreads.

'Yes. Understandable on a human level, but bloody stupid,' Gemma said, refilling their glasses. 'Luckily the reviewer's agent is a friend of mine. She called me and I read Jonathan the riot act. We managed to get it taken down quietly and Jonathan wrote a letter of apology, blaming it on a bad day and one whiskey too many. But I did find a few others.'

'Others?'

'Reviews on Amazon of works by his contemporaries. Highly immature and potentially very damaging to his career. Luckily, only *The Telegraph* reviewer had put two and two together, so they were all removed without anyone taking to social media.'

It was clear to Martha that, were it not for the wine, Gemma would not be sharing half of this. But it was undeniably useful to know. She remembered Jonathan's tight smile as he listened to the news of another Shakespearean neologism being taken down.

'Uneasy lies the head that wears the crown,' she murmured.

'Indeed. Now, are you doing anything over the bank holiday? And what about the Coronation?'

Martha was halfway through admitting her plans consisted entirely of reading and walking, with the possible exception of May Day morning, when her phone rang. It was Alex.

28

vanitarianism, *noun (nineteenth century)*: the pursuit of vanities

Returning to the office late on a Friday evening felt strangely illicit. Martha buzzed Alex and Safi in with her keycard.

'I can't believe we missed it,' she said as she pushed the door open and the automatic lights flickered on. 'Is Simon coming?'

'He hasn't returned my call,' Alex replied, glancing at her phone. 'No, hang on, he's messaged. He's on his way.'

They walked through the reception area past the deserted cafeteria and turned down a side corridor to the familiar, ordinary-looking office door marked 'Slips'.

Safi recalled the disappointment she'd felt when she first entered the 'Slips Room'. She'd expected the same sense of majesty she'd found in the inner sanctum of the dictionary archives, a repository of the oldest evidence collected for the First Edition together with other memorabilia, including sepia photographs of the staff, whose impossibly long and hoary beards almost obscured the bulging pigeonholes behind them. By contrast, today's home of the slips was utterly devoid of charisma, a curiously dead space housing dozens of metal filing cabinets beneath a buzzing sea of strip lights. A few desks and chairs had been prised into the narrow intervals between them, but this was not a place you wanted to linger.

And yet, as Safi knew, within its walls was wonder. Every one of the curled and yellowed slips bore witness to more than the word it illustrated. Take the entry for 'supper', drafted in the early 1900s and, Alex had told the team, once been dropped on the street (perhaps after a boozy re-enactment of its definition) and returned to the dictionary by a diligent member of the public. Another set had been mistaken for kindling and tossed on a bonfire, leaving only the charred remains of the beginning of 'put'.

The slips for 'hart' were organised into groups and held together with string. One pack contained the original submissions for examples of use in the current edition, another gathered those included in previous editions. By far the largest bundle comprised additional quotations that had been sent in by readers but never used.

Martha laid them out on the largest of the formica tables at the edge of the room. 'Do you think we immediately put aside all of the obsolete meanings?'

Safi sat down at the end of the desk, her chin in her hand. 'You mean where "hart" was just a variant spelling of "hard" and "heart" and the rest?'

Martha nodded.

'Yes, I think so,' Alex replied. 'The psalm is about the animal, so I guess we should start there.'

'But what are we looking for?' Simon had appeared on the threshold, his face flushed, his messenger bag slung over his shoulder.

'Simon!' Martha said. 'Thank you for coming.'

'Of course, I don't have the girls till tomorrow.' He shivered slightly in the chill of the room and set his bag on the floor. 'Good call on the punctuation, Safi. But Douglas Adams is a bit of a change for Chorus, isn't he?'

'He is. I loved those books growing up,' Martha said, still frowning at the slips of quotations. 'Dad used to read them to us.'

'I had the radio version on cassette at college.' Alex picked up another bundle and began to go through them. 'I think half our conversations at that time were carried out either in *Hitchhiker's* or Monty Python quotes.'

'My introduction to sci-fi,' Safi added. 'It's definitely a gear change, though, I agree. And "hart" can't have anything to do with antedatings or Shakespeare, surely? It's Old English.'

Martha undid a bundle of slips and sat down before beginning to go through them in the same fashion as Alex. 'I suppose we're looking for something that doesn't fit. There could be a Shakespeare reference to a hart?'

Simon was looking at his phone. 'It comes up a few times.' He twisted the phone round. 'I'm looking at the online concordance to the First Folio. In hunting metaphors mostly.' He raised his eyebrows. 'There's mention of an inn, the White Hart in Southwark. Maybe we're supposed to go there and ask for Charlie.'

He glanced up, waiting for the payoff, but caught instead a frown from Alex, who nodded towards Martha.

'Sorry, Martha.'

Safi turned each slip in the bundle she was given, slowly reading each one. All that nineteenth-century handwriting: swooping italics, the uneven distribution of ink, a little soot on the edge of the card. Each one carried her into some anonymous study, another moving hand.

She felt her heart rate increase before she had consciously understood what she was looking at.

'Oh. So there's a slip here which isn't for "hart" at all. It's for "besmirch".'

'What?'

Safi held it between her hands. This one wasn't yellowed with age, it was a modern index card, written in a mix of ballpoint and pencil rather than ink. 'It's more like a scrap or draft than a proper slip,' she said. The citation had been crossed out and rewritten a couple of times. It took her a moment to absorb the intensity of the faces looking back at her.

'"Besmirch" – as a verb?' Alex asked, a note of urgency in her voice. Safi nodded. 'That *is* a Shakespearean coinage. Read it out, Safi.'

'"My reputacion faire by this scoundril now besmirched." Ballad of the Spinner, Anon. Before 1599.'

'When's the first recording of "besmirched" currently?' Martha said, then reached up for one of the bound volumes of the dictionary in the room to answer her own question. They carefully moved the bundles of slips aside while she set it down and turned the pages, then ran her finger down the column.

'*Hamlet*, 1604.'

Simon sat down next to Safi and plucked the card from her hand, holding it at arm's length. His breath smelled of beer, but then she wasn't sure what she smelled like after her run.

'Then this is five years earlier,' he said.

'What's the rest of the citation?' Martha asked, looking up from the page.

Safi took the card back from Simon while he patted his coat, looking for his reading glasses, then swore softly under her breath before replying. 'It's in pencil and rubbed out and rewritten. OK. "Recorded in The Commonplace Book of J. H., A Provincial Woman, ed. Charlotte Thornhill".' She squinted at it. 'Hang on, did Charlie publish a book?'

'No, she didn't.' Martha put out her hand and Safi meekly handed the slip to her. Martha held it very delicately, as the others held their breath.

'It's her handwriting,' she said at last, setting the card on the tabletop. The strip lighting flickered. 'Charlie's, I mean.' Then she put her hand to her forehead. 'But what . . . where does this take us?'

'Martha,' Alex said slowly, 'sit down before you fall down. Did you eat this evening?'

Martha lowered herself into a chair, her eyes still on the card. 'Yes, it's just that . . . What the hell does this mean?'

'A new antedating,' Safi said slowly, 'citing a book that doesn't exist, edited by a woman who didn't publish . . .'

'And citing a ballad I've never heard of either,' Alex added. 'Do you think it's a joke? Is that the sort of thing Charlie would do?'

'I don't know,' Martha replied. 'Maybe, but if it's just a joke, why is the citation written and rewritten? It's like she was trying to decide what to call her book.'

'My God,' said Simon. 'Is it possible Charlie stumbled on a commonplace book with rhymes and songs from Shakespeare's time? That's the holy grail! Jesus, where is it?'

'Maybe the lost treasure Chorus mentioned wasn't Charlie after all,' Safi breathed. 'If this is real, if it contains material like this . . . then maybe it was this manuscript.'

29

intaglio, *noun (Italian)*:

a figure etched into a substance

SUNDAY EVENING: FOR MOST PEOPLE the gloomiest time of the week, when work raises its head again and anxiety and insomnia come knocking. Even though the current prospect of a bank holiday took away some of the sting, Martha had never quite understood it. For her, Sunday was a time to breathe and gather, to walk, watch, eat cake, and do all the things that on any other day of the week would be considered indulgent. She remembered the Sunday mornings she'd spent with Jack, her university boyfriend, sharing croissants and reading the papers side by side on her narrow student bed. Later they'd watch a movie or pretend to work, laptops open across their knees and fingers curled around mugs of tea. She recalled a sense of anticipation at the week just coming into view.

Charlie, on the other hand, had hated Sundays, latching on to the word 'mubble-fubbles' – seventeenth-century speak for a heavy, eve-of-something-unpleasant dose of the blues – as proof that no sane person had ever liked them. She'd consequently done all she could to defy them, organising drinks or dinners with the deference normally paid to Saturday nights. Another of her thrilling rebellions, Martha had thought.

This had been neither a restful nor an indulgent weekend. Martha had spent it going through every box in Charlie's shoe cupboard, and every volume on her bookshelves. Wary of her father, she'd been careful and methodical, replacing everything where it should be when she was done examining it, before moving onto the next box or book. Nothing. Or rather, worse than nothing: a torrent of Charlie and, today especially, memories of shared curiosity and laughter. The scenes she recalled had a filmic quality to them, of two characters walking down familiar streets, animatedly engaged in conversation the viewer couldn't hear, or lying side by side on the floor, their legs swung up behind them as they pored intently over a book. Martha wondered if she was subconsciously making amends for the negativity that had attended her sister in recent weeks. She took some blame for that. She needed to remind herself that she had loved her sister with an intensity that still allowed for the realities of imperfection.

But she found no sixteenth-century manuscript. Every antique book Charlie had acquired was printed.

Maybe she had put it in a safety deposit box somewhere. Might one be linked to the bank card? She had phoned Caldwell on Saturday and spoken to him briefly, but it had been difficult to hear. It sounded like he was either at a football match or watching one in a noisy pub.

Late on in the afternoon, Alex called.

'George finally got back to me,' she said without preamble. 'And he sounded pretty sheepish. Suggested I pop down to London tomorrow so we can have a chat.'

'Alex, I'm . . .'

'It's really not your fault, Martha, so please don't apologise. I'll ring you tomorrow when I get back. Have a good May Day.'

Martha looked at the phone in her hand and wondered about calling Sabine. No, she'd have to explain all this, and she didn't think she had it in her. Not yet. The last time she'd been to the May Day celebrations, she'd been with her mother. She'd go tomorrow, listen to the choir greeting the morning with heavenly madrigals, and try and work out, as dawn broke, what the hell she was going to do next. The crow-shadows from the lamps flitted across the walls. She thought of the lines from the Song of Solomon.

The winter is past, the time of the singing of birds is come.

30

desiderate, *verb (seventeenth century)*:
to long for something now lost

SHE SAW HIM BEFORE HE saw her, twenty feet away in the crowd as the prayers ended and the quarter peal began, the sound of the bells seeming to force its way into the stones of the street beneath her feet. Caldwell, a little taller than the men around him, was looking up into the May morning, shielding his eyes, as if he could somehow see the vibrations in the air. Then, in that mysterious way, he seemed to feel her eyes on him, prompting him to turn and smile, before immediately making his way towards her.

'Good morning!' he said as he reached her. No suit today, just jeans and a woollen jacket against the morning chill. 'Are you on your own?'

She nodded. 'Yes, you?'

'No one I know gets up this early for hymns.' He smiled. The crowd was beginning to move around them, and in the middle of the road an accordion started up. The Morris Men were getting ready to dance. 'Do you have a minute? I want you to explain to me what this slip you found might mean. I'll buy you a coffee.'

'My treat,' she said, falling into step beside him.

They weaved around the crowds who, like them, had gathered at dawn to 'bring in the May' and listen to *The Hymnus Eucharistus* from the choristers of Magdalen College, as their ancestors had done for five centuries or more. For as long as she could remember, Martha had been part of this celebration of rebirth and resurrection. It was one of the few occasions that as a family they had never missed, cycling in convoy from home as the sun was rising, Martha already looking forward to the hearty breakfast they would enjoy afterwards. She never begrudged the gentle shaking of her shoulders by Gabriel as he roused his two daughters: sometimes she and Charlie would bunk down together the evening before, whispering conspiratorially far into the night, knowing that in just a few hours their father would come in to wake them.

Martha adjusted her scarf around her neck. When she'd asked Gabriel a few days ago if he'd like to come with her this morning, he'd only shaken his head and looked vacant. He'd been in bed by the time she'd got home last night, and this morning the door to his room remained firmly shut. She'd hesitated outside it, studying the scuffed paintwork and wondering if she should knock, then decided it was easier to make this pilgrimage alone, preferring to be with the memory of the man who'd once lifted her up towards the bells.

Their mother had been the instructor. Each year, as she swapped their bike helmets for garlands of flowers beneath Magdalen Tower, Rebecca would explain anew the significance of May Morning, the victory of summer over winter, birth over death. She would tell them how the Puritan government had banned maypole dancing, dismissing it as 'a heathenish vanity, abused to superstition and wickedness'. The same doubters, Rebecca explained, saw Morris Dancers as followers of Satan. Martha and Charlie would look only at each other as their mother spoke, mouthing the lines they knew off by heart.

Perhaps entertainment would always have a dark underbelly, Martha thought, as she took in the costumes and brightly painted faces around her. Performance was the mark of the outsider who, since the time of the Shakespearean fool, was looked on either as a madman or a soothsayer; not for nothing did the word 'funny' look both ways.

She looked about her now as they made slow progress along the pavements flanking the Botanical Gardens. Many in the crowd were dressed in green, a nod to fertility and to Floralia, the Roman goddess of flowers. These revellers were lucky compared with their forerunners a few centuries before, for whom May Day morning had been more Bacchanalian than beatific, and who risked being pelted by eggs rather than music. Not that all mischief had vanished: Martha took in the scores of stewards lining Magdalen Bridge to stop anyone clambering perilously over the balustrade and jumping into the river below: a tradition that threatened annually to get out of hand.

She and Caldwell took a left off the High Street to enjoy the comparative quiet of Magpie Lane. This narrow walkway, Martha knew, was once called 'Gropecuntlane', because within its shadows sex workers had plied their trade. No squeamishness over that word in the Middle Ages, when the biggest taboo was not bodily functions, but religious profanity. She refrained from telling Caldwell this, lest he think her even madder than he probably already did.

They stopped at a pop-up café in Oriel Square, grabbing takeaway cappuccinos and a couple of sticky cinnamon buns. Finally there was space to talk.

'So, a commonplace book? What was that exactly?' he asked.

'Good question. It was a journal, a sort of personal archive in the early modern period – well, say from the fifteenth to the eighteenth centuries.'

He blew over the top of his coffee. 'So, Shakespearean times.'

'Yep, and a couple of hundred years either side. Writing a commonplace book was a way of creating your own external hard drive of quotations, in a way. But not just quotations: thoughts, philosophy, news items, anything that caught the writer's eye. Or ear.'

'Refresh my memory, what was going on then? In terms of culture.'

'Well, this.' Martha smiled, waving her hand towards the May Day hordes. 'But, roughly speaking, the Renaissance had spread from what is now Italy. The printing press had been invented, which hugely accelerated the sharing of knowledge. Books were still luxury items, but they didn't have to be hand-copied anymore, so greater numbers of people had access. More and more were becoming literate too. Grammar schools, like the one Shakespeare went to, taught their students how to keep commonplace books, making notes of quotes and passages from great authors, grouped by subject so they could refer back to them. A fair few have survived, and they are cornucopias for dictionary-makers.'

They were back on the High Street now, standing at the edge of the pavement and watching flashes of a Green Man parade as it headed for Radcliffe Square. A little girl, sitting on her father's shoulders, was applauding enthusiastically with her mittened hands.

'I thought commonplaces were just ordinary sayings – like clichés.'

'Well, that's what "a commonplace" came to mean,' Martha replied, 'because keeping a commonplace book became so widespread, and people would copy down the same quotations, under the same headings. In the end you could get pre-printed ones so you didn't have to do any of the actual reading yourself. It's a bit like some self-help books today that are just a selection of quotable bits from famous philosophers.'

'Like those inspirational sayings you see on Instagram?' he asked, then smiled at something he had noticed in the crowd. She followed his gaze to a pair of teenagers, one of whom wore a T-shirt printed with 'Boys get sad too'. She double-checked. No, the smile wasn't mocking; he looked approving – touched even.

'Yes, exactly like that. But the older commonplaces contain all kinds of useful odds and ends. Sometimes the people who kept them would write down songs or stories they heard, summaries of plays, fragments of rhyme. And those are really precious. We have so little from that period.' He raised an eyebrow. 'OK,' Martha continued, 'I know if you're in school reading Shakespeare it seems like we have plenty, but even his plays weren't pulled together until after his death. Think of all the performers who were travelling around the country putting on entertainments, or the mystery plays that the guilds organised in towns. We only get glimpses of the sort of thing they put on, the songs they sang. A commonplace book can really fill in the gaps. There's one by a London merchant called Richard Hill, for example. We only have the words to "The Boar's Head Carol" because he wrote them down.'

'But, forgive me, it seemed you were very taken with the idea there might be a new song in this commonplace book . . .'

'If the book actually exists . . .'

'Indeed,' he allowed, 'if it exists, but would it really be that important?'

She looked directly at him. 'We are really lacking in the voices of ordinary people. There are even great gaps in what we know about the more famous ones, like Shakespeare's. That's one of the reasons people debate the authorship of the works credited to him. We get endless letters about that at the dictionary.' She cradled the coffee in her hands, trying to work out how to put it. 'But songs and rhymes can tell us so much about the age they were born in. And the fact that this is a spinning song means it would almost certainly have been voiced by women. It could tell us about their attitudes to many things: sex and marriage, faith and family. Careers are built on finding and fitting together these sorts of fragmentary clues.'

'OK, so what do you conclude?'

She ran her hand through her hair. He really did seem interested in all of this, his expression serious and engaged. 'It might be a prank, but it's possible, just possible, that Charlie found a commonplace book during one of her country house visits, and that it contained some lines from songs and ballads we have no other reference for.'

'And that could be . . .'

'Huge. If there are several items like that in it, it could be, I don't know, Tutankhamun's tomb for English literature.'

Martha watched both interest and scepticism flash across his face. 'That's big.'

She laughed, suddenly giddy at the thought the discovery might be real. 'Yes. And not only is the spinning song likely to belong to women, this is a woman's commonplace book, too, according to Charlie. It would be a treasure house for historians and linguists.'

He considered, watching the Morris Men clear a space and begin to dance. The Hobby Horse clowned around the edge of the crowd, making a group of children, their faces sticky with toffee apples, laugh hysterically.

'It was marked as before 1599?' he asked finally.

'That's right.'

'How would Charlie know that?'

'Internal evidence probably. The writer might have dated their passages, although that's uncommon. Sometimes you get lucky. They might make a note of some event that we do have a historical record for. I would imagine that's how Charlie dated this rhyme. If the passage written under it says "the Mayor visited today and gave Fred the freedom of the city," it allows you to cross reference and conclude that, as Fred received that honour in 1599, the rhyme must have been written before that.'

'Gold?'

'The discovery of a lifetime.' She shivered.

'Come on, let's walk before you freeze to death.'

They moved off down the High Street, making their way through noisy groups whose caffeinated clamour prevented any further conversation. Martha breathed in deeply as she walked. Oxford felt alive this morning, its mix of youth and history on full display. They reached the wide thoroughfare of St Giles, whose undeniable grandeur was tempered by a scruffiness about the edges, like so much of Oxford. At its south end loomed the Martyrs' Memorial, a Gothic monument erected in memory of three Protestant bishops, condemned for heresy and burnt to death on nearby Broad Street. There is nobility in these sudden glimpses of the past, she thought. This city could never be understood in a single sweeping assessment: instead it yielded a slow series of realisations, unlocked over time.

Caldwell resumed the exchange as if there had been no interruption. 'So why keep it hidden? Presuming this book exists and she did find it.'

Martha was quiet for a long time. The sounds of the parade were distant now, and the smell of frying onions from the burger stalls and the caramel bite of roasting nuts were replaced with the more subtle scents of earth and greenery. She thought of her father, his trowel scraping in the flowerbed. 'She obviously intended to publish it eventually, but perhaps she was guarding her hoard. I suppose she wanted to do as much of the work as possible herself – dating it, transcribing it, following up the references – before sharing it publicly.'

'Is that the sort of thing she would do?'

Martha considered. 'Maybe. She liked to keep things to herself and then make a big announcement. Maximum impact.'

'What would have happened if she'd just turned up at the dictionary, say, or her college, and said, "Hey, guys – look what I've found!"?

'She'd have lost control of it.'

'So you would have kept it secret too?'

Martha shook her head. 'No. I might have sought legal advice first, found some way to establish ownership. Put it in a bank vault and controlled access maybe.' She sighed, a short, exasperated gasp. 'No, scrap that. Charlie was in her early twenties, a PhD student, for heaven's sake. I hope in her shoes I would have had the humility not to impound it, not when it was so important! God knows what else is in there. A find like that – it needs a team of scholars, specialists in the vernacular literature of the time. Historians, too. She had no right to try to keep complete editorial control, if that's what she was doing. And actually, I don't believe she would have done in the end. Maybe in the first flush of excitement . . .'

She thought of that neatly pencilled line again. *Ed. Charlotte Thornhill.* What a grand reveal that would have been.

'And now it's lost?'

Martha nodded. 'I think so. Unless . . . unless Charlie made the whole thing up.'

He came to a halt again and looked down at her. His expression was one she was getting used to: sympathetic concern. 'But having it – that could be a motive for murder, couldn't it?'

She looked away from him, pretending to sip the remains of her cold coffee. 'Did you know the whole curse of the Tutankhamun thing is probably completely made up? Most of the people involved in the investigation died peacefully in their beds.'

He didn't press the point. 'We like to punish the lucky, though, don't we?'

'Well, those who don't share their luck, yes. Folklore is full of stories like that.' She turned towards him again. '*The Pardoner's Tale*! That's the story Chorus told us to read.'

'What's it about?'

Her own words caught her off guard. 'It's about friends who end up murdering each other over gold.'

31

tacenda, *plural noun (nineteenth century)*: things to be passed over in silence

'GIN AND TONIC?' ALEX CALLED from the kitchen.

'Please,' Martha bent down to pet the black cat that had silently stalked into the room. It rubbed its head against her fingers, and she ran her hand over its glossy back until it jumped up onto the desk under the window and started licking its paws. Martha looked at the bookshelves. There was a row of contemporary novels next to the armchair, but the rest of the space seemed to be devoted to non-fiction: folklore, magic, churchgoing in the medieval period. A four-volume scholarly collection of English folktales butted up against volumes on the Gothic in contemporary literature and a collection of horror with garish spines.

'Here you go,' Alex said, coming back into the room and handing her a tumbler. 'Have a seat.' She pulled her phone from her back pocket and sat herself down on another tightly stuffed armchair on the other side of the empty fireplace.

'Safi will be here in a minute. Simon has his daughters this weekend, remember?'

'What's your cat's name?' Martha asked. They seemed to have made a tacit agreement that they wouldn't discuss Alex's visit to her ex-husband before Safi arrived.

'Rags. Short for Lady Raglan. After the folklorist.'

She put her phone face down on the coffee table, staring at it.

'You have a gorgeous home,' Martha murmured. She had, she realised, been making various assumptions about Alex: her lunches out and her excellent clothes. She'd fallen into the stereotype of the wealthy husband whose money had been shared in divorce, but she knew a scholar at the British Library wouldn't make enough to set up his ex-partner with silks. And hadn't Alex said she'd needed to save for this house? Martha knew little about interior design, but she had browsed enough glossy magazines in her time to recognise the quality of the furnishings. There was both a simplicity and a solidity to them, from the wood of the bookshelves to the fabric on the chairs, and she knew they'd be expensive to achieve.

'Where did you grow up?' Martha asked, and Alex smiled.

'You've been practising your small talk, I see! I was born in Newcastle. My father was a solicitor and my mother a teacher.'

'You don't have an accent, though.'

'There are middle-class people in the north-east, too, you know.' Alex said wryly. 'And it was a different time. My father was sent to public school, and my mother had elocution lessons, can you believe? My soundscape growing up was Radio 4. I could still go full Geordie on you if I wanted to, but at home I was taught to speak "proper". Most of us are pretty good at code-switching.'

No family wealth, then.

The knock at the door startled them both. Alex let Safi in and brought her a beer before they settled again in the living room, allowing themselves the preamble of half-absorbed pleasantries.

'So.' Alex had decided it was time for business. 'I saw George, obviously. Safi, I know you are itching to get out your notebook. I don't mind you taking this down. Easier than me having to go through it again.' Safi reached into the bag and took out the familiar book and pencil. Alex waited for her. 'First things first, for all Tom's suspicions about Charlie seeing someone, I don't think George and Charlie were having an affair. For one thing, she'd never have given him the time of day, and for another, he was hopeless at lying. He met his current wife at a conference in the last year of our marriage and I knew within a fortnight. There's no way he was seeing Charlie.'

Martha nodded and sipped her drink. She didn't interject that even the unlikeliest people had secrets.

'And he denied it?' Safi asked.

'Yes.'

Thoughts flew erratically across Martha's brain like moths seeking the light. Could Alex be lying? This mysteriously wealthy friend and colleague? If Alex in the throes of her divorce had discovered that Charlie was having an affair with her husband, what lengths would she have gone to? Confronted Charlie before going to Jonathan's party? Or had she found the manuscript, killed Charlie for it, and then sold it to some private collector? Was that where all the silks and expensive handbags came from?

Caldwell's suspicions were getting to her. It was like an intellectual Morgellons disease, she thought, where you imagine something crawling all over your skin. The idea that Charlie could have been killed was still anathema to her, but the implications were worse. That whoever had killed her had just continued their lives in peace. That she might know them.

'I'll start at the beginning,' Alex said. 'George was embarrassed when I saw him today. He claimed at first that he hadn't written the postcard.' She leant forward, suddenly earnest. 'Look, I mean it when I say I don't think they were having an affair, but that doesn't mean George didn't hope they might, or that Charlie didn't help his fantasy along.'

'When did they meet?' Safi asked.

'At one of the dictionary symposia. Charlie went with her parents occasionally,' Alex replied. 'They talked for a while – George's speciality is the early modern manuscript holdings, and he told her that much at the time. She rang him a couple of months later. Just before Easter.'

'Easter again . . .' Safi said, the pencil bobbing up and down.

'Exactly. She said she had something she wanted his advice on, a manuscript she had found – late-sixteenth century – and she wanted to check if it was genuine. He agreed, of course, and she came down to see him at the BL. She'd brought a single manuscript page with her and told him she'd found what looked to be a nineteenth-century memorabilia album, with the pages of this earlier manuscript stuck inside.' She registered their looks of distress. 'Only at the corners. Whichever Victorian put this album together wasn't that much of a vandal. Anyway, the page she brought him was a handwritten recipe for a cold remedy. It all looked in order at first glance for the late-sixteenth or early-seventeenth century: the paper, the ink, the spelling. He asked her to leave it with him so he could take a closer look, but she refused, so they went to the research rooms together and looked it over with a microscope. It all checked out.'

'Did he say anything about the handwriting? Any other details?' Martha asked. She had half convinced herself that the citation in the slips was a joke, but now her eagerness to believe in the existence of the manuscript surged, crowding out any other considerations.

'It wasn't a scholar's hand, but he could say nothing more than that. And everything he saw was in English. No Latin or Greek, but pure vernacular. He loaded her up with reference material and she went back to Oxford. The next week she sent him an email with a photograph of another page. This one looked like notes of a play the writer had seen, a version of *Edward II* – in a church hall, by the look of it – and Charlie had sent him a transcription to check. It was very good, he told me. That's when he sent her the postcard. He's looked for the photo she sent, but no luck, I'm afraid. It was so long ago.'

'And after that?'

Alex sat back in her chair, her expression suddenly weary, her skin sallow under the light of the standard lamp behind her. 'He emailed her a couple of times, he said, asking about her progress and suggesting they meet up again. She ghosted him, and he felt like an idiot. I think that's why he didn't say anything when she went missing. And anyway, he assumed these finds were all part of her PhD research. He hadn't seen anything to make him think they were stunningly rare or unusual.'

'But now we suspect otherwise,' Safi said. 'Bloody hell, it might be real!'

Alex nodded.

'I suppose it's possible Tom was just wrong about Charlie seeing someone else,' Safi continued slowly. 'She found this manuscript and was working on it instead of her PhD. Going to London to get it authenticated.'

'She told Gemma she wanted to publish a book: that was supposed to be why they were having lunch that day,' Martha elucidated, another piece slotting into place. 'Charlie told her it was something important, but Gemma thought she was just showing off.' The pencil twitched into life again as Martha told them what she remembered from Gemma's description of the meeting being set up, and the conversation around it.

'But what about Jonathan?' Safi said slowly, looking between both of them. 'I . . . there are stories about him, you know. That before he was married he had a bit of a thing for undergraduates.'

'And an expert in the period,' Alex said thoughtfully. 'I see what you mean, a predatory man with useful knowledge . . .'

'Of course, it looks like Charlie was incredibly protective of the manuscript, so perhaps he would be the last person she would share it with,' Safi went on. 'But if she was having an affair, isn't Jonathan the most likely candidate?'

Martha felt that seashell buzzing in her ears, the pulsing pressure of her own blood.

'She wasn't having an affair with Jonathan,' she said. All these days it had been coming. Had she known this was inevitable from the moment she understood the meaning of the first letter?

I feel the glass between my fingers. I see the zigzag pattern of Alex's Persian rug. I hear my own breath.

'How can you be sure, Martha?' Safi asked. 'I mean, I know he was a friend of your family, but he got really involved in the search, didn't he? That would make more sense if he had a stronger attachment to Charlie than any of you knew. How do we know she wasn't sleeping with him?'

Martha swallowed. It turned out the words were there all along. 'Because I was.'

32

uhtceare, *noun (Old English)*:

the anxiety before dawn

THE WORDS WERE SO DIRECT they felt almost physical, as though they were printed in capitals across a piece of paper. Alex and Safi said nothing at first, but their faces spoke for them, a combination of sympathy and mild distaste.

Martha couldn't stomach the silence. In a low voice she tried to explain how Jonathan had been kind to her at a party at her parents' house early that summer. How he had enthusiastically questioned her about the A-levels she'd just completed and the course she was about to embark on. How he'd felt so different from her parents' other friends: so much younger and more charismatic. And how she had noticed Charlie watching them.

'The thing was, Jonathan didn't seem to notice Charlie, and I can't tell you how attractive that made him to me just then.'

'I get that,' Safi said finally. She had put her notebook down and was curled up in one of Alex's armchairs, cradling her beer.

'It's easy to get swept up at that age. Falling in love seems so simple. Then that ability to dive right in falls away without you realising it, and it's never quite the same again. I ache sometimes for the look I see on kids' faces, all shiny and expectant.'

Rags jumped up into Alex's lap and made herself at home, a pool of midnight in the shadowy room. 'That's a melancholy thought, Safi. I'd like to think it's not true. Not to mention the fact you are still incredibly young to me.'

Safi smiled at her.

Martha knew they were giving her time, and she was grateful for it. Her fingers went to her necklace and ran the hearts back and forth, as if an immutable ritual might order her thoughts in some way. She had tried very hard not to think about that period over the years, and now all the small humiliations and apparent victories of that summer swam to the surface, mocking her with her own naivety and neediness. A word nudged its way into focus. Remorse: from the Latin *remordere*: to bite back. Boy, could she feel its teeth now.

'Did Charlie know that you were seeing Jonathan?' Safi asked at last.

'Not at first. He told me we'd better be discreet, that Charlie had shown a lot of interest in him, and it would hurt her feelings to know we were becoming close. He said he thought she'd got the job at the dictionary to spend more time with him.'

'Whereas she probably just wanted to spend more time with the slips and research materials,' Safi said, tilting her bottle and examining the distorted light through its glass.

Alex shifted sharply in her chair, enough for Rags to look up at her with an expression of surprise and mild rebuke. 'I'm sorry. Let me get this straight. Jonathan, while in his early thirties, had an affair with you – a, let's face it, slightly vulnerable teenager. Urged you to keep quiet because he was supposedly thinking of Charlie's feelings, and within a week of you leaving Oxford for university he had a *different* teenaged undergraduate in his rooms until the early hours? Jesus.'

Martha winced. The words were like thorns scratching at her skin, looking for purchase.

'That's why you looked so surprised when Jonathan mentioned Olivia going to his place after the launch,' Safi said, eyes widening in realisation. Martha nodded, conceding the point. 'He never mentioned her?'

'No.'

'OK,' Safi said. 'So I get Charlie probably wasn't seeing Jonathan, given what you've said, but I hope he never needs you as a character witness, Martha.'

'God, yes,' Alex said. 'Charlie was probably too old for him.'

The thorns dug their way in and Martha held up her hand, still staring at the weave of Alex's hearth rug.

'No, don't paint me as a victim here. Yes, I probably was vulnerable. Aren't we all, even now, to a bit of flattery and affection? He paid attention to me, and I thought for the first time in my life that I'd managed to win some prize that Charlie hadn't.' She could feel their steady attention, but didn't want to look at either of them. 'I was sure she really admired him, even though she had Tom, and I told myself that she hated the fact Jonathan was ignoring her. I never fell in love with him, I slept with him because I wanted to stick one finger up at Charlie. I never felt betrayed, nor used. It was a crush. I wanted to feel grown up, and while it was going on I felt like a goddess: sexy and powerful and brilliant. Like, all of a sudden, I was leaving Charlie in the dust. But then she disappeared, and I thought that it was because seeing me and him together broke her.'

'Jesus, Martha,' Safi said. 'You've thought that all these years?'

Martha passed her hand over her eyes, her fingers unsteady. 'Yes, I suppose I have. At first it seemed obvious. It sort of calcified into a truth.'

'And she found out that you and he were having a fling?' Alex pressed on.

Martha nodded. 'Yes. The day before I went back to university, she saw me sneaking out of his rooms early in the morning. It was the weekend before she disappeared. We didn't speak. I just saw her on the other side of the road.'

'No reaction at all?'

The scene was scored into Martha's brain. It had replayed itself frequently over the years: ugly, repetitive flashes that had an electricity of their own. Alex's living room disappeared and her mind was filled with the liminal light of early morning, the smell of dew on stone, birdsong rising up from the garden in the square, soon to be drowned out by traffic noise. She was in her own teenaged body, still warm from bed, running her hand through her frumpled hair when a tremble of movement on the other side of the road caught her eye. Looking up, she saw Charlie. She had stopped her bike in the middle of the road to stare at her.

'She looked astonished. I suppose I expected to feel triumphant, but I didn't. I just felt guilty. And then I walked away and it was never even mentioned. But she knew, and I knew that she knew.'

'Did Jonathan think that was why she left too?' Alex asked.

Martha tried to recall the conversation she had had with him on the doorstep a couple of days ago. 'I thought he did, in that first week or two. He spent a lot of time at the house.'

'And did you and he . . . ?' Alex asked.

'God, no!' Martha said quickly. 'I don't think we were ever even alone after Charlie disappeared. Perhaps that's one of reasons I thought we both believed it was our fault. A sympathetic look, a snatched squeeze of the shoulder, that was it. But I was very glad he was there, and so were my parents. I was surprised when he didn't even seem to acknowledge Charlie had a crush on him when we spoke the other night.'

'He didn't remember?' Alex said.

Martha thought of that moment at the door, the flush of embarrassment shadowing his throat. 'He seemed confused, then said perhaps he'd exaggerated out of arrogance. That Charlie hadn't been obsessed with him, the way he'd suggested.'

'Martha,' Safi said, glancing between her and Alex. 'I get why you didn't feel like a victim, and why you don't want to feel like one now, but whatever you felt then, what would you think of a colleague in their thirties today having an affair with someone still in their teens?'

'Not much,' Martha said eventually.

33

zugzwang, *noun (twentieth century)*:

the obligation to make a move, but every move is detrimental

When she saw Simon in the office on Tuesday, Martha felt an unexpected sense of guilt. Alex and Safi knew about her brief affair with Jonathan, but he didn't. It was as though they were unfairly arraigned against him in some way, and she disliked the idea he might feel excluded.

He smiled at her as she walked past his desk and slung her denim jacket over the back of her chair. But for once he seemed disinclined to chat.

'You're in early, Simon. How was your weekend?'

'Yep. I have a few things I wanted to crack on with, and my weekend was OK.' He was still reading an email on his screen. 'I took the girls to the whole May Day thing. Now they're teenagers they're obliged to act like they are professionally bored, but Chloe ended up getting a bunch of likes for her photographs of Magdalen Tower and couldn't stop grinning.'

'I was there too. It was beautiful.'

'Were you?' He turned away from the screen. 'I found I missed it during the pandemic years. Not that I got up early enough to see it very often, but I liked the fact it was happening.'

'Me too. I bumped into DS Caldwell there,' she said. 'Explained to him why a new commonplace book would be such a find. It brought it all home: the thrill of it. But he did give me a rather dark warning.'

'What was that?'

'That it might have been a motive for someone to harm Charlie. I don't know whether I'm ready to believe that. But what if someone did go after her for the book? Caldwell was reminding us that anyone who felt that desperate might also be very dangerous.'

Simon considered the idea carefully, his hand reflexively stroking his beard. It looked dishevelled today, Martha thought. But then Simon had never been the particularly shevelled type.

'You said you weren't sure if you wanted to know the truth,' he asked her. 'Do you still feel that?'

'No . . . I don't know. It's as though it's out of my hands somehow. Why?'

'You're a fatalist, I think.' He looked as though he might say more but then decided against it. He looked at the floor. 'Fear could explain why Chorus is being so cryptic. But surely, if someone really had taken the book when Charlie died, they would have published it by now? Then again, maybe they've been too scared to, thinking it might expose the link with Charlie and their guilt along with it.'

Martha tried to appraise the scenario objectively. The missing book being read by some scholar who valued it enough to kill for it, yet was too scared to share it. 'Wouldn't that sort of guilt drive you mad?'

'Some people are able to live with it. Think of all the stories that are resurfacing now: new science solving old murders, and countless people uploading their DNA to genealogy sites and accidentally exposing their second cousins as killers. Even serial killers sometimes, who've managed to fly below the radar for decades, live ordinary lives.'

Martha shuddered. 'I need coffee. Want one?'

He held up a takeaway cup by way of answer, and turned back to his screen while she went into the kitchenette to boil the kettle.

Perhaps you could kill someone and parcel it away, stuff the memory of it like a discarded dress into the back of the wardrobe. She had tried to do something similar after her affair with Jonathan, only that dress was forcing itself back into view. She filled the water reservoir and spooned grounds into a clean filter, acutely aware of her own small movements, of the crisp white of the paper, the rich aroma of the coffee, the cool of the metal as she snapped the lid back on the tin. The miraculous fragments of existence: she had thought that Charlie would be enjoying these, too, somewhere. How had she believed that so completely until now? For her mother's sake, perhaps, as well as for her own.

As the coffee dripped into the pot, she considered what to do. She had to tell Simon about her and Jonathan before anyone else did, although the way he had reacted to the postcard George had sent Charlie gave her pause. When she'd woken that morning into the eerie, panicky space before dawn, she'd realised Simon might well believe she had used her relationship with Jonathan to get this job. Worse, he would have legitimate grounds for complaint. He had wanted that job, after all, as Mike had qualmlessly told her during the handover period. He had worked at the *CED* for well over a decade, and Martha knew his work was good. Wouldn't a reasonable observer think that Jonathan campaigning for a former lover to get the job over anyone else was an entirely legitimate cause for concern? People might even suspect that Martha had blackmailed Jonathan into giving her this position, threatening to make it known he'd had an affair with a girl of eighteen while teaching at the university. She'd kidded herself that Jonathan had had no hand in her hiring; of course he had. In that same pre-dawn clarity she knew that he would never have mentioned any personal interest beyond a friendship with the family, a connection through Gemma. Could last night's moment of candour bring down the house of cards?

Martha played out her own story in her head, frame after frame, finally turning up the sound to the past's subliminal whispers. She had fled Berlin after pushing the boundaries of professional behaviour, only to be settled into a comfortable prestigious job by a former lover. The facts stank even to her. It was the kind of story – a little dark, heady with illicit sex – that clung to a person throughout their career. In her haste to get away from Berlin she hadn't even considered any of this. Well, she had to now. And do the right thing, even if it cost her.

She returned to the office, coffee mug in hand. 'I read your book over the weekend, Simon. It's really good. I hope you write another.'

He looked boyishly pleased. 'Thank you! I would . . . I should. I even have a decent idea, it's just a matter of parcelling out some time.'

'What's the subject?'

'The language of influence, and I think I have a new angle on it.' He smiled a little crookedly. 'What it takes to persuade, particularly on social media. But I need to find a snappy title for it. *Putting on the Rizz*, maybe?' 'Rizz' was a word on their watchlist. A likely shortening of 'charisma', this was sex appeal with bells on, the successor to the 'It' of the 1920s and the gateway to results in dating and beyond. Another of English's semantic time-warps.

She smiled. 'I like it. But how much of these influencers' success is really down to luck?'

'A fair amount, and a certain psychopathy helps too,' he added. 'But, of course, none of them would ever accept that. They have to believe they deserve their good fortune or their brains would explode. Self-belief can get us almost anything. At the very least it can carry us over our failures.'

'But if you don't doubt yourself, how can you ever learn?'

He smiled, and Martha felt a sudden rush of kinship for him. 'Indeed. So we clever, empathetic curators of the mind end up in house-shares worrying about the heating bills, while the narcissists rule over us from their yachts! *Vive la revolution*.'

'"Out of the crooked timber of humanity, no straight thing was ever made",' Martha quoted. 'Could you take a sabbatical from the dictionary to work on it?'

He grimaced. 'I could. But only at one third pay, and I can't live on that. Not these days. Meanwhile, any updates from Alex's husband?'

She told him about the page, the tests they had run.

He balled his hands into fists. 'God, so it might actually exist! Doesn't sound like a prank anymore, does it? A sixteenth-century commonplace book? Where is it now?' His eyes gleamed. 'Does Chorus know? We have to find it. Just think . . .' His face crumpled suddenly. 'Though that period, I mean, they'd all just want Jonathan to talk about it.'

'They?' Martha frowned.

'Radio, TV. I mean, he's made that period his sole preserve, hasn't he?'

'It's a big if, Simon, and *if* we rediscover the manuscript, whatever it contains, it is and always will be Charlie's discovery, not ours. And certainly not Jonathan's.'

He shrugged. His expression might have been one of agreement, but she couldn't be sure.

'Look, Simon, there's something else. It's personal, but I think you have to know.' If she faltered now, she'd blow it. The words tumbled out of her as she stared straight ahead, confident he would understand after those few moments of communion. But as soon as the bare facts were spoken, she knew she'd lost him. He drew back in his chair as if she was contagious.

'So you . . .' He stared at her, a ripple of disgust pulling at the corner of his mouth. 'When you got the job here . . .'

She felt sick. He'd gone straight to her hiring.

'I never thought for one moment about it when I applied! I didn't even know Jonathan was still closely involved with the dictionary. It never occurred to me . . .'

'He mentions his work here in every fucking interview he gives!' Simon hissed. 'Are you really that naive?'

She recoiled. The office, long since her oasis, had shrunk to a pale, cold version of itself, like a house that had been boarded up for winter. She tried to focus on the bold stripes of Simon's scarf that hung over the desk partition, but they began to merge jerkily into each other.

He got up, shoving his hands in his pockets and crossing over to the window, as though he, too, was trying to cling to the ordinary. The first tour party of the day was beginning to gather outside the gates.

He spoke to her with his back still turned, his voice quiet and draggy. 'Look, Martha. You've done the job perfectly well since you arrived. You're obviously qualified.' He put his fingers on the window and stared at it, his focus shrinking to the glass right in front of him rather than the view. 'But I mean, Christ almighty! Why don't I ever . . .'

Alex arrived and quietly took off her coat, glancing between them. She let the tension pass without comment and settled herself at her desk.

'No Safi? Oh, she booked these days off, didn't she?'

'I'm going to get back to "avatar",' Martha said, squeezing as much blandness into her voice as she could, even as the mortification surged inside her. Judging by the twitch in Alex's eyebrow she hadn't managed to convince one iota.

'Mike's in town later this week. He suggests lunch on Sunday at the Trout Inn. Twelve thirty. Could you both make that? I'll text Safi.'

Martha simply nodded.

'The Trout? Ha! I used to think that was such a romantic spot. Our perspectives change as we age, don't they?'

'Are you coming or not, Simon?' Alex asked.

'Wouldn't miss it for the world,' Simon replied, something arch and waspish in his tone. He yawned artificially, then returned to his desk. Martha couldn't look at him; she could almost hear the threads snapping around her.

34

prend, *noun (fifteenth century)*:
a mended crack

SAFI HAD NO PARTICULAR PLANS for her days off. She wanted to read, run, help Josh set up the art show, and not much else. She'd quietly neglected to tell her parents she wasn't at work. Much as she loved them and her two younger brothers, she guessed her mother would be in full Coronation celebration mode, and she wasn't sure how much uncritical monarchism she could take.

She got up slowly, then showered and shuffled into her off-duty trackie bottoms and T-shirt – her 'hufflebuffs', as she and a few nineteenth-century Scots liked to call them. She thrust open the sash window in her room to let in the spring air, and marvelled again at her decision to leave London for Oxford, a place that felt simultaneously beyond normal space and time, and yet deeply rooted in them. But even this gilded paradise had its share of poverty; behind the sunlit spires and lamplit interiors lay shadows of reproach and rebellion, thought and counterthought. Every cause in the world could find an advocate in Oxford, and Safi loved the city all the more because of it.

She opened her laptop and flicked through the news, remembering what Martha had told them the night before. Josh and his gossipy boomers had been right: Jonathan was a creep. She googled his name. Nothing of interest, pictures of him in Waterstones Piccadilly signing the first book on the day of release. An 'At Home' feature linked to one of the TV series he'd done when the children were little.

Next, she typed in 'Charlotte Thornhill'. Old newspaper articles popped up, mostly marking the anniversary of her death, while another in the *Oxford Mail* concentrated on the letters to the *CED*. It was just a brief summary, smothered by features on Royal Oxford and where to watch the Coronation in town. The writer had essentially reproduced the press release that the Communications Team had sent, rounded off with a quote from Jonathan: 'Charlotte was a valued member of the *CED* family. We urge anyone with information about her disappearance to contact the police directly.' Safi wondered when it had begun, this corporate habit of describing a company as 'family'. Why did they do it? Because they expected you to be available at all hours out of love and loyalty, perhaps. Yet she couldn't help but feel that, recently, that's exactly what the dictionary team had become: a circle of people she wouldn't want to be without.

She rose from her chair and tidied her room, slotting the books she'd been given by Brin into the shelves. What next? The plans she'd had for her days off didn't seem so satisfying now, and her thoughts remained stubbornly with Martha and the others. She tried to shake them off, but when her phone buzzed with news about lunch with Mike at the weekend, the surge of adrenaline she felt confirmed it was a lost cause. So what could she do? Get some historical perspective on spinning poems? Maybe. Go through the notes Jonathan had emailed about the quotations and coinages? No, she didn't want to think any more about that jerk today.

She texted Martha:

You got a copy of the picture of Charlie from her desk?

The reply and the photo came quickly:

Brin said he didn't recognise it. And you're supposed to be off work.

She tapped her fingers on the table.

Not work. Curious. Leave it with me.

Martha sent her a thumbs-up emoji.

Then she called Brin.

The exchange of texts dragged Martha out of her embarrassment, at least for long enough to email Charlie's supervisor asking to meet. When she received an answer suggesting a time at the end of the next working day, she told the others.

'Would you like to come?' she asked them both. 'It's possible she might know something about what Charlie was working on.'

Simon had been focusing on his computer screen since their exchange.

'I think she might have mentioned it back then if Charlie had said she'd found something significant, don't you?'

'Probably,' Martha replied, appalled to hear a note of appeal in her voice. 'But perhaps Charlie hinted at something which didn't seem important at the time. I get that it's a long shot, but surely it's worth a try?'

'What's the point?' Simon said, his voice bitter now. 'My theory is Charlie flogged it to some private collector for a fortune, then ran off with the loot. Found her moment, took her chance and skedaddled.'

'But only this morning you were . . .' Martha began.

'That was then,' he said. 'I've had a cold lesson in realism since then.'

Alex sighed. 'Oh Simon, do stop sulking! I'm guessing Martha told you she had a fling with Jonathan? And you've decided that's why she got the job rather than you?'

'What a strange assumption for me to make,' he shot back at her.

'You don't think you were passed over because you got into stupid fights on social media? You don't think turning up drunk at the office after lunch during your divorce from Nancy had anything to do with it? You don't think, perhaps, that your updating the entry for "bitch" with "an ex-wife" played some role in the matter?'

His face went red, then white. 'That was a joke, and never intended to go live!'

'Which is what I told Mike when he was on the verge of sacking you!'

'How kind of you, Alex! Jesus, you're so bloody superior, swanning in with your fancy shopping bags every week,' he exploded. 'I bet life looks very easy when you pop into the office between mini-breaks. You've never had any sympathy for the pressure it puts on a man, taking shitty wages, being passed over. You women are all in it together. Sisters can't be wrong.'

'I just told you I campaigned for you to keep your job, and how I spend my money is nothing to do with you.'

'Cagey about where it comes from, though, aren't you? Can't imagine poor old George keeps you in style. So, are you running an illegal poker circle or have you been shagging one of the bosses and blackmailing him too? Maybe Charlie found out about *that*!'

Martha picked up her notebook and slammed it down on the table, making them both jump. They turned and looked at her, a flicker of nerves crossing their faces as they took in the stony stare from her pink-rimmed eyes.

'Enough,' she said quietly. 'I should have banned any discussion of Chorus and his letters in this office from the outset. Look what's happened to us.' Simon and Alex both started to speak at once, but she held up her hand. 'This is a place of business, and as long as Alex works the hours she's contracted to, the rest of her life is nothing to do with us. Simon, if you are worried that my hiring was in any way irregular, go to HR and make a complaint. You both have drafts due at the beginning of next week. So do I. Shall we actually get on with them?'

Neither replied, although Alex opened her mouth as if to object, paused, and then thought better of it. Each turned back to their screens. The sounds drifted up from the pavement again: traffic, the laughter of passing strangers.

'Horror novels,' Alex said a few minutes later.

Martha put down her glasses. 'What?'

'That's how I make my money. I write supernatural horror novels, selling myself as a cross between M. R. James and H. P. Lovecraft. Only my next-door neighbour knows, because she helps me with the marketing, and there's my agent in London, of course. But I can't tell the boys. Jacob makes so little from his writing, he'd be crushed. And so would Ethan, he's so proud of his sensible job.'

'My God,' Simon said. 'Horror novels?' He half laughed and covered his mouth. 'OK, I'm actually impressed.' He paused. 'Do you sell more than Jonathan?'

She snorted. 'Oh God, yes. Of course I do.'

'Ha! It would kill him to know that!' He held up his hand. 'Don't worry, I shan't tell him. Sorry about . . .' Alex shook her head quickly. Martha couldn't tell if she was saying the apology was unnecessary, or that she wasn't interested in hearing it right now.

'Congratulations,' Martha said carefully. 'That's quite the achievement.'

Alex smiled briefly, but didn't look up. Martha had never seen her look vulnerable before; it softened the angles of her face.

'So where do your kids *think* the money comes from?' Simon asked. 'Last question, then I'll leave you alone, I promise.'

'I had to invent a legacy in the end,' she conceded. 'A cousin in Canada. Thank God they never probed too far. And it's possible they have a slightly unrealistic idea of how well being an editor here pays.'

All three of them smiled at that. With some sort of peace re-established, they returned to their work.

Safi called Brin as soon as she received Martha's thumbs-up. When he said he couldn't remember the various sales that Charlie had attended in 2010 before she stopped working for him, she pushed.

'You must have records, Brin,' she urged, trying to keep her voice friendly. 'I mean, she didn't ever come back from those sales empty-handed, did she? Even if she kept the pick of the lots for herself. You'll have records of what you took in from those sales somewhere.'

'It was more than ten years ago!' he protested.

Safi glanced at her watch: 10 a.m. He had hours before the school rush. 'But you'd have made notes on your database, surely? Date acquired and so on? I mean, I'm sure your record-keeping is good.' There was the nudge, now the shove. If Brin occasionally worked in a grey area, paying Charlie under the counter, not to mention whatever was going on with Simon, then he might want to spend a bit of time cleaning up his paperwork. 'We had another letter, and DS Caldwell agrees Charlie's visits to those sales might be significant. If you could look them out for me, perhaps I can do the legwork and pass my notes on to him. Without him having to come and go through everything himself.'

She hoped she'd managed to pitch that right, without overplaying her hand.

He sighed. 'Yeah, OK. It'll just be a list of addresses, though.'

'That would be wonderful. And thank you again for the books. Really kind of you.'

He hung up without replying.

Now that was in progress, Safi enjoyed the rest of the morning. She had a pile of unread novels on her bedside table, but decided a break from the printed word might do her good. She started a new audiobook instead, and sat in her wicker armchair by the window working on a tapestry kit her mother had bought her for her birthday. It felt good to be working with her hands: the small physical pleasures of pulling coloured thread through fabric, watching a pattern develop. Life wasn't bad, she thought: rich reds and blues humming through her fingers, an actor reading to her as she worked. She revelled in a slow moment of concentration and touch, feeling the breeze from the open window, warm and silky with spring.

The email from Brin buzzed on her phone a while later, just as her attention was beginning to drift. She opened it together with the attached document. There were no niceties, none of the usual greetings or sign-offs – his way of showing his irritation. She was glad to realise it didn't bother her. The list he'd sent was long: Charlie had definitely been busy.

Perhaps 2010 had been a bumper year for sales, with fortunes still stumbling in the wake of the financial crisis. She put aside her sewing and paused the book, switching to one of her running playlists instead. Then she cracked her fingers and rolled her shoulders. Time to swap the manual for the digital, she thought, enjoying the knowledge that the roots of each word were strangely close: 'manual' from the Latin for 'hand', and 'digits' because people counted on their fingers. She smiled at finding another reason to appreciate her fellow editors. Observations like these were their default, a tribal way of speaking that bound them together in their search for sense and adventure. They could never look at a sentence without seeing the stories within it.

Scouring the web for the houses on Brin's list, checking to see whether they matched the photo on Charlie's desk, was laborious in the extreme. Every picture on Safi's phone had GPS coordinates wrapped around its metadata: every moment was pinned to its own geography. No such luck here.

She balanced her sandwich on her laptop and took both into the living room for a change of scene while she worked through the remainder. She began slowly, methodically, crossing off each sale that didn't seem to match any of the online pictures available.

Her phone buzzed again. A sudden flurry of texts at once.

The first was from Alex:

Drama. Simon pissed off about Jonathan/Martha thing. Got unpleasant.

Shit, she replied.

OK now. Martha read us the riot act and both behaving.

The three circles pulsed again on Safi's screen.

Want to know where my money comes from?

Yes! If that's OK.

Am horror writer. Keep secret. My kids don't know.

Safi let out a yawp of surprised laughter, startling the birds picking up toast crumbs on the patio outside. She waved in their direction by way of apology. 'Nice going, Alex.'

That's cool!

She received a heart emoji back. The other text was from Martha.

I am meeting Charlie's supervisor tomorrow at six. You'd be welcome to come if you want to join me. Martha always texted in complete sentences.

Yes please. Send me the address?

It came almost immediately.

Safi finished her sandwich and returned to the screen. She found the house in the photograph twenty minutes later. Maybe. A thirteenth-century manor house with eighteenth-century additions, now an agricultural museum with a café and farm shop. The distant stonework in Charlie's picture looked right, and the original sale had been held a fortnight before Easter. That would work. She rang the number on the website. Yes, the family that had held the sale still owned the property; yes, there had been a lot of bric-a-brac and papers. She'd be welcome to pop in to discuss it.

35

obmutescence, *noun (seventeenth century)*:
a wilful speechlessness

THE TENSION IN THE OFFICE slowly dissipated as the day went on. Martha noticed an email from Safi later in the afternoon about a possible lead on a house sale and felt guilty, briefly, that her colleague was spending her days off working on Charlie's disappearance and the mysteries accruing around it. She completed the draft on 'parasocial' and sent it to Alex, glad to see the back of it; the entry had proved gnarlier than she'd thought. But being a lexicographer necessarily meant working with words that jagged the nerves as well as those that soothed and satisfied. All of them were precious seams in the mine they dug each day.

She noticed her inbox was beginning to salt up with enquiries about the letters, and about Charlie. The article must have come out. Most she thought she could ignore, at least for now. Many were tentative offers of support from old acquaintances, professional and personal. There was one from Gemma: *Shall prepare vulture defences!* It made her smile, and the memory of the olives, wine, and her godmother's seaglass necklace was comforting.

Her father must be getting similar ones.

Simon left at half five on the dot, issuing a grunt of farewell, and Alex began clearing her desk a few minutes after. She hesitated as she put her coat on, and Martha wondered if she was about to suggest going to the pub. She had no desire to go, but would be reluctant to refuse, and Alex must have picked up on her indecision because she left, tactfully, with only a warm smile. Martha began to tidy away her work, and spent half an hour sending bland thank-yous which she hoped would suppress further correspondence without coming off as rude.

She left just after six, then stood on the pavement not wanting to go home, but not wanting to stay here either. Perhaps she would leave her bike and walk through the twilight, see if that allowed the dogged undertow of thoughts to retreat a little. The road seemed strangely quiet, just a smattering of passers-by with tired and dyspeptic faces. Many people, perhaps, had done what Safi had done, and taken these days between bank holidays off. The emptiness was unnerving.

'Martha?'

She turned, startled to see Jonathan's wife Olivia standing a little way behind her on the pavement.

'Olivia! Hi.' She forced a polite smile. Olivia was dressed as elegantly as ever, a sky-blue scarf wound artfully around her neck beneath a pale leather jacket, a convincing mix of sobriety and elegance.

Olivia approached with a swift firm stride.

'I know what you are doing, and it has to stop.'

'What are you talking about?' Martha replied, taking a step back. A man in a tweed jacket cycled past them and Martha felt him glancing over, his attention snatched by the hint of aggression in Olivia's voice and stance.

'Jonathan is my husband. The father of my children. How dare you think you can just turn up and wheedle your way into his affections? And to use your sister to do it? It's disgusting.'

Martha hated herself for the hurt percolating through her body like bile. 'What on earth . . . ? I've no interest in Jonathan.'

'Really?' Her mouth twisted scornfully. 'Turning up at our house all dewy-eyed? Summoning him in to play at your treasure hunt? You're embarrassing yourself.'

Martha was shocked into silence.

'You missed your chance with him so back off.'

She turned away and Martha recovered enough to protest again.

'Olivia, you couldn't be more wrong.'

When Olivia turned around her face was ugly, contorted. 'You're not the only silly bitch to tail after him. Shameless, all of you.'

Graceful, perfect Olivia. Not so graceful, not so perfect, the portrait of composure smashed to smithereens.

'If you think I give a fuck about anything other than my sister, you are sorely mistaken,' Martha said. 'I don't know what your problem is, Olivia. But it's your problem, not mine. Leave me alone.'

Olivia's face was suddenly drained of animation. 'Just leave *him* alone,' she said feebly, as she jabbed her car keys in Martha's direction. She opened her car door. 'Your sister was a self-righteous arsehole. And so are you.'

Martha said nothing, just watched as Olivia swung into the car, then accelerated away to the end of the road.

* * *

The following day Safi took the bus to the centre of Witney, planning to walk the rest of the way to the manor house. She had assumed from Charlie's photo that it would be out in the countryside, but Witney Place lay close to the outskirts of the largest market town in the Cotswolds. Like Burford, Witney had been famous for its woollen industry, as well as for some significant breweries. Both trades had given the town a prosperity that was amply reflected in the grand frontages of its High Street. But there was much more history to tell. Safi had read somewhere that, in the nineteenth century, Witney had been used by several Oxford colleges as a retreat from the plague. Today, it was a town in thrall to a changing climate, crowned and occasionally submerged by the river Windrush.

She turned down Church Lane, whose narrow avenue was flanked with the blossom of Queen Anne's Lace. Safi loved the flower, which had grown in thick wild banks in the London parks she'd roamed as a child. It had been named for poor forgotten Queen Anne, last of the Stuart monarchs and now, thanks to her eighteen failed pregnancies, associated with the loss of children. A melancholy history for such a delicately exuberant flower, Safi thought, as she nudged some stray fronds aside.

The road ran alongside a pale stone wall, above which rose the thatched roofs of some outbuildings belonging to the manor. So far so Oxfordshire, though there had been no sign of thatch in Charlie's photograph. The moment of confidence Safi had felt on looking at the pictures online felt suddenly foolish; here she was, an outsider once again amid the shiny families in their SUVs, quite possibly on a fool's errand. She shook herself. She had as much right to be here as anyone.

The car park was full, and newly arriving cars were being directed onto a neighbouring field by a man in a high-vis vest.

The driveway opened into a large courtyard filled with picnic tables bedecked with Coronation tablecloths, assembled beneath Union Jack bunting that had been strung between a cluster of renovated barns. The largest building had a sign reading FARM SHOP AND CAFÉ, but other small units around the courtyard were apparently businesses too, and the whole scene had the buzzy vibe of a street market. Safi took in a candle-maker, artisan cheesemonger, and a local honey producer. Someone was selling Welsh rarebit from a pop-up stall; she could smell the sweet apple tang of cider. Through the gate at the other side of the courtyard, she noticed areas of fenced-off pasture. Goats gathered by the path and small children sticky with ice cream reached their hands through the wooden fence to stroke their noses, while the animals tried to steal whatever was left of the cones.

Safi glanced at her watch; she still had a few minutes, so she walked towards the house itself and took in the view. She let out a quiet 'aah' of relief, no thatch. Instead she noted painted white stone and a slate roof: just like Charlie's photo. She followed the path to the east of the house and felt a sudden tug of recognition. This was it, the weathered gable-end of the manor house, punctuated with small, irregularly shaped windows. Safi crossed the path to get the right angle, then pulled out her phone to compare the picture of Charlie that Martha had sent her with the view she was looking at now.

It was a perfect match. She must be in almost exactly the place the photographer had been, standing in a small, gravelled courtyard with a low wall off the main track. She lowered the phone, expecting Charlie to be standing in front of her, squinting into the sun with that whimsical smile. The sense of time collapsing into this one place gave Safi a sudden swooping vertigo. Charlie's presence was almost tangible in the spring sunshine: a pulse of connection. The words of the old man in the Burford church, warning against waking ghosts, came back to her.

She steadied herself and took a picture to send to the others. 'Depends on the ghost,' she muttered, and headed back to the tea shop.

She spotted him at once. The man was alone, with a tall glass of something fizzy in front of him. It was the way he surveyed the room, with a mix of bemusement and praetorian pride, that made Safi sure this was the person she had come to meet. The old barn had a high roof of heavy, exposed beams, and half the space was given over to low lamplit shelves stacked with colourful books, and tables covered in fancy goods – wooden shawls, tins of biscuits and chocolates, jewellery and ceramics. There was a strong scent of varnish and pine.

She weaved her way through the busy tables. Every one of them had a tiny vase with a posy of spring flowers.

'Sir Walter?'

He stood up and offered his hand. 'Miss Idowu! Please, Walter is fine.'

'And I'm Safiya.' She took her seat.

He was a thin man, a little shorter than Safi and with a thick head of snow-white hair. He wore what Safi had come to regard as the uniform of the rural upper classes: a cracked, moss-coloured Barbour jacket over a checked shirt, and fawn-coloured cords. Safi glanced down at her own ensemble: a crimson wrap-dress emblazoned with ranks of ruby roses. Around it she had slung a long woollen shawl in an attempt to hide a trace of lipstick she'd somehow managed to smudge across a sleeve – a 'cover-slut', she remembered Simon telling her: a garment worn over the top of another to hide an unsightly stain.

'Thank you for seeing me,' she said.

'A pleasure.' His handshake was firm and dry. 'Can I get you anything? The lemonade is very good. Made here, you know.'

'That would be lovely.'

Walter lifted his hand and caught the eye of one of the girls behind the counter, waving his empty bottle and holding up two fingers.

'One of the privileges of ownership,' he said with a chuckle. 'I don't have to queue.'

'This is a lovely space,' Safi replied as the waitress, a teenager with a bouncy ponytail, brought them their drinks and eyed them curiously.

'Beth said to bring you this too,' she said and set down a plate of fruitcake.

'Thank you, Jess,' Walter replied, and nudged the plate towards Safi. 'All of this is down to Beth, my daughter-in-law. She's the entrepreneur in the family. My son and I are farmers, but the estate was on its uppers when my father died. Death duties. We thought we'd have to sell the whole shebang. It was Beth who encouraged us to have the clear-out and use some of the capital from the sale to build the shop and tea barn. It's no exaggeration to say she saved the place.'

'I'm glad it's doing so well.'

'So am I,' he agreed with great feeling, as he bit down on some fruitcake he'd reached for. 'Looking at it now reminds me how much these houses were hubs of industry in the past. When my ancestors built the original in the 1400s, there would have been a brewery and a bakery on site, both supplied by the local Corn Exchange. Right up to the end of the eighteenth century they would have been making cheese for local markets, curing their own meat and dying their cloth. We're just reinventing those old traditions.' He took a sip of lemonade. 'It was the sale you wanted to talk to me about, wasn't it?'

'That's right, particularly about the books and papers you might have sold.'

He rubbed his hands together, knocking off the cake crumbs, then reached into the pocket of this jacket. 'I found a copy of the catalogue for you.'

He flattened it on the table between them. It was glossy, with a large picture of the house on the front. He opened it and started flicking through the pages. There were pictures of various hulking pieces of furniture and a range of oil paintings and objets d'art. Perhaps it was the light spilling in through the barn's skylights, but every one of the photos seemed suffused with a warm haze of antiquity and opulence. 'We had a few very nice bits and pieces that brought in most of the money,' he said. 'Turned out we had a Humphry Repton sketch hanging in one of the back corridors, and a pair of Beardsley originals in the attic.' He hesitated, and Safi wasn't sure whether it was a gesture of modesty given Beardsley's penchant for dark erotica, or because he assumed she wouldn't recognise either artist's name. Neither scruple was necessary.

He ploughed on. 'My mother hated those drawings. Thought them far too louche, but they paid off the mortgages and funded the barn conversion. But you asked about the books and papers . . .' He found a page and pressed it down with the heel of his hand. 'Here we go! God, the library was in a terrible state. My father basically locked the door after his mother died and never used it. My grandmother was the reader in the family, you see, and her mother too. Very clever women. My father was rather anti-intellectual, I'm sorry to say, and married a woman just like himself.' He shook his head.

'Grandmama had some nice signed first editions, and *her* mother was something of a historian. We had boxes and boxes full of her notes and "researches", but we couldn't make sense of half of them ourselves.'

'Was there anything noticeably old?' Safi wasn't sure how to explain what she was looking for, or what criteria she should mention, given his heavy-handededness towards this job lot of material. 'We have a theory that my friend's sister, Charlie Thornhill, came to this sale and bought something.' It sounded horribly weak when she said it out loud.

He stopped again. 'That was the girl who went missing, that same year? This is to do with her? Well, I never.'

Safi blinked in surprise and momentarily stopped chewing her cake. 'Yes, that's her! So you remember her?'

'She was memorable,' he said with a rueful smile. 'I saw the reports in the paper at the end of the year. She never turned up?'

Safi shook her head.

'Her poor family. I'm terribly sorry to hear that. Yes, she stuck out like a hummingbird among crows. Most of the people who came to the sale were professional dealers, middle-aged men scowling and tutting at everything, then there was this very spirited young woman, so eager and excited.' He sighed. 'I remember she bought a few individual lots and a couple of tea chests of "sundry papers". Mostly old photo albums and postcards we didn't have time to sort out. Or couldn't bear to.' He sighed. 'I'm glad we had the sale, and am relieved we have given this place a future, but it was hard, parting with all those things and knowing they'd probably end up in a junk shop eventually. Too close an encounter with time and mortality for me.'

He wrinkled his nose and turned his attention to the consolations of fruitcake for a minute as Safi tried to work out what to ask next.

'I think,' she said eventually, 'that she might have bought something very old. Older than postcards and photo albums. She went to a lot of sales, but she kept a photo on her desk of this house, so we thought perhaps she bought something really significant here. A manuscript. It might have been a bundle of papers, or looked like legal documents. Could those tea chests have contained something like that?'

He shook his head slowly. 'I doubt it. I don't remember anything along those lines. And when I say we didn't sort things out, I mean not in detail. Anything we thought looked particularly interesting we did set to one side.'

'I suppose it could have been loose pages.'

'Ah, well, yes . . . My great-grandmother did keep some ephemera in albums. We could easily have missed something if she'd put the item you're talking about in one of those. And she might have kept it that way if she thought it was interesting.' He grimaced. 'I hope you aren't about to tell me we sold a missing Leonardo Codex for pennies, or something of that sort?'

'I have no idea, Walter. It might be important, but if this thing exists, and if she bought it from here, it's still missing now. But might those albums have been among the sundry papers?'

'Oh, they definitely were. I helped Ms Thornhill – Charlie – put the tea chests in the back of the car, I think it was an old-fashioned Beetle. She had loaded one case, and was sitting half in, half out of the back seat, looking through the contents of the other.' He paused, lost in the memory. 'As I said, it was difficult watching everything go. But seeing her there, so absorbed in what she'd just fished out of the chest, it made me feel a little better. My great-grandmother had collected so many odds and ends.'

'She didn't tell you what had caught her attention?'

'No! Popped it straight back in the box. We made light chit-chat while I helped her get the crate into the back of the car. It was a nothing conversation really, but as I said, it took a bit of the sting out of the day. She told me she was doing her PhD, and that was some consolation too. My great-grandmother was a frustrated scholar, and she would have liked to pass her research forward. Actually, I remember my father mentioning she regretted not being trained to read secretary hand, which suggests she had some things that were pretty old. I always assumed, if I thought anything, that they'd just be documents relating to the house.'

'But any records of what she found . . .'

'Scattered to the four winds now, I'm afraid.'

Safi finished the cake, picking up the loose crumbs with her fingertip. 'Is there anything else you remember?'

He shook his head. 'Charlie did seem very happy. I said something about it being a lot of junk, and she said she was very pleased she'd come. Then she asked me to take her picture. She had one of those digital cameras.'

'That must have been the picture she had on her desk all summer.'

'Really?' He looked pleased and a little confused. 'Forgive me if I'm being obtuse, but do you think what she bought here might be connected with her disappearance?'

'I honestly don't know, Walter.'

He frowned, a look of deep concentration on his face. 'I do hope not. I'll have a look. See if I can dig up anything else about what my great-grandmother got up to. Any clue what I should be looking for? Anything that might help me spot a mention of this thing?'

Safi hesitated. 'We think it might have been a commonplace book. Though at first glance it could have looked like letters, or recipes. Probably collected over a period of time, so you'd see different inks on the pages.'

'Arthur Conan Doyle had a commonplace book, didn't he?' he noted. 'I read about him collecting criminology theories in his, and then he gave Sherlock Holmes one. I know Charlie did go through the archives we had here. Actually, archives makes it sound very grand: they were more trunkloads of papers going back centuries. My great-grandmother had clearly organised them all, oh, it would have been in the mid-1800s, tied them up with ribbons and stacked them back in the boxes. Those documents were all related to the house, though. Perhaps she would have kept what you describe elsewhere? Beth went through the house stuff with a charming local historian. He was cock-a-hoop with it all, but Beth was disappointed – there is a family myth that Shakespeare was in the circle of acquaintances at one point, and she was hoping to find something to confirm it. Think where that might have led! Nothing turned up that I know of, though.'

'Do you remember the historian's name?'

'Not the foggiest. But I'll ask Beth, she'll remember. I have your email, I'll send you their details.'

Safi gratefully shook his hand and they parted. As she walked through the yard she stopped to pet the goats, who agreed to have their ears scratched in exchange for a handful of oats from the farm shop, nibbled from her outstretched palm. The day was a little cold and a little grey; the buds on the trees lining the path were still tightly furled, with slight hint of the erumpent season of blossom ahead. Safi wasn't quite sure what, if anything, she had learnt. That this house had once held frustrated scholars and trunks full of miscellanea. That the materials had been with this family for centuries. That they'd had neither the time nor the will to check everything, especially when distracted by more obvious finds. If an early modern manuscript was going to survive, unrecognised and intact, these were, she had to admit, the ideal circumstances for it to have done so.

36

fernweh, *noun (nineteenth century)*: the longing to be far away

Martha couldn't remember the last time she'd visited one of the colleges and experienced the thrill of walking under a weathered sandstone arch into one of the quads. Students milled around her, heading towards a seminar or back to their rooms through heavy doors of whiskey-coloured oak. She was ahead of time, so sat on one of the benches and watched them for a while – this parade of youth and potential futures. Most were dressed like teenagers everywhere: baggy T-shirts proselytising bands from the seventies, backpacks slung over one shoulder and AirPods appended like alien earlobes. Occasionally, she spotted someone who had decided to do Oxford 'properly', at least according to outsiders: in a suit and tie. The sort who hung sketches of dreaming spires on their walls and placed a teddy bear on their bed. But these were exceptions, conspicuous in their rarity. This was a far more diverse crowd than those she remembered from her childhood. More ethnicities, happily, and less of a flock. When she was little all the women had long, straight hair which they'd flick over their shoulders; the men had gazed out from squeaky pink faces that seemed too young for their striped shirts and chinos.

'Hiya!' Safi came floating through the quad, her shawl ballooning slightly around her. 'I'm not late, am I?'

Martha chucked her coffee cup into a nearby recycling bin – there had been none of those in her youth, either. 'No, I was early. How was the visit?'

Safi sat on the bench next to her.

'Interesting . . .' She ran through her conversation with Walter. 'He sent me the name of the historian while I was still on the bus home. I've emailed to see if there's any trace of a J. H. in the archives he went through.'

'Thank you,' Martha said.

Safi gave a sad smile. 'Don't thank me, Martha. It's exciting, too exciting sometimes. When I was looking for the house I almost forgot about Charlie, and about you and your parents. It was only when I arrived there that I had a sense of her – of her being gone.' Martha wasn't sure whether she appreciated the honesty or was wounded by it. 'I just don't want you to feel any sense of obligation, that's all,' continued Safi, picking up on her companion's unease and then brightening suddenly. 'Though if you want to, buy something from my housemate at the sale on Friday night! Happy Josh means a happy household.'

'Of course.' Martha laughed in spite of herself. 'I'll be there. He was the one who told you about Jonathan, wasn't he?'

'That's right. Why?'

'I had a very weird encounter with Olivia last night. I'll tell you later. We should probably go and see Charlie's supervisor now.'

They entered the staircase just behind them, ducking beneath an archway engraved with the university motto: *Dominus Illuminatio Mea*, The Lord is My Light. Martha remembered her mother completing the verse from the Bible: *Dominus illuminatio mea, et salus mea, quem timebo?* The Lord is the source of my light and my safety, so whom shall I fear? *Whom indeed?* she wondered.

The pair walked into an ancient lobby with whitewashed walls and stone flags. A corkboard screwed into the wall was thick with flyers for public lectures and student productions; opposite was a wooden box with sliding name panels, designed to show which academics in the building were in situ. Dr Catherine Carmichael's office was on the first floor, up a narrow spiral staircase.

'I only have twenty minutes,' she said with an apologetic sigh after they had made their introductions. 'I thought I had a whole hour but one of my colleagues fell off her bike this morning and broke her wrist, so I'm taking her evening seminar group.'

'I hope she's OK,' Safi said as she fished in her backpack for her pad and pencil.

'Bit of an occupational hazard for an Oxford academic.' Dr Carmichael was in her forties, wearing a pantsuit with clean lines and bobbed blonde hair turning grey at the temples. 'We all end up forgetting to pay attention and a bollard makes us pay for it at some point. Do sit. So, you wanted to talk about Charlie? I saw something in the paper about strange letters turning up at the *CED*.'

'Yes,' Martha responded, perching on the edge of one of the chairs on the other side of Dr Carmichael's desk. 'I'm sorry, I'm not even sure what to ask you. Only my memory is that Charlie had been working incredibly hard that summer, yet my colleague, Simon, mentioned he'd met you after she disappeared . . .'

'And I said she'd been slacking? Yup, that's right.'

Dr Carmichael leant forward on the desk, her chin in her hand. The office was atypical for an academic, Martha thought. The largest wall was taken up with a bookshelf, but the rest of the room was remarkably clear of the usual teaching detritus. The desk, a heavy, Edwardian-looking object, was bare except for a laptop and keyboard, and the other surfaces were lacking the usual broken-backed volumes and piles of essays, holding instead some healthy-looking pot plants and a small gilt clock that gleamed in a circle of honeyed light from a simple standard lamp. This space had none of the creaks or hisses of the usual university offices with their Victorian plumbing; it was as though the building slumbered around them. Martha settled back in her chair.

'We think she was working on something else,' Safi said. 'Would that make sense? Possibly a commonplace book she picked up at a country sale.'

Dr Carmichael nodded. 'Wow, I see. Yes . . . that fits. We had a tutorial just before she disappeared, you know. And she was . . . gosh, I don't know how to describe it. Jumpy? Frazzled? I always blamed myself for not saying or doing anything after that meeting. She kept dancing from topic to topic when she was usually so focused.' She smiled at Martha. 'I very much enjoyed teaching her, you know. She was one of the first really exceptional minds I encountered after coming here. She had a fluency, an ability to absorb and work with highly technical elements of our subject, and use them to build fresh ideas. I was excited about her PhD, so I admit to getting frustrated when she seemed to stop work on it. I thought of her as a friend as much as a student.'

'I worry sometimes she didn't have many friends,' Martha admitted. 'My colleagues tell me she could be heartless. Cruel, even.'

Dr Carmichael sighed. 'We can all be that, from time to time. It's true I saw her get impatient with people at times, or dismissive. But she did have friends. And she could be very kind. I remember we had an extended session in her first year of postgraduate – absolutely exhausting, but fascinating. She said something about families, and my mum had died earlier that year – I had a bit of a moment. Burst into tears, in fact – no doubt very unprofessional. Next time we saw each other, she brought me that.' Dr Carmichael pointed at the tiny clock.

Martha felt a sudden surge of gratitude. It was such a relief to hear her sister being recalled with fondness.

'When was the last time you saw her?' Safi asked. 'I mean, was it close to when she disappeared?'

The older woman looked down at her desk, collecting herself, and when she spoke her voice was thick with feeling. 'It was on the Monday of that week. I was out shopping on the Saturday morning when the police rang to ask about her and I learnt she'd gone. I remember the guilt; she'd seemed so unsettled the last time we met, and I'd done nothing.'

'Can you tell us as much as you remember of what she said?' Martha asked. 'Why did you say just now "that fits" when Safi mentioned she might have been working on something else?'

The academic sat back in her chair and half closed her eyes, tenting her fingertips together.

'We met in my rooms. I was at Somerville back then, but there were roadworks going on outside, so we went for a walk instead. Sat on a bench in St Sepulchre's for an hour. She liked it there. Then we went for a drink.'

Charlie in St Sepulchre's. Martha felt the thread of kinship with her sister, which had felt so thin and threatened, rebinding itself. 'I had no idea. I thought that St Sepulchre's was my discovery.'

Catherine glanced at Martha and smiled. 'We all create our own personal Oxfords, don't we? Geographical idiolects. Some people don't include the university at all; for others everything turns "here be dragons" the moment they step beyond the college walls.' Martha nodded at the reference; she had always found medieval maps compelling. As a child she had marvelled at their colourful dragons and sea monsters, warning of the dangers of uncharted territory.

Catherine went on: 'We were discussing oral culture, in very general terms. It became clear quite quickly that she hadn't made much progress with her PhD work, and she could tell I was troubled by it. I asked if there was anything going on in her personal life, if she was struggling. She was quite vehement. She swore up and down she'd turn her attention back to her PhD by the end of the year. I told her to be careful. Then it became clear she was working on a book of some kind.'

Safi and Martha exchanged glances. 'So she told you she was working on a book?'

'No, I gathered that from a conversation she had in front of me. An older woman who stopped to talk to her.'

Martha thought of her conversation with Gemma, but Safi was ahead of her. 'Did you have your drink outside the Printmakers' Arms?'

Dr Carmichael looked surprised, and a little impressed. 'Yes, trying to squeeze the most out of the September sunshine. The woman stopped by our table. She was reminding Charlie that they were meeting for lunch later in the week.'

Martha searched for a picture of Gemma on her phone, and pulled up one from a *Guardian* feature a few years ago. She was sitting in her living room, the Nicholson painting behind her.

'Is this her?'

Dr Carmichael frowned as she read the headline. 'Gemma Waldegrave. It was so long ago, but yes, I think so.'

'And she was *reminding* Charlie about lunch?'

Dr Carmichael nodded. 'She said, "Remember, you're having lunch with us on Thursday at mine."'

'Only, Gemma told me just the other day that Charlie and she made that lunch date then and there. That Charlie was showing off to you, hinting she had some great project to discuss with Gemma.'

'No. I mean, that was the last time I saw Charlie, so I do believe my memory of it is pretty clear. This woman, Gemma,' she pointed towards Martha's phone, 'she was on the other side of the street and crossed over to speak to us. And she was quite insistent. She said, "I know you're working on a book."'

Safi flicked over a page. 'And then?'

'I think Charlie was embarrassed,' Dr Carmichael said with a shrug. 'She hadn't told me she was working on a book. Just that she needed to take a break from her reading for the PhD for a while. She was quite abrupt with Gemma. Then she got up and they moved a bit further down the road to talk.'

'So she wasn't showing off for you?' Martha asked.

'No. The opposite! She looked positively shamefaced when she came back. I asked her why she couldn't finish her PhD first, and then do this book project.'

'What did she say?' Martha leant forward.

'That I'd understand when I saw it. And that it couldn't wait. No, actually she said, "I won't wait for them."'

'I don't understand.' Martha chewed her lip. 'Gemma, the woman in the photograph, is a literary agent, a friend of the family. If Charlie had a book she wanted to publish, surely she would go to Gemma to find a publisher? Get advice?'

Dr Carmichael glanced at her watch, then picked up her bag. 'Sorry, but I really have to go, and I've no idea why Charlie didn't go to this woman. But she did already have a publisher: a friend of mine at OUP, Giles Baldwin. I didn't know that then, but he contacted me during that first flash of publicity when she went missing.'

'And he didn't tell you what her book was about?' Safi asked.

'No, but he asked who he should speak to in the family about it. I only had Charlie's mobile, so I gave him the contact number in the newspaper.'

Martha had become caught in fog once, out on a country walk with her university boyfriend. A thick brume had wrapped itself around Port Meadow like a giant bandage, and they had stumbled from pocket to pocket of momentarily clear air before whiteness engulfed them again, their voices sliding from mirth to panic. This heavy room suddenly felt no different: the air had lost its comfort, and she had no idea where they were headed.

'Are you still in contact with him?' Safi pressed on, pencil bouncing. 'Do you know how we could get in touch with him?'

She shook her head. 'I haven't seen him for years. But you'll find him with a Google search. He did incredibly well – I think he's publishing director of one of the big houses now.'

37

lion-drunk, *adjective (sixteenth century)*:

the second of the four stages of drunkenness, in which a man becomes violent and quarrelsome

THE ART EVENT WAS TAKING place in a cluster of artists' studios off Magdalen Road, to the east of the city. Martha had declined Alex's offer of a lift and chosen to cycle. She chained up her bike by the Pegasus Theatre, a stylish bronze-panelled structure adjacent to the Magdalen Arms, one of the best-rated pubs in Oxford and home to a flea market on the first Saturday of each month. Charlie had loved dragging a sleepy Martha there, keen to sweep up any bric-a-brac or vintage clothes that fitted her style and wallet. Her finds had featured in many of the treasure hunts she had laid on for her sister.

Safi had sent her notes of the conversation with Dr Carmichael to Alex, but it had not been discussed in the office the previous day. The atmosphere had felt too precarious, too full of caught breaths. Simon had remained largely silent, arriving and leaving first each day and remaining civil to both Martha and Alex, but asking nothing about Charlie, nor making any further enquiries into the mystery commonplace book.

Martha had felt a spurt of anxiety every time an email arrived, in case it was from HR. But so far, nothing. And Simon had said he was planning to come this evening. She was beginning to hope that perhaps, next week, after lunch with Mike and the well-timed bank holiday, they might be able to put the unpleasant scene behind them. Having Safi back, bright, cheerful, and unafraid, would surely help. Make them a team again, ready to deal with whatever Chorus threw at them next. They had heard nothing from him all week. Perhaps he was taking a few days off too.

Martha followed a hand-painted sign into an alleyway opposite a neat row of terraced houses. Not that she needed the sign: the art party had drawn quite a crowd. The alley, flanked with garages, opened out onto a large courtyard surrounded by low industrial buildings, where a man with neon hair grinned at her and thrust a flyer into her hands.

'Studio map!' he said gleefully. 'Enjoy.'

It was only just six o'clock, but the yard was already packed. Martha felt at first that she was the oldest person there, but soon spotted some more mature faces among the throng: men and women with easy smiles wearing jeans and flowery shirts beneath heavy-knit sweaters. How different this slice of the city was to the coiffed and manicured one at Jonathan's reception. Martha much preferred the look of these people. She liked the eclectic clothing, the sparkle amid the ordinary, the rich and warm undertow of friendship. It reminded her of Berlin. Maybe there was a tribe for her in Oxford after all.

She spotted Alex almost immediately. She was talking to someone, but as soon as she glimpsed Martha she extracted herself from the conversation and came over to join her, expertly balancing a bottle of white wine and a pair of plastic glasses in one hand. 'Drink? I nabbed this for both of us. I was afraid they might only have Chateau Forecourt, but they've got crates of a pretty serviceable Pinot. Though I'd drink anything to wipe out dreams of the lost manuscript now. It's tormenting me! From what Dr Carmichael said, I don't think that slip can be a joke.' She filled a cup and Martha took it gratefully. Outside the office, and between themselves, this was still the first and only topic of conversation. It was a relief.

'Did you hear anything back from the publisher she mentioned?' Alex continued.

'I just got an out-of-office reply. He's away and won't be looking at his emails until late next week.' Martha sipped her wine and looked round. Hot food was being served from a converted caravan in one corner, and glasses of wine and beer had been set up on a trestle table, together with some sort of lurid pink cocktail. From a pair of speakers inside she could hear the beginning of 'Anarchy in the UK'. One way to celebrate the Coronation.

'Do you think that perhaps Simon was right, that Charlie sold the manuscript then ran off with the money?'

Alex studied her for a long moment, that affectionate but wry half smile on her face. 'No. But if we don't hear anything more from Chorus, and don't find anything else ourselves, we can all choose to believe that if you like.'

Martha took a deeper draught of her wine. 'Perhaps we'll call that plan B.'

It surprised Alex into a laugh. 'Have you spoken to Gemma yet? Challenged her with Dr Carmichael's version of that meeting?'

'I did.' It hadn't been a pleasant conversation. Her godmother had blustered and denied before making a grudging confession.

'She said she had heard the tiniest rumour Charlie had a book deal for her PhD thesis, some fresh finds, and she was hurt Charlie hadn't asked her for advice.' On the other side of the courtyard a young man and woman in striped aprons were selling slices of pizza from the caravan. The smells of hot bread and melted cheese mixed with older scents of oil and foliage. The couple bantered with the waiting customers, wielded knives, sauces, paddles: making a show of it. The exuberance travelled across the yard like a sound wave.

'She apologised for "confabulating a little",' Martha added.

Alex frowned, looking out over the crowd. 'I hope you don't mind me speaking about these things coldly, Martha, but I'd wondered if the message to Gemma, blowing off lunch, might have been sent by someone who harmed Charlie. But if Charlie had never wanted to go . . .'

Martha heard a burst of laughter and turned her head. Charlie, young Charlie, in the middle of the crowd? But no, another hiccup of time, just a woman in her twenties with unruly hair, posing for a selfie with a couple dressed up as King Charles and Camilla in rubber masks and ragged robes. Art as a festival of misrule: these human impulses to mock authority, and in mocking subtly celebrate it, always found a form in which to flourish, age by age.

'But she told my father she was going out for lunch with *someone* . . .'

'Hey. Thanks for coming!'

Safi appeared beside them, a beer bottle in her hand, her eyes dancing.

'It's wonderful, Safi,' Alex said at once. 'Your friends must be very pleased.'

'Yes, Josh is made up. He wasn't sure something like this would work in Oxford, but it's rammed.' She swigged her beer, moving instinctively to the thrashing punk guitars coming from inside the building. 'So I spent this morning combing through British History Online for anything about the house and Sir Walter's family during the fifteenth and sixteenth centuries. Looking for possible candidates for the writer of the commonplace book.'

'Any luck?' Alex asked, eagerly filling up their wine glasses.

'None. I mean, a few Janes and Jeans, but no J. H. And I spoke to the historian too. He couldn't think of anyone associated with the house having those initials.'

'Could they have been a housekeeper, perhaps? Or a relation?' Martha asked.

Safi shrugged. 'Relation is possible. And I've been reading up on commonplace books in general. Thousands of them survive, even from antiquity, but very few from women. People used them as miscellanies. There are recipes for ink and rat poison, instructions on card tricks, bits of biography, how to converse properly in French . . . Funny though, it's that stuff, the unusual odds and ends, that makes them so valuable now. Not the quotations. I think there's a lesson in there, but I'm not sure what it is.'

Alex smiled. 'Do your own thing, perhaps?'

'Yeah, that works,' Safi said. 'Also, there are plenty of references to people leaving their books to younger relatives or friends as chronicles of their lives. And Sir Walter's lot have been around long enough to have deep roots in the community fifty miles in every direction. There was a cousin buried in St Aldates, and another in Stratford, so their reach would have been pretty extensive.'

'You're supposed to be on holiday this week!' Martha groaned, when Safi finally stopped for breath.

'I told you, Martha, I'm enjoying myself. The farm was great,' she said cheerfully, then waved at someone in the crowd. 'Remember to go and see some art. Simon's in there somewhere.'

Martha and Alex started their tour of the open studios together but soon became separated in the crowd. Martha let herself suspend all thinking for an hour, resting on the bonhomie of the gathering and lifted by the creative pleasure on display. She saw meticulously realistic portraits in one studio, splashy abstracts in another, then layered prints of slightly fantastical cityscapes and bursts of botanicals side by side. All of them were reconstructing reality in an acutely personal way. Just like language, really.

She was glad to discover that Safi's flatmate, Josh, made art that suited her taste exactly. Bold graphics of Oxford in pinks and yellows; neon lights splashing on the pavements and reflected in the rain. The sort of art you could start building an aesthetic around, a home even. Would they work in her bedroom in her parents' house? No. She refused to ask herself what that meant and bought a pair of A3 prints. Josh beamed at her before turning to his next customer; not the moment to interrogate him over gossip about Jonathan.

By the time she'd finished her purchase she'd lost sight of Alex completely. With a cardboard tube containing the prints stuffed awkwardly into her shoulder bag she followed the flow past the remaining open doors, and into the sudden darkness of the yard.

'Martha!' Simon was standing opposite the illuminated doorway she had just emerged from, and was staring at his phone. He thrust it into his pocket as he spotted her. 'You got art.'

He looked unsteady, stumbling slightly as he pushed himself away from the wall.

'Yes, did you buy anything?'

He shook his head while swigging from the bottle. Droplets of beer sparkled briefly in his beard, reflecting the strings of fairy lights garlanded over the doorways and garages, before he wiped them away. 'You know, Martha, I think you are right.'

'About what?'

'Disturbing ghosts. Let them lie. Eyes forward!' He moved his hand forwards and back in front of his own eyes. 'I'm not sure that digging up the past is a good idea.'

'Digging up the past is rather our job, though, isn't it? And it wasn't me who said that, it was that man who Safi met in the church.'

He shrugged and swayed slightly. Martha stepped back. She didn't like flat-out drunkenness. Even as a student it had somehow scared her. It was true she liked its language: on paper it amused her. 'Cherubimical', for example, which once described the happy drunk who goes around hugging everyone; but for every one of those there were dozens of 'lick-spigots' and 'tosspots'. Drunks could turn. And Simon looked very drunk.

'I'm not a bad man, you know,' he said. 'I've been unlucky. I never had those strokes of good fortune, like the way Jonathan became a bestseller, or Charlie found that book. I mean, what were the chances of her coming across it? And she kept it to herself – tried to hold onto it. She *did* that.'

'It looks like she did, yes,' Martha replied carefully. 'Though she obviously intended to publish. But it may have cost her her life, Simon. Caldwell thinks so.'

His mouth twisted a little. 'You like him, don't you? Caldwell? You always look down when you mention his name. Demure little Martha.' He finished the beer and tried to put the bottle on the ground next to the wall, but it toppled and rolled sideways. He stared at it, as though this little demonstration of gravity and physics was uniquely compelling. 'She. I . . . Still . . . she took her chance.'

'Simon, are you OK?' Obviously not, but perhaps asking the question would break him out of the funk. Remind him he was in company. With his boss. At least his boss until he went to HR to get her fired.

It didn't work. 'Yes, no.' He lifted his arms and began to declaim. '"There is a tide in the affairs of men, Which, taken at the flood, leads on to fortune; Omitted, all the voyage of their life Is bound in shallows and in miseries. On such a full sea are we now afloat; And we must take the current when it serves, Or lose our ventures."' A pair of young men glanced over curiously as they passed between him and Martha. They smiled and lifted their hands in silent applause without stopping. Simon swept a grand, low bow to their retreating backs.

'Simon, what are you talking about?'

He half laughed. 'A glitch in the matrix. You know, of all of you, of everyone caught up in the damn thing, I think Charlie would be the one who would really understand.'

'Understand what, Simon?'

She took a step towards him, and some sense swam back into his eyes. He blinked, pulling himself together. 'Ignore me, Martha, I'm just a bitter old fart. This too shall pass. I'll just write another crappy book, while Jonathan's crappy books earn him a mint and I cry hey-ho for a fortune. And I'll tell myself we're all dead in the end and be grateful for the privilege I have in my shitty house in this shitty city.' He put his hand on the wall. 'We all, we all make compromises. Learn to live with our slightly disappointing selves. You should try it, instead of just mooning about while you live rent-free in a bloody mansion. Why sleep your way into a job if you aren't going to have any fun with the money?'

Her hopes that all was going to be forgotten were forlorn. 'I didn't use my relationship with Jonathan to get this job. Honestly, Simon, as I told you, it never even occurred to me. I wish you would believe that.'

'Never-occurred-to-me,' he said in a fluttering tone. 'What happened to cross Martha? Defiant, take-it-up-with-HR Martha?' he snarled, stooping slightly to look her in the eye. 'You never even considered . . . ?' He backed off a little, lifting his hands. 'If you say so. Just tell me to fuck off then. God, it's not like I ever wanted much out of life.'

'Fine. Fuck off,' she muttered, holding her cardboard tube of art slightly in front of her like a defensive weapon. 'And don't talk bullshit. Seems to me you expect quite a lot out of life. You think you deserve whatever anyone else has. Jonathan, me, Alex . . .'

'Just a little of it!' He held his thumb and forefinger together right in front of her eyes. 'Just a squinch!' She saw the anger flare and drain from his eyes again. 'Oh, don't worry. I'm not going to kick up a fuss about you and Jonathan. You're so off in the clouds, it might be true you never even considered it, and he's shagged so many undergraduates he probably doesn't even remember you were one of them.' He slid a long glance over her.

Martha flushed. 'You're drunk.'

He turned away without replying, just began shambling off along the street, one hand raised in farewell.

'What was that about?' Alex asked, emerging from the doorway behind her.

'What do you think?' Martha replied. 'I wish I'd never told him about me and Jonathan. He's beyond pissed.' Alex was carrying an unfamiliar tote bag over her shoulder. 'Did you buy art too?'

'Yes, something for my son, Jacob. God, I hope he ends up a happier man than Simon. I worry about him, still trying to make his books a success. I'm scared what failure might do to him.' They watched as Simon crossed the road and disappeared into the shadows of the spring night. 'I'm sorry I lost my temper with Simon in the office. Of course Jonathan giving the job to someone he once had a fling with doesn't look good, but Simon was never going to be promoted! Not at the dictionary. If he wanted to advance his career, he should have left us and gone somewhere else – clean break. But he's too comfortable.'

'He doesn't seem at all comfortable.'

Alex shook her head. 'Self-pity can be comfortable if that's what you are used to. You didn't rob him of his place in the sun, Martha. He did that to himself.'

Martha was surprised at how relieved she was to hear it. She didn't think she could take another bruise to her conscience.

'Added to which, middle age is not for wimps,' Alex said, adjusting the bag over her shoulder. 'I know I sound like I'm really falling into my role as the office crone, but you don't realise how young you are still, Martha. There are any number of possible futures in front of you, but at some point the opportunities will start to narrow, and you'll need to find joy in what you've achieved already, and in the present. There's a point at which the future can start looking more like a threat than a promise.'

Empathy stirred again within Martha as she stared back at Alex. She'd always thought she had the monopoly on wistful. Perhaps, occasionally, wistful bled into melancholy for both of them.

'Have you read his book?'

'Yes, and it's excellent. Better than most of Jonathan's and it had everything going for it really. Readable, original, erudite. But . . .'

'But what?'

'The planets didn't align for him, and he's never really been able to accept that. Come on, let me buy you another drink, then we can say goodnight to Safi and carry our artistic loot home.'

Safi was enjoying the night. She had exactly the right beer buzz going, she'd seen Alex and Martha buying, and she'd met at least three people her own age with whom she'd promised to get coffee over the next couple of weeks. Sometimes moving between her house and the office made her struggle against the limits of her life, its routine confinement. Tonight reminded her that there was a lot more to be explored. All these cities within a city, just as Dr Carmichael had said. She wandered over to a corner of the large gallery space on the ground floor of the largest outhouse, where they'd invited various artists without their own studios to hang their work on site. A girl of her own age in dungarees and a 'This is what a feminist looks like' T-shirt was telling a small group about her paintings. Collages mostly, from what Safi could see over their shoulders. Spray paint and images of lips and eyes torn from magazines.

'Yeah,' she was saying. 'I really wanted to engage with the lost women of history. The talents we let go by suppressing women, refusing to educate them.'

Safi felt a spurt of irritation. How long must the message be repeated until things began to change? Her beer buzz was fading and she began to feel oddly truculent.

'I mean, you just have to read Virginia Woolf's *A Room of One's Own*,' the artist continued.

Safi knew the essay well. What woman who'd tangled with higher education didn't? It spoke of the centuries of prejudice that had inhibited women's progress, denied them the space to achieve their potential. So that whenever we read of a woman in the past who was ducked as a witch, of one who was thought to be possessed by devils, or who silently mothered a remarkable man, we will be on the track of a lost poet, a forgotten storyteller who also dreamed, wrote, imagined. What if these women had been allowed to let their creativity run free and unimpeded? History had decided instead that they would go half crazed with fear and frustration, their words unsigned and unacknowledged.

'Like Mozart's sister!' the artist added. 'She was a prodigy, too, but they stopped her performing when she got to a marriageable age. Not one of her works survived.'

Shakespeare had had sisters, too, thought Safi, her misgivings fading fast as her mind began to sprint. Anne, who died young. And the mysterious Joan, who married a hatter called Hart. Her brother had left her twenty pounds in his will.

'Fuck!'

The group turned round to look at her.

'Sorry.' Safi smiled at them. 'Great stuff, hope you sell a tonne.'

Then she thrust her way through the crowd back to the yard, where she saw Martha and Alex, heads together over their wine glasses. They looked up and smiled.

'Hart! Why did Chorus hide the slip under "hart"? Maybe the "H" is for Hart. What if J. H. is Joan Hart?' She was talking a mile a minute.

'Joan Hart?' Alex said, frowning. 'That name sounds vaguely familiar.'

'I mean, Walter said there was a rumour that his family knew Shakespeare. And they had a relative buried in Stratford. Perhaps they knew his *sister*! J. H.! The dates are perfect, even down to the dating of "besmirched". She heard it: he used it in a play. What if Charlie found the commonplace book of *Shakespeare's sister*?'

38

pneuma, *noun (sixteenth century)*:

the spirit, soul, or life force

MARTHA WATCHED THE CORONATION IN the living room, sitting on the sofa with her legs tucked under her and a book open on her lap.

The possibility that the commonplace book might be the work of Shakespeare's sister was almost too big to fathom; whenever her thoughts touched on it, they skittered away again. She told herself to wait, to see what Mike, her predecessor, had to say tomorrow. She let her fingers drift across the pages of her book as she read, as though she might anchor herself in the texture of its paper, its pore and grain. She shot periodic glances at the TV screen, registering the musical-chair interviews of historians and royal biographers, interspersed with shots of guests arriving at Westminster Abbey and crowds enthusiastically waving flags despite the rain.

The fact that they had found the slip under 'hart' was as solid as the novel in her hands. Perhaps that tentatively pencilled

J. H. on the slip was indicative of something too, that Charlie didn't quite trust herself to write down the name, knowing that its totality would send ripples through an entire language. *The Commonplace Book of Joan Hart.*

Gabriel emerged from his study just as the formal ceremony began, and Martha offered to make tea.

'I'll do it,' he said as she began to get up, and he returned a few minutes later with a tray. He'd even found some biscuits for the antique willow-patterned plate her mother had always chosen for teatime treats.

Rebecca had enjoyed baking. Martha remembered her and Charlie's attempts to help, a fairly transparent strategy to lick the final spoon. Rebecca's fruitcakes had been especially renowned. 'Almost as good as shop bought,' Gabriel would say whenever he took his first bite, grinning sideways at his wife and waiting to be scolded. Martha glanced at his face now. Angular, hawkish, the laughter lines rarely exercised. No longer the look of a man who would enjoy teasing his wife.

After Charlie disappeared their mother stopped making anything. Even Martha's birthday came and went. Perhaps Rebecca had told herself she'd bake again when Charlie came home to resume the sisterly fight for the spoon. The Christmas cake after that had come from Waitrose. It was another tradition that Charlie took with her, like the treasure trails she'd laid through the house and garden on their birthdays. Hadn't one of those she'd created for their mother been all about baking? Clues full of cherries and sugars, the history of spices, old names for puddings. Each clue had led to another, the way marked with wooden spoons hidden in drawers or tucked behind books, the next riddle wrapped round its handle in a tight scroll done up with ribbon. For her father, Charlie had devised whole crosswords and anagrams, and he had adored them. Words became their private playthings.

Martha wondered if she should let her father into her thoughts. She recalled a moment, distant now, when they had dared to talk about those treasure hunts. It had been a few months after Charlie had gone, one evening when the fading light was beginning to soften edges and they could hear Rebecca singing to herself as she made dinner. Gabriel had remembered one of his favourite puzzles from the hunts, couched as a crossword clue. ENTHRAL EVERYONE, CONCEALING SEARCH'S CONCLUSION (8, 4). 'It was perfect,' Gabriel had said softly, 'worthy of a professional.' Martha hadn't dared intrude upon the private memory, part of a code between Gabriel and Charlie that she would never speak. But it had been one of the last times that talking to her father about her sister had felt like a solace. Now, as they sat together in silence, her hand went automatically to her necklace.

He shot a look at her. 'That will break one day if you keep playing with it.'

She let it fall back against her collarbone.

'We've had another letter, Dad,' she said.

He said nothing, just stared ahead at the ancient ceremony playing out on the screen.

'Are you going to tell me what happened between you and Charlie that summer?'

The awkward conversation with Alex and Safi, and the nasty confrontation with Simon, came back to her so suddenly, and with such force, that her eyes stung.

Still they kept their gaze on the screen. The King had shed his robe of state and taken his place on the Coronation chair.

A screen was placed around him for the anointing while the choir prepared to sing 'Zadok the Priest', the clarion call of sovereignty. Was she not allowed to keep some things private? How was it fair that Chorus remained in the shadows while thrusting her out into this light to be scrutinised and judged?

'It was nothing, nothing important,' she said.

The rising arpeggios on the violins were building to the great entry of the choir; they seemed to thrum in her chest. Her father didn't move.

'"Nothing important" is still something, Martha.'

The choristers began. Their voices seemed to break open the air and Martha could hear her own breath rasping. In, and out.

'*May the King live for ever*,' they sang.

'Don't you want to know about the letter?' she asked.

'No,' he replied. 'If you have anything specific to ask me, then I'll answer. Beyond that I'd rather wait until you are willing to be honest with me.' He stood up. 'I think I'll listen to the rest of this on the radio in my study.'

She put down her tea and retreated to the corner of the sofa.

'Why does everything have to be on your terms, Dad?'

'Because my terms are all I have now,' he said, sharply. He walked out of the room.

'I'm having lunch with Mike tomorrow,' she shouted after him, feeling petty and piqued. 'Shall I send him your regards?'

He paused in the hall. 'You can tell Mike to go to hell,' he said, then went into his study and slammed the door. Martha thought again of that evening in the garden, the last time they'd spoken freely. She remembered its conclusion clearly. 'The answer was ENTRANCE HALL,' Gabriel had said. 'Charlie had hidden the treasure under the stairs.'

* * *

Alex had arrived far too early for the lunch with Mike. When she pulled into the car park of the Trout, the pub wasn't even open. She looked at the ground, examined her shoes, and decided she could risk a walk along the towpath past the ruins of Godstow Abbey.

She locked her handbag in the boot and, feeling vaguely ridiculous in her going-out-for-lunch wear, crossed the pair of bridges that led over the ribboning Thames. As the tumbledown walls of the priory began to emerge on her right she saw that she was not the only one who was early. Martha was standing by an information sign looking out over the ruins, her back to the coal boats moored along the water's edge. Her hair was loose, blowing across her face when the breeze took it, wearing one of her long, patterned dresses beneath a cropped denim jacket. She was lifting her face into the sunshine as it broke between the clouds, her eyes shut.

Alex paused, watching her for a moment, unwilling to disturb. She drew in a deep breath and registered water, woodland, grass, the astringent tang of herbs, and a touch of woodsmoke. The course of this river had run virtually unchanged for millions of years; the nuns of the medieval abbey were relatively recent occupiers of its history. Beyond the steaming pelt of the weir by the inn the water flowed more silently here, inviting passers-by to gaze at the ruins or turn the other way and gongoozle – one of her favourite words ever since Safi had extended its original meaning of lazily watching activity on a stretch of water to the idle staring at a cup of tea.

Martha turned towards her and smiled.

It felt like an invitation, so Alex walked along the path to join her.

'Did you ever read Jan Morris's biography of Oxford?' Martha asked at once. 'Charlie gave it to me; she used to say that humans are rubbish about knowing anything about the ground beneath our feet. It's a wonderful book.'

'It is,' Alex agreed, looking at the remains of the gatehouse that had once welcomed kings but now flourished with nettles. 'Morris said there was a causeway here, didn't she, a path over the tombs of nuns?'

Martha tucked a loose strand of her hair behind her ear. She'd read that in the final years of the Second World War some children playing by the river had discovered a stone coffin protruding from the towpath. It wasn't the first: other coffins were seen to come and go with the levels of the river, a ghoulish series of apparitions in this timeless place.

'She did. A superfluity of nuns. As collective nouns go it's a strange one, isn't it? But I suppose it was all about family disgrace in the end. All those "extra" women, unmarried, tidied away by their families.'

Alex nodded. 'Did you drive here?' The car park had been empty when she pulled in.

'I walked,' Martha replied. 'Through Port Meadow. I love it there. The winter before she died, I used to drive Mum down to look at it when it flooded. At dusk. She called it the twitter-light, the straddling of night and day. Seemed to fit with the way the water caught the sunset.'

'She was a gatherer of unusual words too?'

Martha grinned. 'She couldn't really help it in our family. And she did relish them. She was so curious about everything.'

Alex could picture them, mother and daughter in that strange liminal place, half water, half land. Alex went there, too, when she needed to think or tease out some kink in a plot, her boots sucking at the sodden ground, her only companions grazing cows and horses. Oxford might be known for its damp miasma, but it certainly kept things green.

'Charlie told me about the nuns' coffins before she gave me the book,' Martha said, then pointed down the river, beyond the lock. 'When we went swimming down there. We'd go all the time in summer. I remember once she was meeting up with her friends and I tagged along. She ended up ignoring them and talking to me instead. So then they started talking to me too. I was thirteen, and I thought I was suddenly the most sophisticated girl in the world.'

'You were close, weren't you?' Alex asked. 'You and Charlie.'

'We were. Most of the time. You know, when I said I wanted to study English, I was afraid she'd be angry, think I was copying her, but she seemed genuinely pleased. Then when I said I thought the linguistics course was better in Sheffield than here, she seemed proud. Started making up stories about how we'd become intellectual spinsters living in a cottage in the countryside, writing learned articles and squabbling over the butter and brandy. I thought it sounded wonderful.' She pushed her hands into the pockets of her jacket.

'And all this time, you thought you had driven her away?'

'Yes.'

Alex laid her palm on Martha's shoulder, wishing she could take some of that burden from her. Martha lifted her hand and brushed Alex's fingers with her own, both an acknowledgement and a dismissal. 'Shall we walk through the ruins? We still have twenty minutes before Mike is due.'

Martha walked over the grass and through the gatehouse, slowing her steps so that Alex could follow her in her smarter shoes over the uneven ground. A murder of crows, disturbed from some feast, lifted off, back towards the woods on the far side of the ruins. Martha had never understood why Charlie had wanted to decorate her room with the shadows of carrion birds. 'They're just birds, Marth,' Charlie had said, 'and really clever. Stop being so Gothic!' Beneath the roughness of her voice had been a note of softness, a gentle cajoling and a persuasion that everything would be all right.

Difficult to avoid feeling a little Gothic here, Martha thought. The priory was a shrine for romantics and ghost hunters. The mistress of Henry II, 'Fair Rosamund', had died here in the twelfth century after being poisoned – or so it was suspected – by Henry's jealous queen. Her tomb by the altar had become a sanctum, its inscription a mantra: 'In this tomb lies Rosamund, the fair but not the pure'. To honour her, and in defiance of his wife, the king had lavished wealth upon the convent. Not much left of that now, Martha concluded as she looked around her.

'One of my books is set here,' Alex said, and Martha turned and watched her as she ran her gaze over the ruins. 'A nameless horror emerges from the Thames and picks off the nuns. It's consumed in the fire which destroyed the abbey in 1645.'

'Are all your books set in Oxford?'

Alex shook her head. 'Not all of them. But this city has so many ghosts and monsters to feed the imagination. I think there's something in the water.'

It was getting chilly now that they'd stopped. 'Shall we head in?'

Alex glanced at her watch and nodded. 'Yes, let's. Still, it's very beautiful here, isn't it?'

The dips and furrows of the land suggested old workings; the patches of cobbles, half hidden by grass, were stone echoes of the people who had passed over them. Everything hinted at past glories; the empty windows stranded high above them were the last relics of rooms now resolved into thin air, sanctuary to generations of women who had worked, studied and lived here. *Sic transit gloria mundi.* They must have thought this place eternal, out of time.

'It is special,' Martha agreed. 'Perhaps it's all that prayer. It's got into the soil somewhere.'

They turned back towards the towpath and as they crossed Little Godstow Bridge they caught a glimpse of Safi, sitting on her own at a table on the terrace. Martha lifted her hand to wave, and the greeting was returned with enthusiasm. Safi was wearing huge sunglasses and sipping a pink drink through a straw.

'Do you think she might be right? Could the commonplace book really have been written by Joan Hart?' Martha asked, as Alex fetched her handbag from her car. 'Is it possible she would have been literate?'

'Oh, I think so,' Alex said, pressing her key fob to lock the car again. 'More women were than you might expect. She came from a literate family after all, and a prominent one. God, it would be marvellous. I hardly dare think what could be in it. And Safi's not wrong, Chorus does nothing by accident. He must have put that slip under "hart" for a reason.' Alex took out her phone and glanced at it. 'I texted Simon yesterday. He hasn't responded.'

Martha sighed. 'He said he wouldn't miss this lunch for the world. Do you think he's going to snipe at me over fish and chips about sleeping my way to the top?'

Alex paused. 'I don't think so. I am eighty per cent sure he'll be feeling very ashamed of himself. But then I've managed to preserve an overly optimistic view of human nature into middle age.'

Martha had only been to the Trout a couple of times before. Despite its location, overlooking an island in the middle of the

Thames, it always struck her as a little soulless, full of the forced jollity of work outings, its gastropub fare aimed as much at tourists as the home crowd.

Still, there was no denying its beauty – a view shared by many a producer of Oxford-set TV dramas who tended to view a scene here as obligatory. And however much the trappings of commerce threatened to pull the pub into the ordinary, the water beside it guaranteed a deeper charm, an integrity that no number of cocktails and chips could erode.

Safi jumped up as they approached.

'I'm so glad you are early! I've been doing loads of research. Well, in between watching the Coronation. Did you see it? We all thought we were going to feel terribly arch and snarky about it, then next thing we knew we were eating cake and waving glasses of sherry about.'

'I enjoyed it,' said Alex, simultaneously signalling the waiter. 'A turning point in history.'

'Is it, though?' Martha asked. 'Does it really make a difference? Surely a change of government would mean more.'

'Sparkling mineral water, please,' Alex said to the waiter and waited for Martha to order the same before she answered the question.

'No, I mean that rather literally. When future historians are writing about the first half of the twenty-first century, they'll end a chapter with the death of Elizabeth II. Bound to.'

'A *page*-turning point in history then,' Safi said, and Martha laughed.

'So,' Safi continued, sticking with her habit of introducing most of her sentences with the word; there was no Simon here to pull her up. 'There's virtually nothing to find out about Joan. We know she was Shakespeare's younger sister, that she married a hatter who went bankrupt a couple of times, and was widowed just before Shakespeare died. He left her twenty pounds, his clothes – that was a pretty unusual gift to a woman at the time – and the right to live on in the house on Henley Street for a peppercorn rent. That's it.'

'I wonder what the internal evidence for her identity in the commonplace book might be,' Alex said. Her phone buzzed, and she glanced at it. 'Mike will be a couple of minutes late. I can't say I'm surprised; I remember he was always convinced he had plenty of time to get to meetings, despite all indications to the contrary.'

'A tidsoptimist,' Safi said. 'It's Swedish. A time optimist. I thought we should add it to the watchlist.'

'Definitely useful,' Alex agreed.

Safi looked at her phone, too, then peered into the relative darkness of the bar. 'Nothing from Simon. I texted him about the Joan Hart thing yesterday but haven't heard back. He must have seen it by now. I thought he'd respond, if only to say it was rubbish. And he's surely got over his hangover at this point.' She took off her shades and looked at Martha with a glimmer of chagrin. 'Was he a total arse on Friday night?'

The waiter set down their mineral waters. 'Thanks,' Martha said, and then, 'Yes, he was.'

'Ah! The ministering angels of the English Language!'

They turned round, as did some of the rest of the early lunchtime diners. Mike had emerged from the interior of the pub onto the terrace, his arms akimbo. He looked tanned beneath a neat white beard and closely cropped hair, a touch of Provençal warmth to him. 'How very wonderful to see you all. Do we have menus? I've been dreaming of battered cod for a week.'

They waited until Mike had finished his first glass of red wine to order food, but as texts to Simon continued to go unanswered they made their choices and ate. All the while Mike kept up a flow of light conversation, sharing some genial gossip about the ex-pat community in his village in Luberon, waxing lyrical over the quality of the goat's cheese made by the gnarled farmer next door, and extolling the brilliance of the London Library's Out of Town lending scheme. 'All the joys of an academic life but with vastly improved weather.'

His storytelling was ably supported by Safi, and Alex enjoyed teasing him about his *Year in Provence* lifestyle. Martha sat back, entertained by the chat but taking no great part in it. As the plates were cleared away and they ordered coffees, the conversation found a lull. Martha caught Alex's eye, who nodded.

'Come on, Mike,' she said. 'It's really good to see you, but it's probably time we got to the point.'

'Must we? On such a pleasant day?' Then he glanced up from his second glass of wine at Martha. 'Of course we must. I came here for that, after all. I was thinking of your mother on the train up from Avignon, Martha. She was a wonderful woman.'

Martha could imagine Rebecca and Mike getting on like a house on fire: an explosion of mutual delight. 'Alex has filled me in on these letters. And the postcards. One reached me in Ménebres, you know.'

Before anyone could follow up, Alex said bluntly: 'We want to know what all those dark conversations were about the summer before Charlie disappeared. No flim-flam, Mike.'

He studied the last drop of red in his glass, the supernaculum, then lifted his hand to order another.

'It was a delicate matter then, Alex, and it's still one now. I did what I thought was best at the time, but looking back at it now . . .'

'What was?'

'I'm getting there.' A sudden flash of irritation at his old colleague. Alex seemed unperturbed. 'I was concerned there had been some thefts from our archives. A dealer in London noticed a small set of seventeenth-century Fell types on sale that he was fairly sure came from our old printing presses. No institution is immune from occasional pilfering of course: look at the British Museum, thousands of their artefacts have been turning up on eBay. But it had to be investigated. I consulted with Jonathan and we began an audit, working through our more valuable holdings and reaching out to a few dealers we knew. A few things turned up, sold from various different accounts, most of which disappeared from the web after one or two sales.'

Alex was taken aback. The Fell types had been held in the *CED* Museum, bequeathed to the Press's Printing House in the seventeenth century. They were some of the oldest punches and matrices to survive in Britain. 'How did you manage to do that without Simon and me knowing?' she asked him.

'You were both relatively new back then. A lot of weekends is the answer. And some late nights.'

'And had there really been thefts?' Alex asked.

He shifted in his seat, evidently deeply uncomfortable. 'Yes, and the types were irreplaceable. We had some delicate negotiations with the auction house where they were on sale, and in the end they were quietly returned to us without police involvement. Then I turned detective, started rather haunting the place.'

He received his wine and drank quickly, glancing over the rim of his glass at Martha.

'This is where it becomes delicate. I noticed that Charlie often worked late and alone, but then most of you did from time to time. Then one evening I found her in the slips. She had no reason to be there, not for her work, and she refused to explain what she was doing.'

'And you immediately assumed the thefts were down to her?' Martha asked coldly.

'I did. We'd had none before she started working with us, and to be frank, it wasn't the first time I'd seen her somewhere she had no particular business to be. Of course, we encourage all our editors, however junior, to follow their own intellectual interests, but when she refused to say what she was up to, I came to the obvious conclusion.'

'But you didn't sack her, or call the police?' Alex asked.

He stared at the tabletop, his lips pursed. 'I had no proof. I was fond of Rebecca and your father . . . And I knew Charlie was extremely bright, and under pressure with her degree. I thought it could be kept quiet. So I spoke to your father, Martha. I asked him if Charlie had anything to do with the thefts.'

Safi held her tongue, and Alex frowned. Martha knew her own expression was unlikely to be friendly.

'What else could I have done?'

'You could have reported the thefts to the police, Mike,' Alex said. 'Issued an internal warning and been open about why you ramped up security in the building.'

He knocked back the rest of his wine in a single, jerky swig. 'Well, I didn't. Gabriel caught up with me a week later, saying he'd spoken to Charlie and was absolutely certain she had nothing to do with anything purloined from the dictionary. He said if I ever repeated my suspicions outside that room, he'd sue me for slander. I've never seen him so angry.'

'He could be very fierce in our defence,' Martha conceded quietly. 'When was this?'

'Only a week or so before she disappeared.'

'Gosh, it was all going on for Charlie then, wasn't it?' Safi said, looking through her notebook. 'She'd broken up with her boyfriend, been accused of stealing, had a rubbish meeting with her supervisor when she had to confess she wasn't ready with her new chapter, and had some sort of strange encounter with Gemma.' She glanced at Martha but omitted the part about Charlie seeing her little sister sneaking out of Jonathan Overton's rooms at dawn.

Mike shook his head. 'I didn't know about the boyfriend or the trouble with her PhD. She seemed so resilient. But I *did* do my best to handle the situation gently. I am so sorry this led to her running away, Martha, and staying away so long. I had no idea the accusation would have such dramatic consequences. Lord, it wasn't even an accusation as such! I don't think a month has gone by in the last thirteen years where I haven't wondered if I shouldn't have done things differently.'

'Charlie didn't steal anything from the dictionary,' Martha said clearly. 'And she *was* resilient.'

Mike looked pained. He set the wine glass down on the table in front of him, and spread his fingers wide, as if the terrace was about to pitch sideways at any moment and throw him into the river. 'I am sorry, Martha. But she did steal.'

'How could you possibly know that?' Safi prompted.

'Not long after she disappeared a box arrived at reception.' He spoke firmly, deliberating over his exact words. 'It had come by courier, no indication who had sent it. I assumed at first it was supporting documentation for an antedating from one of the readers.'

On the other side of the river Martha noticed a giggling child being lifted onto a canary-yellow canal boat. The little girl scrambled boldly onto the roof, shrieks of delight tumbling from her mouth. Even at this distance Martha could see the silent conversation between mother and father: the alarm in the mother's face, the slight headshake from him, meaning, 'Don't worry, don't make her afraid.'

Had her parents had exchanges like that when they were young? Probably, though Martha suspected that her father would have been the one vigilant for their safety; their mother would have urged them to go further, faster.

'Was there a note?' Alex asked. 'Why did you think it had anything to do with Charlie?'

'No note,' Mike said, tracing with one finger a knot on the table's weathered wood. 'I couldn't make sense of it at first; there was a series of hunting prints which looked as though they'd all come from the same volume; a folder of song sheets – stuff from the twenties, the sort of ephemera you'd find in any car boot sale; and a couple of nice old editions of Smollett. Why on earth someone had sent them to me, I had no idea. Then I found a packing slip, something to do with the sale of another book to a dealer in London. It had Charlie's name on it as the seller, and her handwriting on the back. And there was a letter from Joseph Wright to Tolkien, obviously from our archives.'

'Let me get this straight,' Alex said, leaning forward. 'Charlie had disappeared, and a box arrived at the dictionary, full of stuff that had never been in our archives, but with a note that indicated the whole box belonged to her. And *one* letter which certainly had been pilfered from us?' She thought of Joseph Wright, a giant in the field of dialectology on whose shoulders every member of the *CED* sat today. And of J. R. R. Tolkien, who had studied under Wright and who had worked as a lexicographer himself before dazzling the world with the mythology of Middle Earth.

He nodded. 'An excellent summary as always, Alex.'

'What did you make of it?' Safi asked.

Martha turned back to the group and answered for him. 'You thought it was from Dad, didn't you? That after Charlie disappeared he had searched her room and sent you what he found. In case you were right about her stealing.'

'And the letter from our archives proved I was right: she had been,' Mike replied. 'I'm sorry, Martha.'

Martha shook her head sharply. 'Don't be sorry. You are wrong.'

He started to protest.

'No, Mike. I can see why you could have thought that, decided it was case closed and then with Charlie disappearing just decided to sweep it all under the carpet. But you were mistaken. Charlie found something at those sales, something huge, and she was working on that. Why would she bother pilfering?'

She looked to the others for support. Safi was flicking through her notebook.

'Yeah, Martha's right. She stopped going to sales around Easter, didn't put in or take any money out of her trading account after that. She'd been doing nicely out of it, too, up until then. I reckon she didn't come to the dictionary to steal, she came to do some quiet research on the antedatings. Staying late, spending more and more time in the slips room and archives in order to find what she needed.'

'Just what she'd have been doing if she'd been researching,' Alex said. 'Honestly, Mike! Why didn't you tell anyone about this?'

'The girl was missing! I was afraid it was the fact she'd been about to be exposed that had caused her to run away.'

'But the police must have called you too?'

'They did. But what was the good? I'd told Gabriel. Gabriel had sent me the material. I felt it was up to him to tell the authorities, if he wanted to. Not me. And there were no more thefts once Charlie had gone. We put in the system of a biannual audit that we have now. I've asked myself a thousand times if I could have handled it better, but each time I decided that remaining close-lipped was the best thing to do.'

'And you never discussed it with Mum?' Martha asked.

He shook his head firmly. 'Absolutely not.' His vehemence surprised them. 'She was so distressed, why add to it? Again, if Gabriel wanted to tell her, it was up to him.'

Martha felt the sting of indignation. She hated the way Mike had talked to her father rather than to Charlie: men sorting things out discreetly over the women's heads. But, despite herself, she also felt for him. After all this, she had not been alone in carrying some burden of guilt. If they had both been wrong about the motive for Charlie's disappearance, who had they been carrying that guilt for?

He shook his head sharply. 'But, I'm sorry to say this again, it must have been Charlie. That letter from the archive was right there!'

'I know, Mike,' Safi said slowly. 'But, knowing what we know now, I'm still not buying it.'

'I wish,' Alex said, her voice brittle, 'that people would learn to speak up. Charlie's ex-boyfriend, Tom, was put through hell, repeatedly, by the police. If you had told them what you knew, Mike, you might have saved him some of that. They would at least have had another theory on the case to follow.'

'People speak up enough in my part of town, Alex,' Safi said quietly. 'You're talking about the reticence of the English middle classes.'

Alex glanced at her, then nodded. 'Point taken. Martha, you're going to have to ask your father.'

Martha looked down at her hands. She hadn't realised she'd been digging her nails into her palms. 'I know.' She sat up a little straighter and forced some lightness into her voice. 'Can't say I'm looking forward to it. He has English reticence down to an art form.'

Mike shifted in his seat. 'Like I said, I had no idea about her boyfriend. I am very sorry for that.' Martha nodded. 'How is your father?' he asked tentatively.

'Honestly? I don't know,' Martha replied. 'He thinks I came back to sell the house out from under him and put him in a home.'

'Did you?'

'I came to run away from a ghost,' Martha said. 'Then ran right into Charlie's.'

Safi tapped her pencil on the pad, as if calling them to order. Their coffee had cooled. 'Mike,' Martha said, turning to face him properly and speaking gently. 'I can't absolve you on Tom's behalf, but I am certain that the accusation of theft did not make Charlie run away. Nor is it the reason Mum didn't get to see her again. Whatever happened to Charlie, it wasn't your fault.'

Nor mine, she realised, and in that moment of comprehension her heart lifted. Her mind was ablaze with images of Charlie: Charlie making faces; Charlie playing the violin; Charlie reading at the breakfast table; Charlie walking along the towpath; Charlie in the water, her breath stolen by its iciness; Charlie's wet swimming costume wrapped in a towel, her feet bare as she ran over the grass.

She reached across the table and put her hand over his. 'I hope it helps to hear that.'

Mike's eyes filled and his voice, when he eventually replied, was clotted with emotion.

'More than you can know. Worth another thousand miles of trains.'

The waiter returned to gather the coffee cups.

39

entelechy, *noun (seventeenth century)*:

the condition in which a potentiality has become an actuality

'HE CAN'T STILL BE HUNGOVER,' Safi announced, nodding towards Simon's empty chair on Tuesday morning.

'I've seen him come in worse for wear plenty of times,' Alex replied, looking up from a bundle of slips on her desk, a sliver of the evidence gathered by readers for the revision of 'dipstick'. 'Drunk he's terrible, hungover he's normally on his way back to diligence. As Hemingway said: write drunk, edit sober.' No one laughed. 'Martha, did he message you to say he was working at home today?'

Martha glanced at her inbox again. 'No, nothing.' Alex and Safi were looking at her expectantly. 'I'll give him a call,' she added, picking up the office phone, whereupon they seemed to relax. She hadn't been particularly worried when he'd missed lunch with Mike – more relieved, if anything. She'd told herself again that things would improve on Tuesday, but now Tuesday had arrived and here she was, and the atmosphere was crooked with his absence.

His phone went straight to voicemail, and she frowned. If he had overslept, she would expect it to ring for a while first, even if he'd set it to 'silent'. Out of battery?

'Hi, Simon, it's Martha. Just checking in. Are you working at home today? Do give me a call when you get this.'

She cut the connection but kept the receiver against her neck. Her mobile was on the desk in front of her; she willed it to buzz, imagined hearing Simon's sleep-roughened voice offering up some excuse or other. The stillness in the room felt unnatural. 'He's been a bit off since we got Chorus's last letter . . . And then of course . . .' She heard a crackle of panic in her voice.

'Still . . .' Safi trailed off. Their sentences were faltering, drifting like liquid symbols without form or permanence. 'Should we worry?'

'I *am* worried,' Alex said. The unease was crumpling the air between them now. 'Look, I fed his cat for him when he was away at New Year. I still have his key. Should I go round?' She didn't wait for an answer. 'I should go round.'

Martha looked up his emergency contact on the staff database. 'Is Nancy Finn his ex-wife?'

'Yes, but we can't call her,' Safi said. 'What if he's been on a bender all weekend and we send his ex round? He'd be humiliated. And he's only missed an hour of work so far.'

'Let me go, Martha,' Alex said. 'Please. We are all in a strange state, what with the commonplace book and everything else. Safi's right, and I'd hate to shame him by overreacting. He's probably in bed with the flu or something. I can pop over and fetch him some soup or he can tell me to sod off. Either way, we can stop worrying.'

'There are a lot of bugs around,' Safi said, brightening. 'Josh could barely get out of bed last month.'

'Probably that, then,' Alex said firmly.

'Probably that,' Martha agreed. 'Yes. Good idea. Tell him to rest up.'

Alex was already shrugging on her coat.

'And Alex?'

'Yes?'

'Call us straight away, won't you?'

'Of course.' She was already out of the door.

'He's fine,' Safi said firmly, pressing her palms down on her notebook. 'He'll be fine.'

Alex walked towards the chipped blue door of the 1960s house, past an overflowing bin perched on a small patch of gravel; one bag had been pierced by foxes' teeth by the looks of things. There was no doorbell, just a brass knocker that had become dislodged on one side and now hung at a sorry angle. Alex opted for her knuckles instead, and looked around her. She knew that Simon had to provide for his ex-wife and daughters, of course, and the road to lexicography was not exactly paved with gold. Still, a pot of geraniums or a bay tree in a tub to brighten the doorstep wouldn't cost much. She knocked again and waited, listening for signs of movement inside, then peered through a filmy window into the living room. Netting and a half-drawn curtain obscured her view, giving the house a blind and battered appearance. She could just make out an empty sofa and a saggy chair with mismatched covers draped over its arms. *I mustn't judge*, she told herself firmly. Her own literary endeavours had made her more than comfortable; just as importantly, they had become a bulwark against loneliness. Perhaps Simon was more depressed than she had realised. They hadn't talked a lot since Martha joined the team. What if Alex and her readers had never found each other? How long would she have stayed hopeful, optimistic enough to plant geraniums, without back-up? How would she feel about herself without her pretty house, her ability to help her children out when they needed it? Martha was right, Simon's book had deserved readers too.

She knew luck played a large part in any publishing success. Jonathan's book had hit the peak of a wave of self-improvement. Shakespeare had added weight and legitimacy to the promise that genius was within the reach of everyone. Simon's book, on the other hand, had never found its niche, had fallen prey to the randomness of bookshop algorithms and bestseller lists. Now he lived here, Jonathan had his mansion, and she had her house, crammed with good furniture.

Silence. She sighed and let herself in, jangling the keys.

'Simon? It's Alex! We've been worried about you!'

No answer. She both craved and dreaded finding him slumped somewhere, beery and unwashed amid kicked-over bottles and fast-food cartons. The house was certainly a mess. A bare bulb on the ceiling illuminated a coat rack bulging with jackets, some with shopping bags crammed into their pockets. A sudden rattle behind her made her jump, but it was only the cat flap. Simon's tabby, Rochester, looped around her ankles, purring enthusiastically. She leant down to stroke him.

'Are you hungry?'

The purring crescendoed.

Alex made her way towards the kitchen. The door to the living room was open and she steeled herself to look beyond it. Curtains were roughly drawn, empty mugs cluttered the coffee table, and piles of books lay haphazardly on a desk against the back wall. She pushed open the door to the bedroom, too, squinting into the gloom.

'I'm just coming in!' She held her breath for a grunted response, a profanity, anything. But she was unsurprised to find it empty too. The whole house had that still, dead air of a place unoccupied. The feeling of disquiet they had all felt in the office redoubled. This was all wrong. Every instinct she had told her so.

Rochester's bowl on the kitchen floor was empty. As she searched for cat food she saw a picture of Simon's daughters on the fridge, a fragment of commonplace, everyday happiness snatched from a sunny garden. Another coffee mug on the sink stood out as the prettiest thing in the place. Its painted letters were thick and uneven, clearly painted by a child. They spelled out the word 'family'.

Alex filled the cat's food and water bowls. The window needed a clean, too, but surely doing that would be overstepping the mark. The kitchen looked out onto an unkempt garden, its paving as cracked as the plasterwork inside. *Oh, Simon.* Suddenly his bright shirts and bad jokes seemed nothing short of heroic.

But where was he? Could he have gone away to work on his new proposal? Martha had said he'd mentioned a new idea, and it sounded promising. But he wouldn't desert Rochester, she was sure of that. He loved that cat. Kept pictures of it on his phone among the multitude of images of his two girls. Perhaps he'd asked some other friend to take care of the cat, and *they* had fallen ill or something. Safi was right: there was a lot of illness around. He'd gone away. A missed email, a forgotten charger, an ill friend . . . More likely than anything else.

She went back into the living room and picked up a box containing two slices of shrivelled pizza. She could bin that, at least; the last thing this place needed was a rodent infestation.

Then she drifted over to his desk, not sure what she was looking for. There must be some sort of clue, instructions for whomever was supposed to be looking after the place, or a leaflet about a writing retreat. Anything that might banish this uneasy feeling of wrongness that seemed to be soaked into the stale air.

She approached the desk. Simon's laptop was there, sitting on a pile of loose papers. Damn. She had almost convinced herself of the writing retreat scenario. She took out her phone.

'Hi, Martha. No sign of him at all. The cat hasn't been fed and his computer is here.' She exhaled, straightening her back. 'I think you'd better ring Caldwell and report him missing. Yes, really . . . No, leave it to Caldwell to ring Nancy.'

She heard Martha on the other end of the line repeating the news to Safi. As she listened, something about one of the loose papers caught her eye. It was sticking out from under the computer. A piece of copier paper, just one letter visible in the distinctive font of an old-fashioned typewriter.

She pulled it out, the phone crooked in the curve of her neck.

'Shit.'

Martha's voice came clear on the line again, alarmed.

'What is it, Alex?'

Alex swallowed as she stared at the sheet lying on the desk in front of her.

Dear Editors,

She froze. *Oh, Christ Almighty, Simon, what have you done?*

'Jesus, Alex, what is it?'

She couldn't quite take it in.

'Alex! Are you OK?'

'Yes, sorry, I'm fine. No, I'm not. I've just found a photocopy of a letter from Chorus on Simon's desk.' The words danced in front of her. 'Martha, it's one we haven't seen before. I . . . I'm coming back to the office now.'

She hung up and looked around again. What the hell was she supposed to do now? One thing at a time.

She took screenshots of the letter with her phone, but didn't touch it again, then found the cat's travel box under the kitchen sink and bundled a confused Rochester into it.

Not wanting to disturb any more of the papers, she tore a page from her own notebook.

Rochester looked hungry, so taking him to mine! Alex

Ah, the glorious exclamation mark. The boing, pling, bang, gasper, startler, slammer, and Christer, as it had been variously known across the centuries. An enforced lightness of tone totally at odds with the creeping darkness of the house and Alex's own thoughts. She locked the door behind her and put the cat box on the passenger seat, then fled as if the hounds of hell were after them.

40

scytheman, *noun (twentieth century)*:
Time and Death personified

'YOU TOOK THE CAT?' MARTHA said.

'I couldn't leave the poor thing there,' Alex said, unwinding her scarf from around her neck. 'He's got the run of my spare room for now, and I'll manage an introduction with Rags this evening. What did Caldwell say?'

'That he'd "get things going", which I think means ringing around the hospitals first. And calling Simon's ex-wife.' A police siren floated up from the streets below. Martha closed her eyes. 'Have we done the right thing?'

'He'd never leave the cat,' Safi said. 'What if he's been hit by a car or something?' She paused, hearing a short ping from her mobile. 'What are you AirDropping me, Alex?'

'The pictures I took of the copy of the letter from Chorus. I don't know how good they are; I was a bit shattered by seeing it.'

Safi was examining her screen. 'We can get a readable version from these. So do we think Simon might be Chorus? I mean, he certainly has some mixed feelings about this place, but I don't think I'm ready to go there.'

Martha lifted her hands, a gesture of despair and confusion. She had a terrible sense of urgency, but no idea where she should direct it.

'That's one theory,' Alex said, sitting down. 'Can I have Caldwell's number? I better tell him I took the cat.'

'What's another theory?' Safi asked, but Alex didn't answer, instead pressing the contact that Martha had just sent and lifting her phone to her ear.

Safi looked again at the pictures. 'Shall I write this up? Do I call Jonathan about it?'

'I honestly have no idea what's best,' Martha responded. 'If we call Jonathan we'll have to tell him how we got it. Do you think we can wait? Perhaps we'll hear from Simon and he can explain why he has it. He had an entrance key to the office. Might he have come in on Saturday? Found it in the post . . .'

Safi was struggling to look as if this sounded likely.

'Yes, I have a key,' Alex was saying into the phone. 'What did I touch? Um, a few things in the kitchen. A pizza box I put in the bin. I didn't take the rubbish out . . . Yes, of course, I'll make a list.'

She hung up, her eyes steady but huge, a tinge of greyness in her skin. 'He sounded . . . He was quite abrupt. He asked if we could stay here until the end of the day. Said he might need to talk to us. And not to touch anything on Simon's desk.'

Safi returned to her main monitor, typing fast and then pressing return, her eyes scanning down the screen. Martha watched her, and felt the dull throb of a headache building behind her eyes. She caught a snatch of music from a passing car outside, all clinking piano and beefy guitar slides that offered the promise of a different reality.

'What are you checking, Safi?'

'Hashtag Oxford on Twitter. Any news should come up there . . .'

'Caldwell is clearly busy,' Alex said. Her voice sounded strangely flimsy. 'I'm sure what he said about leaving Simon's desk is just a precaution, it could mean anything.' Even she knew her sentences were hollow.

Safi yelped and turned the screen towards them. A patch of riverside dominated by a pair of police cars, their lights flashing. A figure in a white forensics gear. A man standing by one of the cars. A phone to his ear. Caldwell.

'It says, "Lots of police in university park. Person in river."'

'But . . .' Alex's voice was now almost a wail, 'that doesn't mean it's Simon. Caldwell is busy with this other thing. That's why he was abrupt. It's not Simon.'

Martha shivered. She started typing on her phone; her fingers thick and clumsy:

Have you found him? Is he dead?

There was a long pause, then the three dots pulsed.

Can't confirm until next of kin have been notified. Please stay at the office. Monroe and Idowu too.

She stared at the screen, still not quite believing it. The circles pulsed again:

I'm so sorry, Martha.

41

wrack, *noun (nineteenth century)*:

the brunt or consequences of an action

CALDWELL ARRIVED AT THE DICTIONARY offices just after one o'clock, accompanied by a sharp-featured woman of roughly his own age in a sober blue trouser suit. Her expression was unreadable, and Martha felt small and insubstantial under her gaze. Caldwell introduced her, but she didn't catch the name. She felt the same sense of incompetence and immobility one has in a dream; the various elements of perception and proprioception no longer slotting into a smooth reality, but seeming instead to clash at their corners.

She was aware that he was telling them they'd found Simon, and that Simon was dead. That he'd been found just before nine o'clock that morning by a man walking his dog. That the time of death had yet to be established, but they thought he'd been in the water for two or three days. She heard her own voice, relaying how she'd last seen him at the art event. He'd been drunk; that they'd expected him at the lunch on Sunday, but he hadn't turned up.

'And how did he seem on Friday night?'

Everyone was looking at her. 'I . . . Not great. Wasted. And bitter. About Jonathan, my getting this job, Charlie finding the book. Too many things.' And then: 'How did he die?'

Caldwell's face was studiedly composed. 'Preliminary indications are that he drowned . . .'

'Those indications being his corpse in a river, I suppose?' Martha snapped, then held up her hand in apology. 'Sorry. I mean, was it an accident?'

The composure cracked a little, softening into sympathy. 'We're not releasing those details yet. Right now we're just trying to establish a timeline. Did anyone else see him leave on Friday night?'

'I did,' Alex said. 'He was already halfway to the road, but waved. Martha and I chatted for a while, then Safi joined us, and we left just before ten, I think.'

'He didn't say where he was going, no indication he was meeting anyone?'

Martha shook her head. 'Was it Friday night, then, that he died?'

'That looks likely.'

Each of them bowed their head.

'Ms Thornhill told me that you found another letter from Chorus at his home, Ms Monroe?' the female officer asked.

'Yes, or at least a photocopy of one. You haven't seen it yet?'

'Our scene of crime officers are at the house,' Caldwell replied. 'We're joining them there next. Did you read the letter? Take a copy?'

'I took a photo, yes,' Alex said.

'Have you worked it out yet?'

'We haven't even looked!' she said, surprised. 'I mean, do you want us to?'

'I think you are as likely to solve it as we are.'

'But . . .' Safi's voice was wobbly. 'We solved the other ones together, with Simon. He's the one who was always best at crosswords.' The infamous collision of tenses.

'I am sorry, but we would be very grateful if you tried,' Caldwell said gently, and Safi nodded.

'Do we . . . Do we tell people?' Martha asked.

Caldwell and his colleague exchanged glances. 'That you reported him missing, and that we believe we have found him, yes. But I would be very grateful if, for the time being, you don't mention the letter you found in his house to anyone other than DS Marche and myself. Is that something you could all agree to? At least in principle.'

Each gave a muted 'Yes'.

'I'll send one of our team to clear his desk this afternoon. I understand that you might not want to be here today, but I do need to ask one of you to stick around to make sure my officer knows what to take and what to leave, and to give access to his emails and records if we need it.'

'I'll stay,' Martha said. 'Give them my number.'

Wordlessly, DS Marche made a note of it.

'Does Nancy know?' Alex asked. 'That he's dead, I mean? We used to be friendly, when they were still married. I'd like to call her.'

'She identified his body an hour ago.'

Alex inhaled sharply. 'His poor children. But, surely, it must have been an accident?'

An Emily Dickinson poem floated absurdly into Martha's brain. *Hope is the thing with feathers/That perches in the soul / And sings the tune without the words/And never stops at all.*

'I'm sorry,' Caldwell said, looking at Martha as he spoke. 'As I said, the investigation is at a very early stage, but I don't think it was an accident, no.'

Martha felt stuck, as though the air had thickened to treacle.

'Does . . . does the copy of the letter mean he was Chorus?' Safi said.

Caldwell held out the palms of his hands. 'It's my job, believe it or not, to avoid making assumptions. It may have been a mugging. It may be that he was Chorus. It's just as possible that Chorus or another person killed him to avoid exposure. The first thing we must do is secure the evidence.'

Martha breathed out slowly. 'We've dug up some more odds and ends – about Charlie's disappearance and the manuscript we think she might have found. If Simon's death is bound up in that . . .'

Caldwell frowned. 'Ms Idowu, Martha mentioned you'd been taking shorthand notes. I was wondering if you've been typing them up?'

Safi nodded. 'I've also made notes on everything Martha and Alex have told me.'

Caldwell smiled at her. It was a good smile: warm, human. 'Our top priority is the routine but vital steps. To find a crime scene if we can, secure the house, get door-to-door going as well as a fingertip search of the riverbank. That means I don't have time to look at them now. But if you could email me that material . . .'

'Of course.' Safi's fingers were flying round the keyboard already.

DS Marche confirmed their contact details. Alex talked them through her route in and out of the house, and agreed to go to the station the following morning to give them her finger-prints for elimination. Then they left, leaving a terrible silence behind them. Martha could hear the air blowing intermittently through the vents at the top of the windows. Were any of them to speak, she wasn't sure they'd be able to stop. But someone had to, and it might as well be her. She was the one earning a few more thousand a year.

'We can't stay in here. Not today. Even if we have to look at the clue, we can't do it right in front of Simon's empty desk.'

'I don't want to sound like a wuss,' Safi said softly, 'but I'd really rather not be alone.'

'The conference room,' Alex said, locating a shred of confidence from somewhere. 'Let's make camp in there and we can start making phone calls – Jonathan, and Pippa in Comms need to know. Let's begin there, then look at the letter later.'

They gathered their things, carefully steering a route around the space that had belonged to Simon, as though crossing it would violate some unspoken law that separated the living from the dead.

Pippa abandoned her home office on the outskirts of town to come in as soon as she heard. Partly, Martha assumed, so that as head of communications she could get the facts straight, and partly to offer them the comfort of her calm, practical company. There were, it seemed, systems for this sort of thing: leaflets with helpline numbers to be distributed, grief counsellors made available, a book of condolence organised. Martha felt grateful to whomever had taken the time to think through such eventualities and prepare for them. It gave a structure to the next few hours that they could collectively cling to.

Only when Pippa had left, leaving doughnuts and coffees behind her, did they mention the letter at all.

'He stole it, didn't he? The letter?' Safi asked.

'He was here before Alex and me every day last week,' Martha said. 'And you were away. So he certainly had the opportunity. But why? What good would stealing it do?'

Alex crossed her legs, one arm hugging her body. 'Did he think he could find it by himself? The commonplace book? And claim discovery of it for himself?'

Safi shook her head. 'That would never have worked! Not when we all knew Charlie had found it. And if that was the idea, why did he take a copy of the letter? Where's the original?'

'Shall we look at it?'

Safi got up from the table and switched on the wall-mounted screen, casting the image of the letter from her phone onto it. 'I don't think we have a choice.'

42

aumbry, *noun (thirteenth century)*:

a repository for books; an archive

Dear Editors,

A return home in short. I have no more fears to whisper, breadcrumbs to drop for you, so offer this final gift. The pattern of a mind, the common cloth of other people's words, stitched with her own thread into a miracle. All these words: numbered, and numberless. Abundant, yet infinitely precious. Catalogued, confined, but ever changing. Study the final marks. Knowledge must be organised to be understood, though arrangements vary, as people do, as times do. Speeches, miscellaneous writings, drama, letters, Old English, poetry, fiction.

Where have I led you? To a book that was, and one that has yet to be, through darkness, down twisting paths.

But I hope the monsters I fear have felt the light of your lamps. Deny them the shadows.

Scholarship, virtue, honour, loyalty all loaned, stolen, betrayed and curdled. I have sent you after these creatures, not knowing how to find them myself. Lift your lamps high.

Go deep into the labyrinth and drive them out.

As time has passed, I realise I do not know what victory looks like. Will there be another homecoming?

In a library, a new volume. A marker. A tombstone. It takes its place among its own fruits. A secret treasure called forth, openly. Find it. Know the labyrinth is a test. We discover not just the treasure in the maze, but ourselves. Our reward will be knowledge. I fear what you will find, and so should you. But I cannot live in this darkness anymore.

Yours,
Chorus

The three women read in silence. Alex shifted in her chair and Safi began a looping doodle in her notebook. Martha exhaled and blinked hard, words ticking across the darkness behind her eyelids. She smelled something dry and musty, the scent of shadows and dust. A low-lit idea began to form in her mind but was quickly smothered, as though the obscenity of Simon's absence could extinguish everything.

Had he died for this? Been killed for it? She thought of what he'd said at the art event – his bitter desire for the stroke of luck he knew he deserved. Perhaps in stealing this, this scrap of paper, he had been finally taking his chance.

'So that's what he's been doing?' Safi said impatiently, pushing away her notebook. 'He's been sending us into his labyrinth to chase out monsters?'

'I'm not sure if we are chasing the monsters out or creating them,' Alex said sadly, then leant forward on the table, her head in her hands. 'I can't think straight. What is this letter leading us to? He must be talking about the commonplace book.' She sighed, straightened her back and turned again to the screen. '"The pattern of a mind, the common cloth of other people's words, stitched with her own thread into a miracle".'

'Is it possible Chorus *has* the commonplace book?' Safi gasped. 'And is telling us where to find it now? Could Chorus have had it all this time?'

'I think that's exactly what this means,' Martha said. 'It has to. A way of organising knowledge – that's the definition of a commonplace book, and it could well be made up of all those elements – speeches, poetry, essays. And note the female ownership: "stitched with *her* own thread". God, what if it really is Joan Hart's!'

A homecoming, a marker, a tombstone.

Scholarship, virtue, honour, loyalty all loaned, stolen, betrayed and curdled.

Simon had betrayed them, betrayed her. Her mind flitted away from the letter again.

'Simon didn't owe me any loyalty,' she said, 'but how could he do this? Steal? Sell something so huge, to someone he thought was involved in Charlie's disappearance? And all because his book didn't sell as well as he'd hoped?' Her mouth formed a bitter half smile. Alex was looking at the floor and Safi was watching her with steady sympathy. 'Or was it because I told him about me and Jonathan?'

The smell of the doughnuts was suddenly nauseating. She stood up and walked back towards their office, flinging the double doors open with the palms of both hands.

A man was standing by Simon's desk. For a long moment she thought it was him, that it had all been some sort of terrible error.

Jonathan looked up as she entered the room, and before she could adjust her eyes he'd walked over and put his arms around her.

She let herself lean on him for a moment. The scent and feel of his body were familiar even after all these years, and there was comfort in them. But it was brief. She pulled away almost at once, the memory of Olivia's ugly snarl evaporating the nostalgia of the moment.

'We aren't allowed to touch his desk,' she said, without looking at him. 'The police are sending someone.'

He looked hurt for a moment. Then confused. 'The police? Why? They don't think there's anything suspicious about it, do they? I heard he slipped while walking by the river.'

'They have to investigate.'

'But surely—'

'I'm just telling you what they told me! What are you looking for anyway?'

He shrugged. 'I honestly don't know. After you called I didn't know what to do with myself.' If he was looking for sympathy, he didn't find it. 'Is there anything I should know?'

Martha hesitated. 'Simon was in an odd mood last week, and wasn't himself on Friday night.'

He perched on the edge of her desk and folded his arms. 'It must have been an accident. Tragic, of course. Nothing new from Chorus?'

His expression was utterly bland. She'd thought he would have made a better job of looking upset.

'Jonathan, I think Charlie had found something before she disappeared. A late-sixteenth-century commonplace book.'

He frowned, his head on one side. 'OK . . .' He dragged out the syllables. 'What makes you think that?'

There was something off about his reaction, and a suspicion began to curl under her skin, like the swirl of black smoke from an extinguished candle.

'You're not . . . you're not surprised, are you? Did you know? How could you . . . ?'

Safi appeared in the doorway. 'Martha, your phone went. The police are just coming up from reception. Oh, hi, Jonathan.'

'Hi, Safiya. Terrible news about Simon. I'll get out of the way, then.'

He began to walk towards the door, but Martha put out a hand and stopped him.

'Jonathan, did you know that Charlie had found something?'

He looked at her, and for a moment she thought she saw something like entreaty in his eyes. 'I think Gemma mentioned something around the time when Charlie went missing.'

'What? What did she say exactly?'

His eyes flickered between them.

'Gemma had heard a rumour Charlie was going to publish a book, that it was something in my period and the publisher was excited about it. A find of some kind. It was all third hand. We were going to talk to her about it. Then she disappeared and it turned out the publisher hadn't actually seen anything! We concluded Charlie must have been making it up.'

'How did you know the publisher hadn't seen anything?' Safi asked, stepping into the room.

'It was a fantasy of hers to cover up the fact she was failing in her PhD and pilfering from the dictionary. Then she ran away.'

Safi moved aside to let someone enter, a police officer in uniform with a cardboard box in her hands. Jonathan retrieved his professional smile but then seemed to remember the occasion and let it fall into an expression of sorry seriousness. 'Welcome, Constable. This is Martha Thornhill, she'll see you have everything you need.' Then without waiting for either of them to reply, he left.

'That your boss, ladies?' the police officer said, walking over to Simon's desk and putting her cardboard box on the chair. Martha looked across at the cardigan over the back of her chair, the coloured pencils scattered over Safi's work top, the small cactus in an artfully simple pot on Alex's. The officer had picked the most unfeminine desk in the office, and it irritated Martha that her assumptions were correct.

'That's right.'

'Reminds me of the assistant commissioner. Smooth bugger.' She opened the box and took out a sheaf of evidence bags. Safi watched in horror.

'Sorry, Martha, I can't.' She fled back to the conference room.

'Poor lass,' the officer said, her sympathy genuine. 'I know this looks all very formal, Ms Thornhill, but it's just procedure. We secure as much as we can straight away as possible evidence. Do you mind taking me through what's company property and what isn't?'

She had taken out her phone as she spoke and photographed the top of Simon's desk. Martha noticed he'd been working on Safi's draft of a new, AI-inspired sense of 'prompt'. The printout was on the table. He'd liked making his alterations on a hard copy first. She took in the terrible ordinariness of the paper, the pencil lying where he had left it, the last marks he had made before deciding to call it a day on Friday. Suddenly his absence exploded through the room, a shockwave that seemed to toss Martha into the tilted air.

43

sinuosity, *noun (nineteenth century)*:
a complexity or intricacy

SAFI ARRIVED FIRST AT THE office the next day. Everything was the same, and everything was terribly wrong. There was no comfort in the ritual of chaining up her bike, hoisting its pannier over her shoulder, and crossing the road. All the ordinary, unthinking actions of an average morning had now been rendered monstrous.

She pushed open the doors and was brought to a sudden halt by the sight of a large frame on an easel next to the reception desk, draped with black ribbon. A younger Simon smiled out at her, and below him the dates 1973–2023. *It is with the deepest regret that the* CED *announces the passing of our friend and colleague, Simon Turner.*

Liz the receptionist glanced between her and it.

'How are you holding up, love?'

Safi looked away and adjusted the backpack over her shoulder. 'Not great.'

The receptionist furrowed her brow. 'He was always friendly with us, would often stop for a chat. I went home last night and made my husband swear on the Bible he wouldn't come back from the pub along the towpath anymore.' She smiled kindly. 'Alex and Martha are in already.'

Safi nodded and mechanically climbed the stairs, heading straight for the conference room. The image of the letter was up on the screen already.

She began straight away: 'I just had the most horrible thought. When Liz said you were up here I found myself thinking, *Can I trust them?* I mean, if this is the clue to a manuscript of unimaginable value, what if one of us works it out and goes to fetch it alone?'

She let her backpack drop and pulled out her notepad.

'*The Pardoner's Tale*,' Alex said with a soft exhalation. 'Chorus told us to remember it. I . . . Yes, I see what you mean, Safi.'

Martha was cradling a mug of tea in her hands. 'I told Caldwell about that story, the three friends murdering each other over a mountain of gold. But what can we do but trust each other?'

Safi looked between them. 'Nothing, and I do trust you. More than that, I trust myself. I trust myself not to do what Simon did. Mark 8:36: "What doth it profit a man, to gain the whole world, and lose his own soul?" If I work it out, I trust myself to tell you.'

Alex nodded. 'Chapter and verse. Yes, I think that is the way to look at it. But I can see how someone might lose their way and forget that.'

'Lost in the labyrinth,' Safi said. 'Found any threads to lead us through Chorus's latest, then?' They all knew the etymology of 'clue': a ball of twine given by the princess Ariadne to the hero Theseus. Its unravelling allowed him to plot a path through the maze of underground tunnels that was the Labyrinth into the lair of the Minotaur, and to follow it back after slaying the monster. The ultimate solution.

'Who are these monsters we are looking for?' Safi added.

'And what is Chorus afraid of?' Martha added. 'What is he scared of finding?'

'The truth behind Charlie's disappearance? But why should he fear that?' Safi pressed her fingertips to her forehead and stole a glance at Martha. Her boss looked pale in the blue light of her screen.

'We have to solve this letter,' Safi continued. 'So, we know the score. A clue concealed within the plain text. Up till now we've had the measures of music and the rhyme scheme of a sonnet. What are we looking for here?'

'There are seven paragraphs,' Martha said slowly, straightening her back. 'If it's the same pattern as the others, the clue must have words from each in it, and the key to working out which word or words we need from each paragraph is in the first few lines.'

'"Study the final marks"?' Alex said, her voice jagged with frustration. 'In the commonplace book? But how do we know what they are if we don't have the book?' Safi saw her make an effort of will to reach some kind of clear thinking. 'Ways of arranging knowledge . . . The commonplace book is one. Dictionaries are another. Could that be part of it?'

Safi stared at the screen. Seven, a mystical number: seven days of Creation, seven Wonders of the World. Seven continents. Seven divisions in the Lord's Prayer. Seven ages of man. Seven liberal arts. Seven paragraphs here, seven . . . 'Yes!' she shouted. 'Look, there are seven sorts of writing there at the end of the first paragraph. Speeches, miscellaneous writings, drama, letters, Old English, poetry, fiction.'

'Could those translate into numbers?' Martha said, putting down her mug and leaning forward. '"Numbered, and numberless" . . . "Catalogued, confined, but ever changing". "Study the final marks. Knowledge must be organised" . . .'

'Numbered, catalogued, knowledge must be organised!' Alex said. 'That sounds like a library to me. But . . . Safi, can you google all those terms and see what comes up?'

She copied the words from the screen and pasted them into a search window.

People also ask, the search engine responded, *What are the ten classifications of the Dewey decimal system?*

'Marks!' Alex exclaimed. 'Shelf marks! And final marks. What's the Dewey Decimal Classification for Old English?'

Safi's fingers scrambled to the Wikipedia page for the classification scheme that dictated the location of every book in libraries across the world. She scrolled down. 'Old English is 829; English literature is 820. Yes: they are all subcategories! Poetry is 821, Drama is 822 . . .'

'So what do the final marks – numbers – give us?' Martha said, snatching a pen off the table. 'Speeches is 825, miscellaneous writings is 828, drama is 822, letters is 82—'

'Six!' continued Safi. 'Then poetry 821 and fiction 823.'

She flicked back to the screen and the letter. 'Give me the numbers and I'll highlight.'

Martha looked at her notes. 'It starts with five.'

A return home in ***short****. I have no more fears to whisper, breadcrumbs to drop for you, so offer this final gift. The pattern of a mind, the common cloth of other people's words, words, words, stitched with her own thread into a miracle. Numbered, and numberless. Abundant, yet infinitely precious. Catalogued, confined, but ever changing. Study the final marks. Knowledge must be organised to be understood, though arrangements vary, as people do, as times do.*

'Second one is eight,' she said as Safi made the word bold on the screen.

> *Where have I led you? To a* ***book*** *that was, and one that has yet to be, through darkness, down twisting paths.*

'Third is two,' supplied Alex. 'That works.'

> *But* ***I*** *hope the monsters I fear have felt the light of your lamps. Deny them the shadows.*

'Letters next, that's six,' Martha said.

> *Scholarship, virtue, honour, loyalty all* ***loaned****, stolen, betrayed and curdled. I have sent you after these creatures, not knowing how to find them myself. Lift your lamps high.*

'And Old English is nine.'

> *Go deep into the labyrinth and drive them* ***out****.*

Safi felt her fingers slip on the mouse as the clue shimmered into view. 'One for poetry,' Alex said, then glanced at Martha.

> ***As*** *time has passed, I realise I do not know what victory looks like. Will there be another homecoming?*

'And the last is fiction, three!' Martha concluded.

> *In a* ***library****, a new volume. A marker. A tombstone. It takes its place among its own fruits. A secret treasure called forth, openly. Find it. The labyrinth is a test. We discover not just*

the treasure in the maze, but ourselves. Our reward will be knowledge. I fear what you will find, and so should you. But I cannot live in this darkness anymore.

'Short book I loaned out as library,' Safi said as she typed it out. 'It makes sense; I mean, it sounds like a clue, but it's not exactly X marks the spot, is it?'

The phone on the conference table rang and Alex leant over to pick it up.

'Alex here.' A pause. 'Yes, yes of course, Liz. Bring her up to the office. We'll see her there.' She replaced the receiver and looked at them. 'Martha, sorry, Nancy has just arrived. Simon's ex-wife.'

She was a tall woman in her early forties, dressed in jeans and a vintage leather jacket. For some reason Martha hadn't expected her to be so striking. Her dark hair was glossy and shoulder-length, her eyes a deep blue surrounded by laughter lines.

'Nancy!' Alex said, rising swiftly to greet her. 'How are you? How are the girls?' She put her hand on the other woman's arm, guiding her to a chair by her desk. 'I'm sorry. Stupid questions.'

Nancy shook her head, coaxing her mouth into a semi-smile.

'They're with my husband. It's grim, Alex. Chloe keeps saying she was grumpy with Simon last time they had a day together and has been crying her eyes out. I don't know how to take that away from her.' She dabbed a tissue under her nose. 'How on earth will they get over it? Losing their dad when they're still so young, and like this!'

'Can I get you a tea, or a coffee?' Safi asked, half standing up and willing Nancy to give her a job to do.

But Nancy shook her head with surprising vehemence. 'God, no. I think I've drunk a swimming pool of tea in the last twenty-four hours. You must be Safi?' She turned round. 'And you're Martha. Simon told me about you both. I think you met my girls once, Safi?'

'Yes, in town one weekend,' Safi said, retaking her seat. 'They were all propped up in a row on a wall, eating toffee apples. I took a picture of them.'

'We have a copy of it at home.' Nancy smiled, a genuine one this time. 'Chloe thinks you are very cool. Simon would say Chloe only ever showed an interest in two things in his life, you and the cat.' Her pupils widened suddenly. 'Oh shit, I suppose we have a cat now!' She ran her hand through her hair. 'God, the stuff that just comes into your mind, I'm sorry. But my husband's allergic, and yet the girls will never forgive me if we don't . . .'

'I'm very happy to keep Rochester for now,' Alex said. 'The girls can come and visit him any time they want.'

'I am so sorry about Simon,' Martha said. She should have better words, she thought, she of all people. But she loved words as individuals. She knew their roots, their rhythms, their skeletons, shapes and stories. Fitting them together to create something meaningful took a different skill altogether.

'I thought we were almost getting to a place when we could be friends again,' Nancy said without a pause. Martha couldn't be sure her condolences had been heard; the woman in front of her seemed intent only on getting the words out, on keeping the pen moving over an invisible piece of paper. 'He came over to ours for Christmas last year; it was weird but it sort of worked. His parents are both dead, you know. Thank God; they are spared this. Can you think what losing a child . . .'

She stopped talking, biting her lip and stiffening her body, making a physical effort to stop the flow of words. 'Martha, I can't believe I said that. I'm sorry. I'm trying to be brave for the children, so whenever they aren't around, I lose it.'

Alex touched her arm. 'You can say what you like here, Nancy. I'm sure of that.'

'Of course!' Martha added. Nancy flashed a quick smile of thanks at her.

'I'm supposed to be going to Simon's place. I was at the police station yesterday talking to DS Caldwell, then I was back there again this morning. I didn't want him asking questions in the house with the girls there, but nor did I want to send them to the park or anything. They have a family suite at the station, you know, with sofas for those interviews where they don't want to scare the shit out of you. Afterwards, I thought I'd go to the house. The funeral home need something to bury Simon in, because of course everything he was wearing is evidence. But I couldn't face it, and I can't face going back home yet. I've just been wandering around the city in circles, trying to walk to his home and not making it. And I just found myself here. I'd rather remember him in this place most of all. Is that stupid?'

The terrible aftershocks of death, Martha thought. Magnified by violence and made more shattering by the suddenness of it. You could never prepare for something like this, the indignities and traumas, the invisible traps. The ground beneath all of them had fallen away. She thought of Charlie, barefoot, walking ahead of her along the path through Port Meadow.

'Not at all,' Martha said. 'Stay as long as you like. We're all too shocked to get any work done. We just came in to be together.'

'That's nice,' Nancy said, looking down at the shreds of tissue in her hands and wiping her eye on her cuff.

'He . . . he was found in the University Parks, wasn't he?' Safi asked.

Nancy nodded. '"There is a willow grown aslant a brook" . . . Yes, he drowned. I thought maybe he'd got drunk, fallen in . . . But today . . . they have ruled it a suspicious death. The pathologist thinks the head wound is too deep, and they found a spot on the bank. Signs of a struggle.' Martha looked up, and saw her own anguish reflected in the faces of Safi and Alex. 'The things they keep asking about! Things from years and years ago. I keep telling myself: just get through the next hour, but my mind keeps running away with itself.' Her eyes looked half crazed.

'Is there anything we can do to help?' Martha asked, her own grief delivering a deep need to offer some sort of practical support. 'Pippa has drafted a tribute for the website and we can call his professional contacts.'

'Oh God, yes, please. Would you? I'd appreciate that. There are so many things. I keep thinking of new ones. What on earth will we do with all his papers?'

'We can help with that, too,' Safi said quietly, then, almost to herself: 'Part of the sadmin.'

'Sadmin?'

'Yes, all the admin tasks that come with a death.'

'He would have liked that word,' Nancy said with equal softness.

She stood up suddenly. 'I must go, be with the kids. Alex, can I bring them over to yours later to see the cat? It's a terrible imposition . . .'

'No!' Alex said. 'Not in the least.' She took a Yale key from her Tiffany keyring and handed it to Nancy. 'Just let yourself in any time if I'm not there. They can spend time with Rochester and Raglan, or just eat junk food and ignore me if I'm around. Help yourselves to anything. You can have a large drink and a sofa and talk or not talk as you see fit.'

Nancy nodded, taking another small sharp breath. 'Thank you. Please don't see me out. You've all been very kind.'

She took a step towards the door, then hesitated. 'The stuff in the past they were asking me about. It was the time your sister went missing, Martha. Charlie? That was her name, wasn't it?'

'That's right,' Martha replied, closing her hands around the edge of the desk.

'They asked me about the night of Jonathan Overton's book launch.' She touched her forehead with her fingertips. 'I wanted to go to the party, and my mother was going to babysit, but Chloe had terrible croup. Poor thing wouldn't settle at all unless I was holding her, or pushing her about, so I missed it. Simon came home quite early. He was in a good mood. He thought the book he was working on was much better than Jonathan's, so he was certain it would be a big success. He was already spending his royalties, promising holidays and all that.' Her smile was affectionate, frustrated, a complex mosaic of feeling that was part of the intimacy with another soul. 'He came home and found me half dead with exhaustion, Chloe fussing, and he just took her from me. Told me he'd take her out for a drive and a walk and to get some rest. Don't think I ever loved him as much as I did in that moment.'

'So he went out again? After the launch?' Safi asked.

'Yes. I didn't hear him come back. He'd always take her on these great loops, get mud all over the pushchair. It was all part of the ritual of being a good dad. I don't know how long he was gone.' She looked at Alex again, held up the key. 'Thank you so much. I'll text, of course, before I bring the girls round. Everyone's been so kind.'

As soon as she left Alex looked at Simon's desk. 'I can't stay here. I'm sorry, but I feel like I can't breathe. Can we go? I need to be somewhere else.'

'I know where,' Martha said.

44

bethel, *noun (seventeenth century)*: a hallowed spot

It was Safi's first visit to St Sepulchre's. The three women walked in under the stone arch and followed Martha to a curved bench on the edge of a small memorial garden. A few remaining bluebells nudged their heads through the choppy grass by the graves.

'God, it's lovely here,' she said as she sat down. Then, as she breathed in the dark smell of earth and resin, she burst into tears. It took only a beat before she felt Martha's arm around her. 'I don't know why I'm crying. Sorry. I can't seem to stop.'

'Shock,' she heard Alex say. 'And don't try to stop. It's miserable. Why shouldn't you weep?'

'Someone *killed* him!' Safi said in a choked voice. 'I mean, I knew when I went home last night that Caldwell had said as much, but . . . then seeing Nancy . . .' For a moment the tears stopped, ousted by incomprehension and fear, but then a fresh storm of them swept in from nowhere. She had never felt so completely out of control of her own body. 'Jesus! Who?'

Martha squeezed her shoulders. 'He said something about a glitch in the matrix, that night at the art thing. About taking his chance.'

'He might have been blackmailing someone. Or selling on the Chorus letter,' Alex said. 'Perhaps he saw something that night when he was taking Chloe out.'

Safi tried to slow her breathing as the storm receded slowly, though her eyes still felt gritty and her whole body burned as though a layer of skin had been flensed from it.

'But what? Charlie was already missing, the launch had come and gone . . .'

'I have no idea,' Alex admitted.

Safi sucked in her breath. 'I was thinking about that conversation Simon was having with Brin. I wonder if he was the one pilfering from the dictionary. And Brin was doing the selling.'

Alex sighed. 'I wondered that. I do remember him talking about how expensive baby things were round then. I even remember him talking about Chloe being fussy and taking her for walks. He had his favourite places. Even as a baby she liked looking at the canal boats, their windows all lit up.' She stopped suddenly. Safi turned to look at her. She was staring at the path, the crumbling rows of Victorian tombs in front of them.

'Alex?' Martha said.

She held up her hand and took out her phone. 'Give me a moment. That was what he was doing on the night of the launch, taking Chloe for a walk to settle her. And remember the way he reacted when we said we were meeting Mike at the Trout. The way time changes your perspective on a place?' She spoke into the phone: 'Nancy? . . . No, no more news yet . . . I'm sorry to ask, but I just remembered something Simon said about those night-time walks with Chloe, and I wanted to double-check. Was one of the places he took her along the path by Godstow Abbey?' A pause. 'OK, thank you. Yes, of course, please go anytime.'

Safi felt Martha's fingers tighten uncomfortably around her shoulder.

'Well?'

'Yes, he used to go to Godstow. It would explain the mud on the pushchair wheels too.'

Safi thought of the ruins, the woods behind them, the high hedges.

'He saw someone, that night,' Safi said. 'Someone who shouldn't have been there. What could they have been doing?'

Her eyes rested on the graves surrounding them.

Alex reached again for her phone and let her fingers shiffle through her contacts with practised speed. Her wide eyes scanned those of her colleagues as she hit the green dial icon. They waited two beats before a distant voice picked up.

'DS Caldwell? It's Alex Monroe . . . No, we haven't worked it out yet. But is it possible Simon saw something at Godstow Abbey on the night of Jonathan's book launch? We know he used to go there a lot.' Another pause. The air felt taut and pressurised.

She murmured a goodbye and hung up.

'Alex?' Martha said.

'The police are already there.'

Martha shot to her feet.

'Martha,' Alex protested. 'They can't know for sure.'

'I do.' Martha was staring at her. 'She's there. I know it.'

'I'll drive us,' Alex said.

As they left the graveyard Safi touched the cold corner of one of the gravestones. Some sort of appeal, a private prayer.

They left the car at the inn. Martha barely waited for it to stop before opening the door and bolting towards the bridge.

'Go with her,' Alex said to Safi as she ground the gears of her car to back into a parking space. Safi clambered out of the back seat and set off in pursuit of Martha.

She had turned into the field, heading off across the grass towards the gap in the north wall, through the ghost of the old building and out the other side. Her stride was long and determined, and Safi was half running to keep up. As they rounded the edge of the ruins, they saw a cluster of unmarked vans and cars parked on the field, just visible amid the lush spring foliage of the trees behind the abbey itself. Safi could make out flashes of white.

A woman in a police uniform emerged from among the vehicles as they approached, a bundle of wooden stakes propped under her arm and a roll of police caution tape hanging from her wrist like a bangle. She drove the first spike into the soft ground ten yards from the treeline, and looped the tape around it, then steadily unspooled it as she took slow steps, her lips moving as she counted. She drove in another stake. The tape flapped between the poles like bunting.

A van had been parked on the turf, a little closer to the ruins than the others. Two men in orange overalls lounged against its open back, vaping and drinking tea from a thermos, surrounded by heavy-looking equipment. Safi recognised it from a dig she'd been on while she was an undergraduate: ground penetrating radar. Perfect for pinpointing areas of disturbed earth. *Christ*.

The two men were watching the policewoman putting out the tape with interest.

'We were right?' one of them called out to her. 'That was more recent?'

'Looks like,' the woman said, lifting up her roll of tape. 'But hang on until the DS gives the word.'

'In no rush,' said the overalled man, toasting her with his thermos.

The policewoman smiled, then noticed Martha bearing down on her.

'Excuse me, madam?'

'Is it her?' Martha's voice cracked. 'Is it Charlie?'

Safi grabbed onto her arm. 'Martha, wait!'

Martha shook her off. 'Just fucking tell me!'

The policewoman blinked hard but seemed to comprehend. She held up her hand and, keeping her eyes on Martha, spoke into her radio. 'DS Caldwell? I've got a . . .' She lifted her eyebrows interrogatively.

'Martha Thornhill.'

'Martha Thornhill at the perimeter.'

A static-laden response buzzed through her radio, offensively loud and mechanical in the quiet.

'Is it her?' Martha asked again.

The policewoman didn't meet her eye, but her tone became suddenly softer. 'If you could just wait for DS Caldwell, madam.'

The light was beginning to fade. Safi took a half step back and stared at the ground. Ancient ground, generations of the dead. She lifted her eyes to the tangle of trees and hedgerow. More white became visible through the gaps, and slowly her mind was making sense of what it saw. They were putting up a tent.

She heard something behind her. Alex coming towards them in her long black coat, her scarlet scarf tight around her neck. She silently took a place next to Safi, who leant in slightly until their shoulders touched.

Another van was making a ponderous approach across the uneven field, and came to a stop alongside the other vehicles. More men in overalls got out, and the side panel of the van slid open. The thunk caused the crows in the treeline to lift into the paling air, calling out in affront. The men unloaded poles and lamps; a small generator was placed on a trolley which they shoved and heaved along the old path leading into the woods. A policeman stood at the spot where it disappeared among the trees, like the guardian of the Greenwood. He made notes as they passed him.

They looked as though they would dig all night.

Finally a tall figure, dressed head to toe in white, ducked out from under the trees. He took off his mask and glasses while he spoke to the guardian. Caldwell.

'Oliver?' Martha called out, her voice unrecognisable. 'Is it her?'

He quickened his pace towards them and ducked under the police tape now marking the barrier between his world and theirs.

'Martha, we don't know,' he said as he reached her. 'We can't know yet.'

She staggered and he caught hold of her upper arms. He spoke to her quietly, quickly, searching her face to check she was understanding what he was saying. 'There are indications that the burial is between ten and fifteen years old. And it's the skeleton of a woman. That's all we know for now. Please, go home, Martha. I'll come and tell you as soon as we know.'

'I'm not going. I won't go. I can't leave her again.'

Caldwell looked stricken. 'Martha, please. I can't look after you here.'

'We can.' Safi touched Martha's arm, and Martha turned and looked at her with uncomprehending eyes.

'Martha? We're not going. We'll wait in Alex's car.'

Martha half nodded and seemed to rally for a moment. 'Yes, OK.'

Safi glanced at Caldwell, and he nodded. 'All right. It will be a while.' He released his hold on Martha very carefully.

'We'll wait,' Safi said.

Dusk thickened into night and one hour folded into the next. Safi fetched them whiskies from the pub, and later coffees and sandwiches, avoiding the polite but curious speculation in the bar as best she could. None of them spoke much. Martha was sitting in the back seat while Alex and Safi stayed in front, allowing her space while keeping her close. Safi noticed an email from Caldwell replying to her own from late the previous evening, thanking her for her notes. She caught sight of a figure on the bridge.

'He's coming.'

Martha stirred and pushed the back door of the car open; the interior lights came on, making the dark outside more complete.

Caldwell had shed his white protective suit, his shadowy face flickering in the unsteady light.

'Any news?' Alex asked for all of them, twisting round to look at him.

He took a moment to gather himself. 'We won't be certain until we run DNA tests, but all the indications are that we have recovered the skeleton of a young woman between the ages of twenty and thirty.' He looked down at the phone in his hand, and then at Martha. 'The clothing has mostly rotted away, but we found a necklace which seems to match the description of one belonging to your sister. May I show you a photograph?'

'Yes, please,' Martha said. She sounded very calm now.

He unlocked his phone and angled it towards her. Safi could make out a small silver necklace lying on a plain background. A black and white ruler lay alongside it. She thought of the standard colour chart they scanned next to manuscript pages, a means of keeping a true relative record. It was dirty, and soil had clogged in the delicate chain, but the pendant itself was brutally clear in the icy glow of the phone. A pair of silver hearts.

'Yes, that's Charlie's.' Martha unwrapped her scarf and lifted her chin, meeting Caldwell's gaze head-on. Her hand went to her neck, and she gently drew forward a flimsy serpentine chain, its centrepiece of two hearts polished by years of touch. 'She bought one for each of us.'

Caldwell nodded slowly. 'I can take you home. We need to tell your father.'

Alex returned to her house in Jericho just after midnight to find a strange man on her sofa. She wasn't unprepared. She'd walked through the door to find the hall light on. The man in question was pinned in place by a sleeping Nancy and two slumbering teenagers, apparently oblivious to the two cats sprawled between them.

He smiled up at her apologetically and whispered, 'I'm so sorry about this.'

'Don't be,' she said quietly, setting down her keys on the table. 'I'm Alex.'

'Marcus,' he replied. He was younger than Simon. Thin, with wavy black hair and tortoiseshell glasses. 'We only sat down for a minute after they'd been playing with Rochester, and they just sparked right out. None of them have slept since it happened; I couldn't bear to wake them.'

'Can you extract a hand to hold a glass without disturbing them?' she said, going to the decanter. The family was nested in a tumble of woollen throws that normally sat neatly folded over the back of the sofa. It was good to see them being used. The girls looked peaceful save for splashes of red beneath their eyes. Alex remembered Simon's photo of them, their pale skin freckled over, a weft of gold in their hair. Both had something of their father in the shape of their eyes.

'Reckon I could dance a tango and not wake them right now, and if that was the offer of a drink, then yes, please.'

Alex poured out large measures for them both and handed Marcus his. He winced as he took it, and she suspected he'd been keeping still for some time. She shrugged off her coat and settled in the armchair opposite him. 'How are your allergies?'

'I took a fistful of antihistamines before we came. Between that and this drink, I'll probably pass out myself.'

'You'd be very welcome. Do you know what's been going on?'

'Beyond Simon's murder? I read that article in the newspaper about the letters, and Nancy told me what the police had been asking her, of course. Has something else . . . ?'

'The police have found Charlie Thornhill's body. I've just come from her father's house. We took Martha there to tell him, with DS Caldwell, of course.'

He glanced instinctively at the girls. 'My God! After all these years! How did he take it?'

Alex sipped her own whiskey. Rochester, now curled up between Chloe and her sister, stretched out a paw, yawned and settled again. 'He was . . . he was terribly relieved, I think.'

Alex had driven Martha and Safi back to the house, with Caldwell following, and Gabriel had appeared on the doorstep as their cars crunched up the gravel drive. Martha had climbed out and gone to him, while Alex and Safi had waited by the car. Whatever words Martha had chosen to tell Gabriel that his eldest daughter's body had been found, Alex would never know. She had seen only their effect as he stooped to wrap his arms round Martha's shoulders and hold her, rocking her gently from side to side, stroking her hair as Caldwell approached, head down. Then, still holding Martha close, he had held out one arm and reached over to shake Caldwell's hand.

She and Safi had tactfully withdrawn to the car and she had driven Safi back to her houseshare, where she had been welcomed in by the artist and a worried, maternal-looking young woman in a thick towelling robe.

All in all she felt very grateful to find Nancy's family in her living room.

'How did they work it out?' he asked, tossing back his whiskey. Alex fetched the decanter and topped him up.

'It was down to Nancy, really; what she had told them about him going out again the night of the book launch, and taking Chloe out along the towpath in her pushchair. It was one of his favourite places.'

'But do you know who killed her?' Again, that nervous protective look at the two girls. 'Please, not Simon!'

She shook her head. 'I don't think so. He saw someone who shouldn't have been there – acting suspiciously, I presume – and finally put two and two together. He'd seen the person who'd been burying Charlie, and never realised until Chorus, the letter writer, stirred everything up again. No, I have my suspicions. I suspect DS Caldwell does too.'

He drank more of the whiskey, frowning in concentration. 'Simon tried to blackmail this person? And that's why he was killed?'

'I suspect so.'

'How am I going to explain that to the girls?'

Alex said nothing. There was no easy answer to give.

'What happens next?' he said, acknowledging her silence.

'I'm not sure, but I think I'm going to head upstairs and make some phone calls. I need to wake up a holidaying publisher.'

'It's very late,' he said dubiously.

'I know, but I make my publishers a decent amount of money and I haven't played the diva card yet.' He looked confused. 'I write horror novels, so I have a bit of pull.' It was getting easier to tell people, she realised. Perhaps she could tell her sons after all and the world wouldn't fall apart. 'Do stay as long as you like. Actually . . . I don't suppose you're any good at crossword clues, are you?'

'Not great,' he said exhaling, 'but I used to do them with my mum. Why?'

'"Short book I loaned out as library". We can't work it out.'

He frowned and asked her to repeat it. 'Short book – that could be an abbreviation of "book" itself. I loaned out as library. An anagram?' Then he smiled broadly, revealing a set of white, even teeth. 'Oh, of course. "B" for book, and "I loaned" is "out", i.e. its letters have to be rearranged. That will then produce the name of a library!'

Alex found his sudden pleasure in the puzzle oddly charming, but she couldn't answer him.

'Bodleian,' he said. 'The answer's Bodleian.'

She shook her head at the sudden simplicity of it.

'Thank you! I'll go and make my calls now.'

45

witterhed, *noun (fourteenth century)*: knowledge and wisdom

THE BODLEIAN OPENED AT 9 a.m., and at a quarter to the hour Alex and Safi were standing on the cobbles with their back to the Old Library, looking up at the Radcliffe Camera, the majestic circular pineapple of a building which stood at a little distance within a circle of perfect green grass.

'You got hold of that ex-OUP guy's number and called him in the middle of the night?' Safi said, and looked, Alex was gratified to notice, both shocked and impressed.

'Giles Baldwin. Yes, and I told him Caldwell would almost certainly be calling him, too – and soon – so he might as well talk to me. He was still up anyway, keeping Spanish hours on holiday. Can't say he was pleased to hear from me, but honestly, Safi, I didn't care. I don't think I'll ever forget seeing Martha bare her throat to show us the matching necklace.'

'So what did he remember about Charlie's book project?'

'I didn't get much out of him last night, but he promised to email first thing.'

Safi sipped from her takeaway coffee cup. 'He still has the proposal, after all this time?'

'We'll see when he emails, but I think he will have. He's been haunted by this thing, too, however much he tried to filibuster on the phone.' She looked over her shoulder at the massive walls of the old library. 'Do you really think it might be here, Safi? The commonplace book?'

'I feel like it is. If Charlie or Chorus wanted to hide a book, what better place than a library? But there are over ten million books in this place! I know there's got to be something in the letter to tell us where exactly it is, but I still can't see it.'

Behind them a porter in tie and jacket was unlocking the metal gate which would let them pass under the Tower of the Five Orders into the Old Library Quad. To his left a more familiar figure slipped into view.

'It's Martha!' Safi said in relief, and Alex turned away from the gate to see her colleague approach. She looked, Alex thought, lighter somehow, and as she reached them, she smiled and put her arms first round Safi, then Alex. The pressure of her embrace felt like a gift.

'How is your father?' Alex asked, as soon as she was released.

'He's OK,' Martha replied. 'Everything feels a little different in the house already. He's calling friends of the family this morning. Well done, Alex, and thank you. For finding the answer.'

Alex shook her head. 'We're not done yet. And this is down to Simon, not me. Do you expect to find it here, Martha? The book?'

'I do.' They walked into the quad together and looked up at the high sandstone wall above the Old Library entrance. The shallow niches carved into the frontage reminded Alex of giant tomes, guarded on each side by brooding faces of stone.

'But where?'

Martha pulled out her reader's card from her wallet. 'I might know that too.'

They were the only people in the Upper Reading Room, and with term coming to an end, the shelves for books ordered from the archive were sparsely occupied. It was a simple system. All those who had a 'Bod card', available to current students as well as alumni and members of academic institutions such as the *CED*, could request a book or manuscript from the archives via an online catalogue or blank request form. After a short period of 'fetch time', the book or box of material would be placed on the collection shelves with a rectangular sliver of paper protruding from it, bearing the name of the lender. More slips, Martha thought: in one way or another, Oxford's intellectual endeavour was underpinned by these precious cuts of paper.

'It was in the last paragraph,' she explained as they approached the shelves. '"It takes its place among its own fruits. A secret treasure called forth, openly."'

Safi smiled. 'So called up and placed on the open shelves, in the same section of the library as English Literature? Nice.'

'Oh, hurry up and look,' Alex said pleadingly. 'This is killing me.'

A single student, her face framed by a deep-blue chiffon hijab, came in through the double doors and took a seat in the corner of the room. She brought out a laptop from her shoulder bag.

'Here!' Martha said. The single document box, used to house more delicate books and manuscripts, was conspicuous among the few volumes nestling up against it. 'Requested by Hart; of course.'

She pulled out the order slip. It looked to a large extent like all the rest, but as her fingers ran over it she realised the paper was slightly wrong, the printing off. She handed the slip to Alex and lifted down the grey box from the shelf before carrying it over to the nearest desk.

A strong feeling of unreality was heightened by a sleepless night. She and her father had sat together on the sofa in the living room, Martha settled into the crook of his arm the way she used to do when she was a child. They had spoken little, had simply shared the acknowledgement that they were watching the world alter and rearrange itself around them. Yesterday had been the world where Charlie was missing; now it was the world where she was found. As she leant against him, she could see her mother in her chair to her right, knitting, listening to the radio turned down to a murmur. Charlie sat curled in the armchair to their left, a book in her lap, twisting her blonde hair round her fingers as she read.

And this could be it. Charlie's great discovery, what she had died for more than a decade ago. What she had been *killed* for, before being left among the prayers of Godstow Abbey.

She folded back the lid, heard Safi's sharp exhale over her shoulder, and gingerly lifted out what was inside.

It was an old photo album. Red buffed leather with an embossed golden rose on the front. The world was narrowing, the room's pink ceilings lit by spring light fading away. This was all and everything. Martha opened the cover.

Heavy black cartridge paper. The first double page held birthday cards and postcards. Mid-Victorian, she guessed, judging by the clothes in the illustrations. They were held in place by paper corners glued to the page. She turned over another leaf: more postcards, and a large watercolour of misty hills inhabited by some slightly wobbly pine trees. Similar on the next. She bit down on her lip and turned to the next page.

An envelope, a modern one, was tucked between the pages. She opened it carefully and pulled out a short stack of index cards, exactly like the one they had discovered in the slips.

'These are all in Charlie's handwriting,' she said, leafing through them.

'Antedatings?' Safi said, her voice thick and raspy. 'There's, like, at least two dozen of them!'

Martha nodded. 'And they only go as far as C.'

'My lord,' Alex said, lifting her hand to her chest as if she was about to cross herself. 'These will change everything. Do they all reference the commonplace book?'

'Yes. Oh, God, is it here?' Safi said.

Martha put the cards back into the envelope and turned another page.

Blank, only the corner anchors remaining. Same on the next page, and the next.

'Is it gone?' Alex said, through gritted teeth.

'She took them out,' Safi breathed. 'The individual sheets of the commonplace book.' Then suddenly, 'Martha! There's something else.'

Between the last page and the back cover was a brown manila folder. Martha slipped it out, pushing the album gently aside before opening it.

It was a thick pile: thirty, forty sheets at least. The top one was written over in a tight, Italianate hand, the ink blacker in some paragraphs than others. At the very bottom of the page were the initials, J. H. Martha was no expert, but she knew enough to see it was the right sort of paper, ink, and penmanship. She was looking at a page of the commonplace book of J. H.

Alex pulled out the chair next to her and sat down heavily.

'Jesus, it's real.' Safi sat down more slowly on the other side. 'Can you read any of it, Martha?'

Martha brought her face closer to the page.

'"Look, what thy memory cannot contain, commit to these waste blanks" . . .'

'That's from one of Shakespeare's sonnets,' Safi squeaked.

'I think this whole page is about memory,' Martha was scanning the rest of the neat script. 'There are quotations here. "The present is the object of perception, the future expectation." That's Aristotle. Oh God. This long paragraph at the bottom of the page. It begins, "My own memories . . ."'

She shut her eyes. 'There's too much here. We can't.'

'What on earth do we do with it?' Safi drew a finger along the edge of the manila folder, as though she doubted its existence.

'We ask the archivist team here to look after it for now,' Martha said. 'It'll be safe here. And we call Caldwell. There's no way of knowing what exactly Charlie found until it's been transcribed.'

Alex's phone buzzed and she pulled it out of her pocket. 'We might have some idea. Giles Baldwin has just emailed me.'

Martha moved slowly, carefully replacing the folder in the album, and the album in the box. It seemed to glow on the table in front of her.

'What does he say?'

Alex was shaking her head as she read. 'That he thought after Charlie disappeared it must have been a hoax. There's something pleading in his tone. Hang on, there's an attachment.' She put the phone down and dug her reading glasses out of her bag.

'Alex!' Safi said.

'Yes, I'm going as fast as I can! It's a list of Charlie's chapter titles. "Internal Evidence of Authorship". "Joan Hart – biography".' She stopped, and looked up at them. 'I can't believe it. You were right, Safi . . . This is Shakespeare's sister.'

Safi allowed them no more than a minute to absorb it. She was frothing with anxiety and adrenaline. 'What else?'

'Songs and verses. Anecdotes of Stratford. Antedatings of neologisms.' She paused, her eyes wide and feverish. 'It's right here. In the contents. An account of the life of William Shakespeare by his sister.' She put the phone down on the table and stared at it. 'My God, Martha. I can't even begin to take this in.'

They retreated into silence. Each of them knew that any new account of Shakespeare in the records was a major event. To have biographical notes from his sister was almost unthinkable.

'Do you think Charlie knew, in the moment Walter took that photograph, what she had found?' Safi asked finally.

'I don't know,' Martha replied. She was thinking of that summer, the rate at which Charlie was working. No wonder she struggled to pay attention to her little sister.

'Martha,' Alex said gently. 'You know that if Charlie had published this in 2010, or 2011, she'd be in Jonathan's shoes now.'

Martha turned towards her and took in her colleague's sad, wise expression. She felt Safi's hand on her arm.

Charlie had been made for television, too. Her looks, her easy laugh, the speed of her mind, and then this monumental discovery. Martha thought of the programmes Jonathan had made over the years and saw instead Charlie looking contemplative as she wandered through an empty Globe Theatre, or in the garden of Anne Hathaway's Cottage. Charlie interviewing creative geniuses in white-plastered rooms. Martha heard her voice coming from the radio, saw her face looking out of the cover of the *Sunday Times Magazine*. Jonathan's work would have become an embarrassing footnote in Shakespearean scholarship. The cold enormity of it seemed to press rational thought from her mind.

The student in the hijab approached their table. Martha looked up at her and placed her hand protectively over the box containing the pages of the commonplace book. The student smiled, pulled out a wallet and showed them a police ID.

'Can I help you?' Martha said, baffled.

'Good morning, I'm DS Norah Faris,' she said. She was wearing a blue sweatshirt with a Disney logo, an incongruous splash of colour in the softly lit room. 'Is it the commonplace book?'

'Yes,' Alex replied for her. 'The pages of one, at any rate. We didn't expect to see anyone here. Did Caldwell send you?'

'He did as soon as you texted this morning, Ms Monroe. I was trying and failing to get ahead of you.' She gave a gentle grin. 'Took a while to get past the guard dogs without a reader's card, and Detective Caldwell said not to disturb you unless we needed to, but time's up. Could you replace the box file where you found it, with the slip? Then if you wouldn't mind waiting round the corner. There's some movement outside.'

Martha pushed back her chair and obeyed mechanically, putting the box back on the shelf and taking the slip from Alex to tuck into place. Then she paused. 'Does Oliver think someone else has worked out the clue?'

Safi covered her mouth. 'Is that what the movement is? Someone's coming?'

'Time is short, Ms Thornhill,' DS Faris said, and nodded to the shelf. 'Please trust me, I'll make sure this doesn't come to any harm.'

'Come on.' Martha felt Safi take her hand, and the three women followed DS Faris's nod in the direction of the Upper Reading Room, round the corner and just out of sight of the self-collect shelves.

The removal of the box felt to Martha like a sudden physical injury. Safi pulled a chair out from one of the desks, and gently lowered her into it. It was so quiet; the walls seemed to curl up over them, pushing them closer together as they waited.

She thought of her father, making tea for the family liaison officer. Of dawn as it broke over the rooftops of Oxford that morning, seeping into the house to reveal its faded colours. She wanted to tell them how she'd sensed that something else was being returned to the house with the sun. Not hope, not love, not yet. But with the discovery of Charlie's body, and the knowledge her sister had spent these years with the crows and ghosts of Godstow, Martha had seen in that dawn light the possibility of hope, of respair. And she'd thought, watching her father as he made tea, that perhaps he felt it too.

She tuned back in, picking up the sound of Safi's short breaths and the fabric of Alex's coat shifting on the wooden chair. She thought of the pages she had just been handling and felt a rush of fear. For all of life's hyperbole, few things were unique and irreplaceable. The *Mona Lisa*, or a Crown Jewel for sure, but everyone in the world knew what the *Mona Lisa* looked like, and the jewel in the crown was made of the selfsame material as a gem in a Bond Street window. Even if the originals were lost, the glance and glimmer could be remade. These pages, though. No one knew the words they contained, their ideas and revelations. Their singularity terrified her. Is that why Charlie had been so secretive? So careful? How in the world had Chorus found it?

She looked up and saw a wall of witnesses. The room's frieze, painted a couple of years after Shakespeare died, was a long ribbon of portraits. Scholars from the ancients on, watching over four centuries of students, researchers, and educators. Bede was there somewhere, peering out of one of the dozens of oval frescoes alongside Ovid, Chaucer, and Dante. No Shakespeare himself: he had been just another playwright when these worthies were chosen – and just one woman: Sappho. Joan Hart would not have been welcome here, nor any sister or daughter of these severe-looking men. Had any of them ever questioned that?

Footsteps.

DS Faris's voice: 'If I could just stop you there, madam.'

'I'm sorry, but I'm in a rush.'

Martha felt the world tilt. She pushed herself up from the chair as Alex and Safi started forward, their shock echoing her own as each of them recognised the distinctive voice. Martha rounded the corner while DC Faris was identifying herself over blustering protests.

'Gemma!' Martha said. 'Gemma?'

DS Faris had one hand on Gemma's arm and her phone in the other. 'Yes, guv. They're here. See you in a moment.' She slipped the phone back into her pocket. 'Detective Caldwell's coming in,' she told them. She turned back to Gemma: 'We'll need you to come down to the station and answer some questions, Ms Waldegrave.'

She turned towards them then. Gemma. Her mother's best friend, who had helped her through those terrible weeks, months, and years after her eldest daughter's disappearance; the source of laughter and lightness in their house while she died.

She looked grey under her foundation.

'Martha! What on earth is going on? I was just explaining to this officer: one of my clients asked me to come and pick something up and now it seems I'm in the midst of a drug sting or something.' She laughed nervously. 'It would be exciting if it weren't so confusing.'

Martha didn't yet have the words to speak.

'You don't just "pick something up" from the Bodleian,' Alex said sharply. 'It's not Tesco.'

Gemma frowned. 'Who are . . . ? Oh, yes, you're a dictionary person.'

'Gemma,' Martha said, stepping forward. 'Was it Jonathan? Did Jonathan send you?'

Gemma put her hand on the shelf for support. 'I need . . . I need to sit down.' Faris guided her to a chair. When Gemma lifted her hand to brush her hair out of the way, it was shaking. 'He said . . . I was asked . . .'

'Ms Waldegrave,' Faris asked, 'who asked you to come here this morning?'

She took out her phone and placed it on the table. A text message from Jonathan glowed on the screen:

Upper Library Bod. Self-collect shelves. Document box.

'I'm very sorry, but I think, in the circumstances, I shouldn't say anything else until I've spoken to my lawyer.'

A terrible rage seared through Martha's blood. Jonathan had read Chorus's last letter, deciphered its instructions and sent Gemma to collect. Successful, charming Jonathan was being blackmailed by Simon. And there could be only one reason for it. She remembered Gemma lavishing love on them as their mother faded, bringing a final blast of colour to her friend before she disappeared beyond reach, but never giving Rebecca the one thing she really needed – the truth of what had happened to her child.

Somewhere on the edge of her consciousness she was aware of Caldwell loping through the door to the staircase behind them and pausing, DS Marche at his heels.

'You knew,' Martha said, stepping forward as Gemma shrank in her chair. 'You knew all these years that Charlie was gone, that Jonathan had a hand in it. And you said *nothing*?'

'I never knew exactly what happened!' Gemma protested. 'I didn't dream . . . I knew Charlie had some crazy book project which might have been a threat to Jonathan, then she disappeared. I don't live in a world where one's mind leaps immediately to *murder*. For goodness' sake, Martha! Why would I? I thought she had gone away for a while.'

Faris and Caldwell exchanged glances. Caldwell lifted his hand, telling her to let it play out.

'Then why not tell Mum and Dad about the book?'

'I . . . Please don't bully me, Martha!' Her voice was cracked and querulous.

'I hope,' Alex said with icy precision, 'you are not going to play the little old lady card, Gemma. You're only a few years older than me and as tough as nails.'

Gemma shot her a look of loathing.

'Martha, the publisher who said he wanted to contact the family, the one who was going to publish Charlie's book . . .' Safi said.

'He rang the number on the flyer.' Martha pressed the heel of her hand to her head. 'God, I can still remember you offering your number, Gemma. You wanted to help, you said. Save Mum from any nonsense.'

'I did want to help!' Gemma said with pained indignation. 'I loved your mother very much.'

'That's not love!' Martha exploded. 'You were making sure he was safe! Then that publisher called, asking about the book and what was happening.' She tried to slow her breathing. 'He must have told you exactly what Charlie was promising to deliver! How could you? What did it take for the publisher to promise to forget about it? How much does that man's career have to do with you?'

'I'm simply doing a client a favour, and I have no idea why you are all making such a fuss about it. Some research notes left here by mistake . . .'

'Jesus,' Safi said.

Martha put her hand to her head. 'What other calls did you lie about or ignore?'

'Oh, it was mostly nonsense. Girl on a bike! What a lead in Oxford! I was shielding your mother from all of that.'

'I've been as naive as Mum was,' Martha said. 'Not anymore. All those times you "defended" us from journalists or true crime podcasts' – she drew air quotes with her fingers – 'you weren't protecting us at all, you were covering for Jonathan.'

'I looked after you, too!' said Gemma. 'That's what I do. Take care of people. I got you the job in Germany.'

'Nice and far away,' Alex said, her voice clipped and dripping with disgust, 'where Martha could keep blaming herself, not risk running into anyone who might cast any doubt on the official story.'

'Then you sat and held Mum's hand while she died, and all the while you knew!' Martha spat out the words at her godmother and Gemma shuddered. 'You knew what had happened to her daughter and you said nothing. I will never, ever forgive you for that.'

Gemma twisted her hands together. 'I didn't know! Not the details. There are just some things we decide not to know. That remain unspoken. You're too young to understand. We all hide from things like that. Infidelity, betrayals. I didn't know what happened, and yes, I suppose I chose not to find out . . .'

'Overlooking infidelity is one thing. Quite another to turn a blind eye to murder,' Safi said.

Martha shivered, feeling feverish waves run through her as the truths of her life spun in kaleidoscopic dances, their fragments changing space and colour like light bouncing between mirrors.

'We're all culpable of something,' Gemma protested. 'It's part of being human. All of us. In fact, in your terms, we are all guilty by definition.'

Caldwell lifted his phone to his ear. 'Yup. Can you send a car for Jonathan Overton? I want him down at the station for questioning. We're bringing his agent in now.' He paused. 'That's interesting,' he said to the voice at the other end. He listened again, and something about the quality of his seriousness drew their attention. One minute. Two. 'Got it. Thank you. We'll be there in half an hour.'

He hung up, then came over and touched her arm lightly. 'Martha, Jonathan Overton has just arrived at the station with his solicitor. They told the desk sergeant he's there to confess to the killings of Charlie Thornhill and Simon Turner.' Martha felt the reassuring pressure of his fingers. 'And he says he wants to talk to you.'

Adrenaline surged through her body. How could she possibly see him now? How could she stop herself pummelling him with her bare hands? 'I don't see how on earth . . .' Then, regathered, 'Would it be helpful?'

'Possibly,' he conceded. 'But only if you are up to it.' She managed to nod, the only language that hadn't failed her.

'Thank you. Marche, could you take Ms Waldegrave to the station?'

'This is ridiculous,' Gemma protested. 'I have a lunch.'

'You can come in voluntarily and be questioned under caution,' Marche said icily, 'or we can arrest you as an accessory straight away. Which would you prefer?'

Gemma stood up carefully. 'I didn't know, Martha, not really.'

'You knew enough,' Safi said, and they watched as Marche steered her towards the stairs.

'Can Safi and Alex come?' Martha asked. 'I mean, they don't have to be in the room, but I'd like to know they were there . . .'

Caldwell considered. 'They can watch from the monitoring room with Marche, if they would like.'

'We'd like,' Safi said.

Faris picked up the pale paper box.

'Oh, no!' Alex said, stepping forward. 'That needs to stay with us.'

'It's evidence,' the young woman said, obviously confused.

'What it is, is a unique manuscript of profound importance to the history of English,' Alex said sharply, while Faris examined it doubtfully. 'You are not putting it in a plastic bag and shoving it in a basement until you see fit to release it. It will stay here, at the Bodleian with people who are qualified to look after it until ownership has been established.'

They looked round at Caldwell.

'Martha,' he said carefully, 'is it as important as you thought it might be?'

'Much, much more.'

He studied her for a moment, then nodded. 'Very well. Faris, can you go with Ms Monroe and speak to someone in authority here? See it secured, and seal and tag the box. Can we take the fake slip as evidence?'

Alex waved her hand. 'Do whatever the hell you like with that.'

He half smiled, pulled an evidence bag from his pocket, and put the slip inside. 'I'll see to the manuscript,' Alex said, then drew the box carefully off the shelf and set off with DS Faris in tow, holding it in front of her with a solemn dignity that reminded Martha of the Leader of the House of Commons, who had just a few days before carried the ceremonial sword at the Coronation like a modern-day Athena.

'He confessed?' she said, turning back to Caldwell. 'Sorry, I need to make sure I've understood this right. Did you say Jonathan had come to the police station and actually confessed to murdering Charlie and Simon? Why did he send Gemma in to collect the manuscript, then turn himself in?'

Caldwell pulled out a chair from behind one of the desks and they sat down. Safi moved in to sit at Martha's shoulder.

'He has confessed to the *killings*,' Caldwell said, and Martha's consciousness shifted uneasily. 'The brief he has with him has come from London and looks like he gets paid my weekly wage by the hour. Jonathan won't be confessing to murder. I'd lay money on manslaughter, or even accidental death in Charlie's case – and self-defence in Simon's. But I'm sure his brief doesn't want him speaking to you. He might slip up, say something that will make that defence just a bit more difficult.'

'But why now . . . ?'

'It's possible he sent Gemma in so he could offer the manuscript to us as part of a deal.'

Martha covered her face, as if she could stop the words from reaching her, could simply obliterate this version of reality by refusing to let its light reach her eyes. Safi put a hand on her shoulder.

'Why, though? Why did he turn himself in at all?' Safi asked. 'The manuscript shows he had a motive to hurt Charlie, and the message to Gemma shows he worked out where it was. He must have seen the letter from Chorus that Simon stole. But he was in the office after Simon died – he could have said he caught sight of it there. I can't see there'd be anything like enough evidence to arrest him!'

Caldwell nodded. 'You're not wrong. The news that we discovered a woman's body at Godstow leaked this morning. I am sure that's what decided him. No doubt he realised he'd have left some trace of himself on Charlie's body: hair, fibres.' Safi was frowning at him. 'He'll get credit for coming forward. He would have got credit for retrieving and returning the manuscript if you three hadn't got there first.'

'Credit!' Martha gasped.

Caldwell looked pained. 'I know. It's a bitter pill, but a confession saves the CPS and the police a great deal of time and trouble. If he is going to tell us Charlie's death was accidental, and Simon's was self-defence, well, we'll be much more likely to accept that now he's confessed, before we've built a case against him.'

'He deserves nothing,' Martha said, her voice steely now. 'I'm ready. Let's go.'

46

remembl e, *verb (twentieth century)*:

to have a false memory of something

SHE WAS SHOWN INTO THE same interview room as the day she had brought in the first letter. It seemed a lifetime ago. She glanced up at the discreet camera in the corner and measuredly scanned the grey-green paint, scuffed linoleum floor, and plastic chairs before bringing herself to look at Jonathan.

He was sitting next to his lawyer, a distinguished-looking older man in a pin-striped three-piece suit, a gold watch chain draped across his waistcoat. Even in silence, the authority he exuded felt expensive. Jonathan himself was as neatly groomed as ever. Martha thought of him staring into his mirror as he shaved that morning. Did he know then that he'd be turning himself in? Or was it only later, browsing the news sites over breakfast, sipping his freshly ground coffee at the kitchen counter while Olivia rounded up the children for school, that he realised this life was on the brink of extinction?

He stood up, as if he were greeting her at a party.

'Martha, thank you for coming,' he said.

She and Caldwell took their seats on the other side of the table.

'I've advised my client against this interview,' the lawyer said. 'Most unwise.'

'Enough, Sebastian!' Jonathan growled. 'I told you this was non-negotiable.'

He sat down again, glancing nervously at Caldwell, who introduced himself to the tape. Martha looked again at the camera. Safi and Alex would be watching all of it, and the thought comforted her.

'Martha, I wanted to tell you that I am so very sorry,' Jonathan began, spreading his hands out across the table. 'Charlie's death was a terrible, tragic accident and there hasn't been a single day when I haven't thought of it. The regret has never left me.' Martha sat impassively and he cleared his throat. 'I had heard from Gemma that Charlie had a book project, something extraordinary and Shakespeare-related—'

'Caldwell's told me what's in your statement, Jonathan,' Martha interrupted. 'You don't need to rehearse it with me. You talked to Charlie at the *CED* and she told you enough of what she'd found for you to realise that your promising new book was about to be blown out of the water. You asked her to wait, to collaborate with you. Repeatedly. You asked Gemma to help you persuade her. Then went to our house to try again. She refused and told you to leave. You grabbed her arm as she was going upstairs and she fell.' Her voice was brittle and icy.

Jonathan had been looking at his hands as she spoke.

'Yes, I panicked then. I don't know what possessed me . . .'

'How did her bike end up in the C. S. Lewis nature reserve?'

The lawyer huffed. 'This is not an interrogation, and certainly not by you, Ms Thornhill. Dr Overton wishes to make a personal statement, that is all.'

'Why?' Martha felt a flash of rage burn through the emptiness. 'Why make a statement to me? What could you possibly say that will make any difference?'

'I care what you think!' he exclaimed. 'I always have.' She stared at him and was astounded to see that he was blushing. 'I rode it up there, before the launch.'

'While my sister's body was still stuffed in the boot of your car?'

He stretched out his hand. 'It was . . . Have you ever heard of a dissociative state? It's a known mental phenomenon . . .'

'Don't give me your pseudo-intellectual bullshit, Jonathan,' Martha flashed. 'You're not on your podcast.'

He cowered, stung. 'I shouldn't have grabbed her. But she was taunting me. She knew about us and . . . and well, I had lost her respect. I just wanted her to listen for a moment. I wanted her to rest somewhere peaceful, so after the launch, I . . .'

Martha felt herself deep in the labyrinth now, a dark narrow passageway of stone flags underfoot and walls whispering truths too quietly for her to hear.

Alex and Safi sat crammed into the viewing room with Marche and Faris.

'Something doesn't fit . . .' Safi said, staring at Jonathan on the screen before realising the other women were looking at her. 'Him going over to talk to Charlie before lunch. Wait, didn't Charlie's supervisor say Gemma was reminding her about having lunch "with us"? He and Gemma were supposed to be having lunch *with* Charlie! Together! So why go and bother Charlie at home? He'd do much better persuading Charlie with Gemma there, surely?'

'Perhaps he went after Charlie had cancelled?' Alex said.

'Charlie's tutor obviously thought she was going.' Safi snapped her fingers. 'And she told her father she was going out for lunch and then on to the library. If she'd gone out for lunch, even with someone else, why was she still in the house when Jonathan came over? It doesn't make sense.'

'And Simon?' Martha asked. 'Why did you kill him?'

Jonathan squirmed in his seat. He looked pathetic, shrinking in front of her like a guilty child. 'He came to me on the Sunday, before May Day, said he knew I was lying about being at home after my launch. That he'd seen me at the ruins. He wanted money to keep quiet, and more to intercept any further letters from Chorus. I got the cash together on the Friday evening and told him to come and meet me.'

'So why kill him?' Martha pressed. 'He wanted money, you have money. Why murder again?'

'It was self-defence! He was drunk, belligerent. Lording it over me, and I was afraid.' His eyes darted around the room. 'I took the letter, but he frightened me, started squaring up to me. I was defending myself when I hit him. He was so drunk, he stumbled and fell into the water.'

'Dr Overton, if we could return to your statement of regret . . .' the lawyer murmured.

'He has two daughters, Jonathan,' Martha said. 'Not much older than your children.'

He winced, and then glanced furtively at his watch.

'No,' Alex said, leaning closer to the screen.

'What is it, Ms Monroe?' Marche asked. 'It seems clear that Simon Turner heard Dr Overton assert he'd been in his rooms late with his now-wife, but had spotted him that night at Godstow while he was out soothing his daughter. Why "no"?'

'You didn't know Simon,' Safi said, catching her breath. 'If he'd seen Jonathan – Jonathan Overton, our boss who he makes snide remarks about all the time . . .' Alex paused, then continued, '. . . if he'd seen Jonathan picking about in the ruins on the evening of his launch, he'd have been making cracks about it every day for the past ten years.'

'And Jonathan afraid of Simon?' Safi said, wrinkling her nose. 'I mean, Simon was a burly man, but Jonathan is at least three inches taller than him, and much fitter.'

Martha felt the hum of the labyrinth grow louder, then it stopped. Suddenly. Some physical change, some cluster of firing neurones, and she grasped something she had not known before.

'Gemma covered for you. She gave her number for the inquiry line. She persuaded Charlie's putative publisher to keep quiet. Then she kept anyone asking questions at bay for a decade. She even kept off the reviewers you hounded online for criticising you . . .'

Jonathan swallowed, and his knee began to jerk. 'I . . . She's been loyal.'

Martha shook her head. 'You've done well, Jonathan, but fifteen per cent, even of what you earn, is not enough to shovel that much shit.'

She thought of the lovely Ben Nicholson painting on the wall behind Gemma's chair.

'Who was Gemma really working for?'

Jonathan was floundering. 'I don't know what you mean, Martha.'

The lawyer frowned. 'This meeting, which I advised against, has crossed the mark. I really think we should stop.'

'What was your plan, Jonathan? Confess so the police don't spend too much time looking closely at the forensic evidence? Get twenty years, serve ten? Leave prison for a comfortable retirement, while your children are brought up in luxury by your wife and her family? You've made a devil's bargain. Your wanting to meet me now: was it just a ploy to buy a little more time for them to get away?'

Martha took a deep breath. The voices in the labyrinth were perfectly audible now. She lifted her lamp high to see the monsters clearly.

'The girl who was obsessed with you, the one whose interest in you meant you and I needed to be discreet, that wasn't Charlie, as you let me believe. It was Olivia. Olivia went round to try and persuade Charlie not to publish and to let you collaborate that morning. Did my sister tell her you'd been sleeping with me? I bet she did. It was *Olivia* who threw Charlie down the stairs, then called you for help while you were waiting with Gemma. It was *Olivia* who cancelled lunch from Charlie's phone. *Olivia* who Simon saw at Godstow, while you were burying the body together.

Olivia who he was blackmailing. *Olivia* pushed him into the river.'

Safi thought suddenly of the picture in the newspaper picking up the moisture from the table in their back garden, the face of Jonathan and his loving wife Olivia curling and distorting in front of her.

She turned to Alex. 'God! Do you remember what Gemma said, in the library? About how "girl on a bike" wasn't a sensible lead. *Olivia* must have ridden Charlie's bike out to the pond.'

DS Marche picked up the phone. 'We need to know where Olivia Overton is right now, please.'

'Jonathan,' the lawyer said. 'This stops now, or I shall have to ask you to find alternative representation.'

'Why?' Caldwell spoke to Jonathan directly for the first time since they had sat down. 'This girl was a student, in love with you to the point of obsession. A groupie, almost. Why on earth would you risk everything to help her cover up a murder?'

'It was an accident.' Jonathan swallowed. 'She was just trying to help. So supportive of my book . . . and I had told her about Charlie's project. I am to some degree responsible for what she did. And I'm certain it all happened just as I described.'

'I am no longer Dr Overton's legal representative,' the lawyer said, replacing the lid on his fountain pen.

'The commonplace book,' Martha said to Caldwell. 'He didn't love Olivia, at least not then, but he thought by covering up Charlie's murder he'd have a chance to get his hands on the book and publish it himself, without anyone ever knowing it was her discovery.' Jonathan flinched as if she had struck him. She felt the light again, the dawn of the first morning of knowing where Charlie was, Chorus's lamp revealing every corner of the maze. 'No wonder he spent so much time at the house after she disappeared, encouraging me to go back to university. He was searching her room, and seized the chance to bundle up the remains of her book-dealing sideline with a letter he took from the *CED* so he could send it to Mike. He ransacked our house under the guise of being our friend, to frame Charlie for theft and steal her discovery. But he didn't find it. Someone else did.'

Jonathan stared at the table, his arms wrapped around himself as he rocked back and forth, saying nothing.

Martha turned to Caldwell. 'I'd like to get out of this room now.'

'Interview terminated,' Caldwell said, and reached over to switch off the machine.

Safi's housemate Paula, deputy head of maths at one of the top private schools in Oxford, would not normally look at her phone during the working day, let alone take a call, but given what Safi had been through in the last few days, she answered at once.

The exchange was short, and before it was over she was already running to the school secretary's office.

'Edgar and Miranda Overton. Are they in school today?'

'Yes, but how strange you should ask. I literally just took a call from their mother. A family emergency. She is coming to pick them up now.'

'Dial 999 and do not, absolutely do not, let those children leave.'

Epilogue

untwining, *noun (sixteenth century)*:
an unravelling of threads

HUNDREDS CAME TO CHARLIE'S FUNERAL, filling the pews of the university church of St Mary's. A few wore black, but the majority respected Martha's request for colour, and the light-filled nave was decked with garlands of wildflowers as though for a wedding.

Martha recognised many of the faces as she walked up the aisle, arm in arm with her father. The staff of the *CED* had come en masse, together with several of the police officers she had met: Caldwell, of course, in a thin black tie, as well as Marche and Norah Faris. Tom and Tanya had come with their boys, squirming in the heat, and Dr Carmichael was accompanied by an editor from the OUP who was helping them prepare for publication *The Commonplace Book of Joan Hart,* edited by Charlotte Thornhill.

Family friends had come out in force, and it pleased Martha to see her father brighten as he spotted them in the crowd. Sir

Walter, whose family had unknowingly guarded the commonplace book for centuries, attended with his son and daughter-in-law. Martha noted a smattering of journalists and scholars, drawn to the congregation as news of the book spilled into the press. Even in death Charlie could pull a crowd, Martha thought, with a mixture of sadness and pride.

Jonathan had taken Charlie's laptop on the day she died, but he had never got rid of it, keeping it among the proofs of his first book, where it was found during the search of his home. The police's technical team had managed to get it working again and found the draft of Charlie's book in its entirety.

Olivia had managed to leave the country before she was arrested. The sirens of the police car summoned to the school must have alerted her. She had been forced into a choice: run and leave her children behind, or stay and be charged with murder. The children were now under the guardianship of her parents. In the weeks since she had gone the forensic evidence against her mounted, and Jonathan had withdrawn his confession. The charges against him – obstruction of justice and prevention of a lawful funeral – would not keep him in prison long, but his career would never recover. His publishers withdrew his books overnight and his programmes were erased from every platform, while column after column in tabloids and broadsheets feasted on his descent into iniquity. A documentary chronicling the fall of the literary star and his murderous wife had already been optioned for Netflix. Gemma 'retired' from her agency and was to be charged with obstruction of justice; Caldwell said she would most likely be given community service. Merton College had formally requested that she leave her house. Martha resolved to think of her as little as she could.

A private burial took place after the service, and Martha and Gabriel were accompanied only by Alex and Safi to see Charlie laid in her final resting place, next to her mother. Martha wondered how long it would be before Charlie's new fans found it. By the time they were able to set the headstone, Martha was sure it would be surrounded by the devotional offerings that had started to appear outside the *CED* since the story broke. Miniature busts of Shakespeare, art works, embroideries, pens, and accumulated notebooks lay fattening in the summer rain.

Among the many riches contained in the commonplace book, alongside its ballads, rhymes, and descriptions of plays that Joan had seen performed in Stratford and London, were a thousand words on her brother, written shortly after his death. Uniquely, it documented the lost years of his life, between the baptism of his twins and his arrival on the theatre scene in 1592. This mysterious time had long attracted a mythology of its own; speculation ranged from the young Shakespeare's escape from justice for poaching deer and his enlistment as a soldier, to a spell as a player in a successful touring company. Joan's book put an end to the conjecture. The truth, it turned out, was rather more prosaic, yet still sensational in its revelation. Her brother had become a schoolmaster, burning the midnight oil in writing the plays that flowed from his imagination.

But it was Joan's own voice that was for many the most precious jewel in the find. It supported the theory that it was women who were pushing the boundaries of Renaissance language, women who were innovating as they wrote their letters and commonplace journals. Martha had found delight in such details as Joan's replacement of 'hath' with 'has' and 'maketh' with 'make'. The book's conversational tone was worlds away from the formality and poetry of her brother's public output.

For etymologists, it was the vast number of antedatings provided by Joan that would change the entire lexicographical landscape, remaking the foundations of the historical dictionary. In her quiet and unofficial way Joan had been her brother's muse, collecting words and phrases from the mouths around her and artfully creating her own, for which he himself would go on to be credited. It was entirely possible that the biggest source of neologisms in the *CED* was about to be changed for ever. Simply, yet seismically, the single nomer of 'Shakespeare' against such entries as 'askance', 'vouchsafed', and 'bedazzle' would gain the initial J.

The wake was held back at the house, its French doors thrown open and tables scattered around the lawn. The editor at Oxford University Press had brought along glossy cardboard cutouts of the proposed book cover, and received enthusiastic consent to his suggestion he put them up on the patio. The caterers served champagne, and the mood was festive.

'It doesn't feel like a funeral,' Alex remarked. She, Martha, and Safi had taken possession of one of the tables in a far corner of the sunny garden. Martha couldn't help watching her father. He was moving fluidly between groups of people, smiling, welcoming them. He looked ten years younger than when she'd arrived back from Berlin.

'No, more like a book launch,' Safi replied. 'Do you mind, Martha?'

She smiled. 'No, it's much better like this. How is Nancy?'

Alex shrugged. 'As well as can be expected. The whole media storm has made it impossible to shield the girls entirely from what Simon did, but they have a sort of refuge at my house.

They spend hours playing with the cats. Nancy hopes you understand why they didn't come today.'

'Of course,' Martha said.

Jonathan had told the police what Simon had seen. Olivia, keeping a lookout by the ruins while he finished burying Charlie among the crows. Simon hadn't grasped its significance at first. His funeral had been a rather bleak affair. Well attended, but suffused with disbelief and anger as the news of what had happened started to swirl through the newspapers. Sales of his book had increased dramatically.

'The girls will be well provided for,' Martha added. 'The commonplace book is now the property of the British Library, and they got it at rather less than the market rate. We avoided estate tax on it that way, but it's where it should be, money aside.'

Safi looked confused. 'But the book was Charlie's, so the money goes to your father, or you. How does that affect Simon's family?'

Martha reached into her handbag and pulled out a pair of envelopes. 'Proceeds from Charlie's book are going into a trust. There are five equal beneficiaries. Us three, Walter's family at Witney Place, and Simon's family. Dad will be a trustee with a couple of friends and a lawyer or two. These . . .' she handed two typed envelopes to Alex and Safi, 'are your shares of the purchase price of the commonplace book.'

Safi opened the envelope and looked inside, carefully, as if she thought the contents might detonate. 'Oh! Is that . . . What? Does that actually say half a million pounds?' Her voice was rather weak.

'It does.' Martha lifted her glass of champagne and sipped. 'Charlie would have liked you, Safi.'

'I think bloody well of her, too, right now,' Safi said, and Martha laughed.

'I . . .' Safi said again, then with a huge effort of will tucked the envelope into the inside pocket of her jacket. 'Martha, can I ask you something?'

'Yes.'

'Why did you come back from Berlin? I've always sensed there was another reason, more than just getting the job here.'

Martha studied the base of her champagne glass. She'd been waiting for the question for weeks now, had discussed with her new therapist how to answer it. 'Truthfully' was the best formula either of them had been able to come up with.

'You know that I thought it was my fault. That Charlie was in pieces over Jonathan and that was why she left. It seems ridiculous now, but at the time it felt horrifically true.' She pushed the hair off her face. 'As I got older, I added into her story the pressure of being a golden girl. I think I made up a very tragic version of her, projected a lot of my own melancholy. Maybe that's why I made it my project in Berlin to look after young scholars who reminded me of Charlie. I got a reputation for managing troubled brilliance over the years, and it made me feel wanted, valuable. My friend Sabine once told me that I was seeking out other people's shadows to avoid my own light. I should have listened to her.'

'I like her even more now,' Alex said, picking up her glass and leaning back in her chair. Sabine had visited in the immediate aftermath, and had stayed until a clean draft of Charlie's book had been rescued from the old laptop. She'd helped to supervise the scanning of the commonplace book and the correction of the full text.

Gabriel had so taken to Sabine that he had started spending less time in his study. More than once Martha had come home to find them sitting together in the garden as the summer progressed, gossiping over crossword puzzles or picking over the implications of the discoveries offered up by Joan Hart.

'Anyway, last year I was working with a young woman, Andrea König. I became really excited about her project, sold it hard in-house. Then she started missing deadlines. I pushed, ignoring warning signs. Kept offering her extended deadlines, counselling, more money. But when I went to see her, she said I loved the project more than she did, and that my "help" was the exact opposite of what she needed.'

'And you left because of that?' Safi said doubtfully.

'I left because I had been telling the wrong narrative. I'd seen her as a troubled genius, another Charlie. She was perfectly capable of working out what she needed and getting on with it. I felt a fool, realised my whole story of myself in Berlin had been wrong. So when the job at the *CED* was advertised, I began to question whether any of my narratives were true. I thought coming home might let me work that out.'

'So when did your father find the commonplace book?' Alex asked.

The words hung in the air. The silence was punctured finally by a gasp from Safi.

'What the *fuck*?'

'I'm right, aren't I?' Alex said. 'Gabriel is Chorus.'

'How?' Safi mouthed. Alex lifted up her envelope and pointed at her typewritten name. It had the same wear pattern on the 'e' as Chorus's letters and the returns between the lines of her address were abnormally large.

Martha nodded. Her father was talking to the OUP editor and laughing. He'd put on some weight since they'd found Charlie. She picked up her glass.

'It was one Christmas when Mum was still alive; I was home and we were talking about the treasure hunts Charlie used to set for me. Dad must have gone looking in her hiding places and found it, carefully wrapped under a loose floorboard under the stairs in the hall.'

'But he didn't tell anyone . . .'

Gabriel approached them over the lawn, his hands in his pockets. There must have been something in the way Safi was looking at him, because he hesitated before taking the last few steps.

Martha looked between them, seeing the shock in Safi's face, the tumbling together of facts that she herself had experienced when she'd learnt of her father's role. It had been the day after Gemma and Jonathan were arrested, and Olivia had been named as a suspect in the killings of Charlie and Simon. The betrayal of Gemma had hit them both hard, but it had also opened a door, toppling the reserve that divided father and daughter, and he had told her the truth. The following day Gabriel had made a full confession to Caldwell. There was nothing illegal about what he'd done, though he'd received what he referred to afterwards as 'a bit of a talking-to' from the younger man.

'So now you know?' Gabriel said as he approached gingerly.

Alex held up her envelope again. 'Bit of a giveaway. Why? Why on earth didn't you tell anyone about the book?'

He looked at Martha, his eyes pained but clear.

'It's OK, Dad,' she said, nodding towards a free seat at the table, 'you can tell them.'

Gabriel sat down and ran his hand through his hair. His expression, as he looked between Safi and Alex, seemed to Martha both shy and hopeful.

'Rebecca was so sure Charlie was coming back,' he said. 'Or at least that's what she kept telling me. When I found it, I was afraid that the book meant something terrible had happened, and I didn't want to take that hope from her.

Then . . .' He blinked, looking down at the table. 'You see, when I saw what the book was, saw the antedatings cards and the references to Shakespeare, I did begin to wonder about Jonathan. I may be an old fool, but I'm not blind. I suspected Martha and Jonathan were involved.' Martha remembered those long conversations she'd had with Jonathan at her parents' house during the summer. The supportive squeezes on her arm or shoulder while they waited for news around the kitchen table. She'd thought them invisible. 'So when I found the book I was terribly afraid that Jonathan had something to do with Charlie's disappearance, and that' – he shot a rueful look at his daughter – 'Martha might have known something about it. I couldn't risk it. What if, in her final year, Rebecca found she had lost both her daughters?'

'That would be unthinkable,' Alex said quietly.

'It was,' Gabriel admitted.

'But you did ask Charlie about the thefts?' Alex asked.

'Yes, for some time I thought that conversation had driven her away. Though she just laughed when I asked her about it. Told me Mike was crazy for suspecting her and she had her money on Simon.'

'Did you tell Mike that?' Martha asked.

Her father shook his head. 'I was angry at Mike for accusing Charlie without evidence. I couldn't do the same. Though I did accuse Simon in the postcard.'

Safi pulled out her familiar notebook and rifled through the pages. 'He told us his said "God keep me from false friends".'

'No.' Gabriel sniffed. 'It was "Thou art a robber".'

'No wonder he lied to us.' Alex's voice held both contempt and sadness. 'I suppose Brin helped him get rid of what he pilfered?'

Martha lowered her eyes. Brin had admitted he'd sold some items on Simon's behalf in the year before Charlie went missing, but insisted he'd had no idea they were stolen. Martha didn't believe him for a second.

'Yes, I'm glad he didn't come today,' she said. 'Oliver would like to charge him for handling stolen goods, but it was so long ago.'

'I wish I'd heard more in the bookshop that day,' Safi spoke gently, then frowned. 'Gabriel, why didn't you do something about all this after Rebecca died?'

He reached out and put his hand over Martha's.

'I discovered I didn't want to lose both my daughters either. Suspecting her was terrible, but the thought of losing her entirely was worse. Or that was how it felt for a long time.' Martha turned her hand to hold his for a second, then released it.

'So what changed, Gabriel?' Alex said. Martha looked at her: she had that strange half smile on her face, but her tone was gently curious.

'My plan was simply to leave the commonplace book to Martha in my will with a letter of explanation. Then she came home, and seemed so lost, so guilty. I realised I had to do something, and I thought back to those treasure hunts. I'd been sending those postcards to Mike for years. Stupid, really, but he had hinted to a couple of people that Charlie was the thief at the *CED* and that enraged me. I never wanted him to forget what he'd done. I realise now he thought he had proof . . .' He brushed a daisy poking up from the lawn with the toe of his shoe. 'I couldn't face it head-on.' Gabriel swallowed. 'We've all lost ourselves in words. They are our oasis, and our downfall. And working on those clues, losing myself in them: it was a solace.'

His gaze became distant and he seemed momentarily lost again, somewhere beyond their reach. As she watched him Martha thought of the etymology of the eye's 'pupil', named after the Latin *pupilla*, little doll, because when we look into the eyes of another, we see a tiny, doll-like reflection of ourselves. *I was there in his eyes all along.*

'As for bringing a card into the slips,' Gabriel went on, 'I'm still known at the *CED*, and it was easy to pop in on the pretence of seeing Martha. Mike's security measures might stop people taking things out, but taking things in is simple.'

'And you really hoped to learn the truth through such a convoluted process?' Alex asked.

He nodded and smiled briefly. 'It worked, didn't it? I thought I could use the letters to open a door. I wrote about the monsters in the labyrinth, but think perhaps the person lost in the labyrinth was me. I knew these few things . . . that Charlie had been accused of theft, and had been working for Brin. That she'd found the commonplace book somewhere, that Jonathan and Martha had been in some sort of relationship. That Charlie had just split up with Tom. But it all felt like a dead end. I needed your help to find a way out. Thank you, all of you.'

'None needed,' Alex said.

A look of pain passed over his features. 'I had no idea writing those letters would get someone killed.'

'Simon made his own choices,' Safi said firmly. 'That's not on you. Or you,' she added, looking at Martha.

Caldwell separated himself from a group of admirers nearby and approached, resting a hand briefly on Martha's shoulder. She smiled up at him.

'So this is where the cool kids are,' he said. 'Martha, the publisher is looking for you. He's offered to say a few words if you'd rather not.'

'No, I want to do it. Thanks, Oliver.'

She stood up and walked down the garden to a shady spot on the patio. Caldwell called for silence and the crowd turned towards her. The few dressed in black looked incongruous in the summer garden, a little like gathering crows. She thought of Charlie and smiled, then took a printed sheet of paper from the pocket of her jacket.

'Hello, everyone, we so appreciate your being here with us today. I've decided not to fill this afternoon with my words; there were so many from my sister that we never got to hear. But now some of them have been returned to us in this book, and so I'd like to read a short extract from Charlie's introduction to her extraordinary find, to give her voice to its significance.' She breathed in and briefly closed her eyes, then slowly lifted the page.

'"The commonplace book of Joan Hart contains many revelations, but I want to take a moment here to say what it means to me. Joan recorded the voices heard outside the courts and palaces of England; she netted the songs and words of the people around her, the itinerant players, the poor, the cutpurses, spinners and tavern-keepers. Above all, she reproduced the words of women, and in doing so captured the blossoming of a language that sprang up like weeds between the heavy paving slabs of literature. Many of her fragments were carried back into the theatres by her brother, to be immortalised in the canon of his work, but most would have faded for ever had not this one woman taken the time to notice what others didn't, to listen to the music of language swirling around her in one of its most vigorous periods of growth.

'"I have never believed in God or the afterlife. But the very existence and survival of this book have almost persuaded me to believe in both.

'"Charlotte Thornhill, Oxford 2010."'

Martha lowered the page and took the glass of champagne Alex was holding out to her.

'To my sister,' she said, then keeping the glass high, she quoted, '"But thy eternal summer shall not fade, Nor lose possession of that fair thou ow'st; Nor shall death brag thou wander'st in his shade, When in eternal lines to time thou grow'st: So long as men can breathe or eyes can see, So long lives this, and this gives life to thee."'

They applauded, and as the light began to dim towards evening, a swirl of jackdaws lifted into the air at the back of the garden, adding their own dark and chuckling plaudits to the crowd's.

Acknowledgements

When I was around eight or nine years old, I entered a short story competition at school. I don't remember all of it, but I do know that my tale involved a breathless chase through a misty forest by some unknown source of danger, and that I called it *Pursuit*. My early attempts at creative writing began and ended there, for not long after I discovered far greater adventures, ones that have preoccupied me in the many decades since. They were contained, of course, in dictionaries, whose stories needed no further drama. The secret lives of words have held me captive ever since.

Why then, this book? The honest answer is that it would not exist without the inspiration of the editors at Zaffre, who sent me into a whole new level of betwitterment when they suggested I might like to try my hand at fiction. Much like my invitation into *Countdown*'s Dictionary Corner, which I turned down three times before agreeing to give it a go, my instinct was to politely decline, and to stay safely thrilled within my net of dictionaries. But the idea began to take hold of an approach to writing that could combine my love affair with etymology with a glimpse into the people who pursue it.

It was the title that came to me first. Definition is such a weighty word. We look to define every aspect of life as we navigate it, just as we are constantly defining and redefining ourselves. Those definitions are expressed through words, which in turn are given definition in a dictionary. I began to consider a mystery that could only be solved through the unravelling of language, one that compels a group of lexicographers to be far more than simple word detectives.

The fact that the consideration was realised is down to the encouragement and considerable support of that team from Zaffre, who from start to finish led me through the complexities of plotting and of giving proper voice to the thousands of linguistic stories I wanted to share. They are led by Kelly Smith, who over numerous lunches and phone calls lent me both her ears and her wisdom.

Bonnier's publicity and marketing team have been equally thoughtful and effective, notably Eleanor Stammeijer and Sophie Raoufi. Their efforts have gone hand in hand with those of the sales team, including Stuart Finglass, Vincent Kelleher, Mark Williams, and Stacey Hamilton, while Stella Giatrakou has been indefatigable in selling the rights to the novel overseas. I am so grateful to all of them.

Once again, my agents Rosemary Scoular and Natalia Lucas have given me endless support. They willingly read every word as I went along so that they could cheer me on from the sidelines.

More personally, I would like to thank those who read early drafts and always gave me their honest opinion; this book rests on their feedback. They include Chris Price, the kindest of critics, and Rebecca Gowers, who thrashed out many an aspect of the story with me as we walked. The very substance of the novel owes a huge amount to two friends in particular: *Oxford English Dictionary* editor Andrew Ball, and Charlotte Scott, whose profound knowledge of lexicography and of Shakespeare respectively inspired much of my writing here.

Two crossword experts gave me invaluable help in making some of the book's word clues as fiendish (yet solvable) as possible: my thanks go to Ashley Knowles and Don Manley, to whose coat-tails I can only hang on for dear life.

Finally, this book is dedicated to my father, Malcolm Dent, who never failed to ask me about its progress even when he was slipping away. I still remember his pride when that childhood story was printed in the school magazine; I hope he might feel a little of the same now.

Susie Dent
April 2024